Implementing Success: Strategies for Effective Caregiving and Care Support

Schieloh Wolfe, M.S. and Naomi Latini Wolfe, M.S.

Published by Rainbow Weather Publications, 2023.

While every precaution has been taken in the preparation of this book, the publisher assumes no responsibility for errors or omissions, or for damages resulting from the use of the information contained herein.

IMPLEMENTING SUCCESS: STRATEGIES FOR EFFECTIVE CAREGIVING AND CARE SUPPORT

First edition. August 11, 2023.

ISBN: 979-8223172956

Written by Schieloh Wolfe, M.S. and Naomi Latini Wolfe, M.S..

Table of Contents

Implementing Success:

Strategies for Effective Caregiving and Care Support

Written By:

Schieloh Wolfe, M.S.

Naomi Latini Wolfe, M.S.

Published in the United States of America

First Edition, 2023

Acknowledgments

We wish to express our deepest gratitude to the many individuals and organizations whose contributions made this comprehensive caregiving guidebook possible.

To the tireless caregivers who dedicate their lives to providing compassionate support for their loved ones, you are the inspiration behind these pages. Your experiences, insights, and advocacy shaped this work.

We are indebted to the researchers and scholars whose evidence-based studies formed the foundation of many of the recommendations in this guide. Your rigorous analysis and pursuit of knowledge drive progress in caregiving practices.

The perspective of medical professionals across nursing, medicine, social work, psychology, and rehabilitation therapy was invaluable in ensuring a balanced, multidisciplinary approach. Your hands-on expertise and wisdom enriched this book tremendously.

Additionally, the input of community organizations, nonprofits, government agencies, and policymakers that strive to address caregiver needs helped tailor the practical tools in this guide. Your tireless efforts to uplift caregivers are admirable.

To our colleagues: Your thoughtful feedback and collaboration pushed me to sharpen our focus and writing. You helped refine core themes and content.

Most importantly, we want to thank the readers of this guide. We hope the knowledge gathered here provides you with evidence-based insights to enhance our shared mission of enabling a community of empowered, resilient caregivers.

Together, through understanding, compassion, and determination, we can transform the caregiving experience for the better. This work is but a small contribution toward that vision, and there is still much meaningful work ahead. With research as our foundation and a single goal in mind, let us move forward.

Disclaimers

Medical/Ethical Disclaimer

This book is intended to provide helpful and informative material on the subject matter covered. It is not meant to be used, nor should it be used, to diagnose or treat any medical condition. For diagnosis or treatment of any medical problem, consult your own physician.

The author and publisher are not responsible for any specific health or allergy needs that may require medical supervision and are not liable for any damages or negative consequences from any treatment, action, application, or preparation for any person reading or following the information in this book. References are provided for informational purposes only and do not constitute an endorsement of any websites or other sources.

Please consult your healthcare provider regarding the applicability of any opinions or recommendations concerning your symptoms or medical conditions.

Disclaimer of Opinions and Views

The views and opinions expressed in this book are those of the author and do not necessarily reflect the official policy or position of any organization, employer, or company. Examples of analysis performed within this book are only examples. They should not be utilized in real-world situations as they are based only on minimal and dated open-source information. Assumptions made within the analysis do not reflect the position of any organization, employer, or company.

While every effort has been made to ensure the accuracy of the information contained in this book, the author and publisher assume no responsibility for errors or omissions or for damages resulting from the use of the information contained herein.

This book is intended to provide informative material on the subject matter and is presented as the author's opinion based on personal experience and field research. The strategies and information contained herein may only be suitable for some situations. This work is designed to provide a general overview of the subject matter covered and is not intended as a substitute for professional medical advice, diagnosis, or treatment.

Readers are advised to consult with a qualified healthcare professional for any medical concerns and verify any information they plan to rely on.

Readers are encouraged to conduct research to enhance their data and subject matter.

Acknowledgment of Redundancy

Given this textbook's comprehensive nature, some approach similarities will be seen across chapters pertaining to topics. For instance, the importance of conducting assessments to identify caregiver needs and challenges is a recurring theme across multiple sections. These assessments form the foundation for understanding the status of caregivers and designing appropriate interventions.

Likewise, techniques and strategies to prevent caregiver burnout are discussed in several chapters, tailored to the specific focus of each section. Promoting caregiver well-being through respite, self-care practices, counseling, and other supportive resources remains an overarching priority addressed from various perspectives.

Furthermore, nurturing caregiver competencies through education and skills training is a recurring recommendation aligned with the goal of empowered, effective caregiving. While this theme is woven throughout the text, each chapter's specific competencies discussed are unique.

Essentially, core, unifying themes related to providing robust caregiver support manifest in various ways across the topics presented. We hope that through this multifaceted, comprehensive approach, readers will gain a holistic understanding of caregiver needs and best practices to address them. By integrating collective wisdom across chapters, we aspire to present a guide that enhances our shared mission of uplifting and celebrating caregivers everywhere.

Author's Note

It has been an honor to contribute to the caregiving field through this comprehensive textbook. As educators with personal experience caring for a loved one, we profoundly understand the joys and challenges of this journey. We hope that the insights, strategies, and perspectives presented in this guide will provide caregivers everywhere with the knowledge and support needed to navigate their vital role with greater empathy, effectiveness, and fulfillment.

The worldwide compassion, tenacity, and dedication shown by caregivers never cease to inspire us. We dedicate this work to them with the aspiration that it will lead to more inclusive, holistic caregiving practices that uphold the dignity of both the caregiver and the care recipient. As we strive towards this vision of empowered, supported caregiving, may we always lead with wisdom, courage, and boundless heart.

Introduction

The global landscape is witnessing an unprecedented surge in the aging population and chronic illnesses, necessitating the need for high-quality caregiving (Lee et al., 2022). Caregiving, often provided by unpaid family members or friends, is a lifeline for those unable to care for themselves. However, it also poses substantial challenges for caregivers, potentially compromising their physical, emotional, and mental health (Williams et al., 2021). To prevent caregivers from becoming overwhelmed and susceptible to health complications or burnout, there is an urgent need for robust, evidence-informed caregiver support programs.

Implementing Success: Strategies for Effective Caregiving and Care Support is a comprehensive guide that serves as a holistic resource for healthcare professionals, caregivers, and others involved in the field of caregiving. This guide offers a comprehensive exploration of evidence-based practices for caregiver support, covering key areas such as:

• Understanding caregiver support programs

• Competencies essential for caregivers

• Caregiver needs assessment

• Implementation and management of caregiver support programs

• Caregiver connections to community resources

• Recognition and management of caregiver burnout

The guide stresses the integration of empirical evidence, professional expertise, and caregiver perspectives to develop support strategies that are scientifically grounded, practical, compassionate, and adaptable to unique situations (Smith et al., 2020).

Moreover, Strategies for Effective Care Support emphasizes the importance of contextual factors such as cultural norms, resource availability, public policies, and systems-level issues. By accounting for these factors, caregiver support programs can be more effective, sustainable, and impactful (Johnson & Brown, 2021).

This guide brings together the wisdom of psychologists, healthcare professionals, researchers, educators, caregivers, and policymakers. It underscores caregiving as a shared responsibility that affects us all, with the ultimate goal of providing the knowledge, tools, and motivation to foster supportive, inclusive caregiving environments that respect the health and dignity of caregivers and care recipients alike (Martinez & Davis, 2022).

As a comprehensive resource, this guide serves as both an informative manual and a call to action. It invites readers to acknowledge the growing importance of caregivers in our communities. By embracing the strategies and perspectives presented, we can better appreciate the complexities and rewards of the caregiving journey, thereby ensuring caregivers receive the empathy, compassion, and support they deserve (Thompson et al., 2020).

Caregiving in the Contemporary Landscape

Today's world faces a growing urgency for caregiving support. Global demographic changes, such as increased life expectancy and aging populations, have contributed to a greater prevalence of chronic illnesses and conditions like dementia (Carter et al., 2022). This trend has heightened the demand for both formal and informal caregivers.

Informal caregivers, typically unpaid family members, provide the bulk of long-term care globally (Riffin et al., 2022). These caregivers' shoulder immense responsibilities, often without formal training, intensifying the strain they experience. Providing suitable preparation, respite, and support is crucial for maintaining their well-being and capacity to deliver quality care.

For formal caregivers, such as nurses, social workers, and home health aides, the escalating demand for caregiving services often translates to heavy workloads and potential burnout (Shea et al., 2023). Their needs include manageable staffing ratios, continuous education and training, and organizational policies that promote employee wellness.

Addressing these diverse challenges requires comprehensive, evidence-based support programs. Strategies for Effective Care Support provides guidance on developing such programs and offers practical strategies to support caregivers across the care continuum.

Roadmap of the Guide

This guide offers an in-depth exploration of crucial topics in caregiving support:

Chapter 1 delves into understanding caregiver support programs. It discusses evidence-based practices, contextual factors, and the integration of empirical evidence with professional expertise.

Chapter 2 explores the core competencies of caregivers, including self-care, stress management, medication management, problem-solving, and communication strategies.

Chapter 3 covers the assessment of caregiver needs across domains such as physical health, emotional well-being, social support, and ability to provide care and discusses needs assessment strategies and tools.

Chapter 4 examines program implementation, covering stakeholder engagement, funding and resources, program evaluation, and quality improvement.

Chapter 5 discusses the educational needs of caregiver families and strategies to meet these needs through tailored educational initiatives.

Chapters 6–8 delve into the roles and experiences of caregivers, connecting caregivers with community resources and addressing the critical issue of caregiver burnout.

Chapter 9 discusses special populations that have unique and different care requirements.

Based on evidence-based research, this guide aims to advance the understanding of caregiving support and provide healthcare professionals, educators, policymakers, and caregivers with the knowledge to implement effective, compassionate initiatives. It highlights caregiving as a crucial shared responsibility and sheds light on the dedication and commitment displayed by caregivers worldwide.

Chapter 1: Understanding Caregiving Support Programs

The Crucial Role of Evidence-Based Practices in Caregiving

The current landscape of healthcare is continually evolving, making it imperative to optimize patient outcomes using the best available evidence. The principles of evidence-based practices (EBPs) and evidence-based programs (EBPs) have become critical in enhancing the effectiveness of healthcare delivery, influencing diverse facets of healthcare, including caregiving (Sackett et al., 1996; Institute of Medicine, 2001).

Caregiving, both formal and informal, is an indispensable component of healthcare, often forming the backbone of a patient's healthcare journey (Rainville et al., 2020). Caregivers, whether they are looking after the elderly, those with chronic health conditions, or individuals with disabilities, are instrumental in improving their care recipients' quality of life (Roth et al., 2019).

However, the caregiving journey, while rewarding, can also be fraught with challenges that can adversely impact caregivers' physical, emotional, and socioeconomic health (Stall et al., 2019; Adelman et al., 2014). These challenges underline the necessity of equipping caregivers with the most effective tools to navigate their caregiving journey, and EBPs serve as such pivotal tools (Gitlin & Hodgson, 2015).

Significance of Evidence-Based Practices in Caregiving

The integration of evidence-based strategies in caregiving can enhance a caregiver's ability to provide effective, high-quality care (Gitlin et al., 2015). These practices offer a scientific foundation for caregivers, enabling them to make informed care decisions that align with the best available evidence (Montgomery et al., 2017). Such alignment ensures optimized care that is tailored to the unique needs and preferences of the care recipient (Gitlin et al., 2017).

The use of EBPs in caregiving has the potential to empower caregivers by bolstering their caregiving skills, knowledge, and self-efficacy (Lyons et al., 2015). It provides them with a solid foundation to navigate the complexities of their roles confidently and effectively (Vandepitte et al., 2016). This empowerment can lead to improved caregiver well-being, reduced caregiver stress, and enhanced outcomes for care recipients (Pagan-Ortiz et al., 2014; López et al., 2019).

The Intersection of Empirical Evidence, Professional Expertise, and Caregiver Perspectives

In embracing evidence-based strategies in caregiving, it is crucial to understand that the most effective caregiving support programs are built at the intersection of empirical evidence, professional expertise, and caregiver perspectives (Drake et al., 2009). This approach ensures that the strategies are scientifically grounded, practical, compassionate, and adaptable to unique caregiving situations.

Empirical evidence provides the scientific foundation for effective caregiving practices (Drake et al., 2009). Professional expertise enables the translation of this evidence into practical strategies that can be implemented in real-world caregiving scenarios (Aarons et al., 2011). Meanwhile, caregiver perspectives offer invaluable insights into the lived experiences of caregivers, ensuring that the strategies are not only effective but also empathetic and responsive to their needs (Lewin et al., 2001).

By integrating these three elements, caregiving support programs can be robust, comprehensive, and impactful, promoting a high quality of care while supporting the well-being of caregivers.

Understanding the principles of evidence-based practices in caregiving is pivotal for healthcare professionals, caregivers, and other stakeholders involved in caregiving support programs. These principles serve as the foundation for effective caregiving, fostering improved outcomes for care recipients while simultaneously enhancing caregiver well-being.

In the subsequent chapters, we delve deeper into the core competencies of caregivers, the assessment of caregiver needs, the implementation of caregiver support programs, and strategies to tackle caregiver burnout. By embracing the strategies and perspectives presented in this guide, we can appreciate the complexities and rewards of the caregiving journey, ensuring caregivers receive the empathy, compassion, and support they deserve.

1.1: Evidence-Based Practice

Evidence-Based Practice vs. Evidence-Based Programs: A Comprehensive Understanding

Evidence-based practices (EBPs) constitute a framework or set of guidelines established through a vast range of scientific research. The purpose of EBPs is to inform clinical decisions and provide a structured approach to patient care (Leung et al., 2023). EBPs are a blend of various types of evidence, such as empirical research, clinical experience, and patient preferences. This amalgamation ensures optimal patient care that grows and matures with the advancement of scientific knowledge (Santos et al., 2022).

On the other hand, evidence-based programs (EBPs) are specific interventions or methods that have been scientifically proven to produce positive outcomes (Chen et al., 2023). These programs are usually designed to cater to specific populations and conditions, addressing unique health or care needs. EBPs follow structured protocols and guidelines to ensure that the intended outcomes are achieved. A substantial body of research supports such programs and provides scientific validation of their efficacy (Lutz et al., 2021).

Operational Distinctions between Evidence-Based Practices and Programs

EBPs play unique yet complementary roles in improving the quality and effectiveness of care (Ferguson et al., 2022). EBPs function by distilling the most modern and reliable research evidence into practical guidelines that inform the decision-making process (Peterson et al., 2021). By offering access to the most recent research findings on a specific subject, EBPs enable caregivers to make knowledgeable care decisions that are rooted in scientific evidence (Kumar et al., 2022).

Contrarily, EBPs act as structured interventions designed to achieve targeted outcomes in specific populations (Zhou et al., 2023). The effectiveness of EBPs relies on the research-backed evidence supporting their success in achieving the intended outcomes.

EBPs offer a roadmap for caregivers, providing a structured approach to care that is efficient and effective (Davies et al., 2022).

Evidence-Based Practices and Programs in Caregiving

The application of EBPs in caregiving is a potent tool that can significantly enhance the quality of care provided (Jensen et al., 2023). EBPs guide caregivers in making informed decisions about care provision, while EBPs offer structured support and interventions tailored to the needs of both the caregiver and the care recipient (Harper et al., 2022; Gonzalez et al., 2023).

EBPs ensure that care aligns with the best available knowledge by distilling the latest scientific evidence into practical guidelines (Peterson et al., 2021). EBPs serve as a valuable resource, providing guidelines and strategies that are grounded in science and proven to be effective (Singh et al., 2023).

EBPs, meanwhile, offer structured support to caregivers, addressing their unique needs and challenges. They provide a roadmap for caregivers, offering a structured approach to care that is both effective and efficient (Zhou et al., 2023). By empowering caregivers and equipping them with effective strategies, EBPs can significantly improve the caregiving experience, alleviating caregiver stress, enhancing caregiver well-being, and ultimately leading to improved outcomes for those receiving care (Mills et al., 2023).

Frameworks for Implementing Evidence-Based Practices and Programs

Implementation science focuses on understanding the best methods to incorporate EBPs into real-world settings. This requires a comprehensive strategy that takes into account various factors, like organizational culture, leadership, and workforce development (Harrison et al., 2023).

Several frameworks guide the implementation of EBPs, such as the Exploration, Preparation, Implementation, and Sustainment (EPIS) framework (Aarons et al., 2022). The EPIS framework acts as a roadmap for organizations, guiding them through the various stages of implementation. It recognizes that successful implementation necessitates a combination of factors, including effective leadership, a conducive organizational culture, and robust workforce development (Smith et al., 2023).

By employing a structured framework like EPIS, organizations can effectively implement EBPs, improving the quality of care provided and enhancing the caregiving experience (Aarons et al., 2022).

EBPs represent invaluable tools in the healthcare landscape, particularly in the realm of caregiving. By understanding their characteristics, operation, application, and implementation, caregivers and the organizations that support them can better navigate the complexities of caregiving. The caregiving journey may be challenging, but with the support of EBPs, it can also be a journey of continuous learning, growth, and fulfillment (Mills et al., 2023).

1.2: Evidence-Informed Practice

Evidence-Informed Practice (EIP) represents a comprehensive approach to healthcare decision-making, incorporating the best available research evidence, experiential evidence from healthcare professionals, and the unique values and circumstances of each patient or client (Leung et al., 2022). Similarly, comprehensive programs grounded thoroughly in research, known as Evidence-Informed Programs (EIPs), aim to address specific health issues or problems (Grimshaw et al., 2022). Both forms of EIP aim to provide optimal care and support to caregivers and their loved ones.

Understanding Evidence-Informed Practices and Programs

Evidence-Informed Practices

EIPs aim to optimize healthcare practices based on the most current and relevant research findings, providing a clear, scientific rationale for healthcare professionals' decisions (Leung et al., 2022). They span numerous areas of health and social care, including preventive care, treatment modalities, recovery, rehabilitation, and palliative care (Melnyk et al., 2022).

EIPs are particularly pivotal in areas where there's significant variability in practice or a dearth of comprehensive guidelines (Pearson et al., 2023). The use of EIPs involves an ongoing, iterative process that starts with formulating the right questions, seeking answers in the research evidence, and critically appraising the quality of this evidence (Leung et al., 2022).

EIPs provide a general framework that allows flexibility for individualized care while maintaining an approach based on rigorous scientific research (Melnyk et al., 2022). Within this framework, there is room for individual tailoring to match each patient's unique needs and circumstances, including their comorbidities, personal preferences, and cultural context (Pearson et al., 2023).

EIPs facilitate the continuous advancement of healthcare by encouraging regular review and updating of practices based on new scientific evidence (Leung et al., 2022). This ensures that healthcare delivery remains dynamic, responsive, and up-to-date. For caregivers, this means they can be confident they are providing the best possible care, grounded in the most current understanding of effective strategies and interventions.

EIPs promote a culture of accountability and transparency in healthcare, as every decision is backed by scientific evidence that can be critically reviewed and scrutinized (Melnyk et al., 2022). This underpins the principle of 'doing no harm,' safeguarding patients from ineffective or potentially harmful practices.

Evidence-Informed Programs

EIPs are more extensive than individual practices, integrating multiple practices to tackle specific issues (Proctor et al., 2023). These could be complex health conditions, systemic problems in healthcare delivery, or public health issues. EIPs are often multidisciplinary, engaging various sectors of healthcare and society to produce a comprehensive, holistic solution (Park et al., 2023).

In designing EIPs, extensive research synthesis is conducted to ensure that each component of the program is evidence-informed and that the program as a whole is likely to be effective (Proctor et al., 2023). This involves combining findings from a wide array of studies, including randomized controlled trials, qualitative research, and gray literature such as policy documents and expert reports. The goal is to create a program that is effective, feasible, acceptable, and sustainable in the real-world context (Park et al., 2023).

EIPs typically operate on a larger scale compared to individual EIPs, reaching out to entire communities, healthcare systems, or populations (Proctor et al., 2023). This broad scope allows EIPs to achieve a more significant and systemic impact, often tackling underlying issues that cannot be addressed by individual practices alone (Park et al., 2023).

Implementation of EIPs often requires strategic planning, collaboration, and continuous evaluation (Powell et al., 2023). Rolling out a new caregiver training program based on the latest evidence might involve partnerships with healthcare organizations, community groups, and policymakers. Furthermore, it would require rigorous evaluation to assess the program's effectiveness and identify areas for improvement (Proctor et al., 2023).

EIPs play a critical role in empowering individuals and communities by providing them with reliable, evidence-based tools to improve their health and well-being (Melnyk et al., 2022). By addressing the needs of caregivers holistically, EIPs can lead to improved quality of life for both caregivers and the people they care for (Park et al., 2023).

How Evidence-Informed Practices and Programs Work

Both forms of EIPs work by utilizing various strategies to improve outcomes. These strategies are multifaceted and tailored to the unique needs and circumstances of each patient or client (Proctor et al., 2023). They may involve screening for specific conditions or risk factors, implementing specific interventions or treatments, or providing education and training to caregivers (Leung et al., 2022).

Screening

Screening is a fundamental aspect of Evidence-Informed Practices (EIPs) that serves as an initial step to identify those at risk and plan the subsequent course of action (Melnyk et al., 2019). The identification of potential risks helps to formulate a clear treatment path, prioritize necessary interventions, and customize the care plan as per the needs of the individual (Straus et al., 2019). For instance, in a setting focusing on elderly care, screening might involve assessment for cognitive disorders like dementia, physical ailments, or nutritional deficiencies. Once the screening is complete, the individual can be directed toward the right resources, interventions, or therapies.

In the context of trauma-informed care, screening helps to identify individuals who have undergone significant trauma and might be at risk for mental health issues like post-traumatic stress disorder (PTSD) or depression (Muskett, 2014). Given the deep-seated impact trauma can have on an individual's physical and mental health, early identification is key to providing effective care. Evidence-Informed Programs (EIPs) can incorporate various trauma-focused interventions based on the screening results, which in turn can prevent the exacerbation of symptoms and improve the individual's overall quality of life (Ramirez et al., 2018).

Moreover, screening is not a one-time event but should be viewed as an ongoing process. Individuals' needs can evolve over time, and therefore, regular screenings help update the understanding of those needs, adjusting the care accordingly (Melnyk et al., 2019). A person-centered approach to screening promotes engagement and collaboration, making the person an active participant in the care process (Barry & Edgman-Levitan, 2012).

Screening in EIPs also plays a crucial role in identifying the level of stress and burnout among caregivers. It can highlight the need for interventions targeting their emotional well-being (Del-Pino-Casado et al., 2019). By recognizing caregivers' distress, the system can proactively address it and prevent a potential decline in the quality of care provided to patients.

Education and Training for Caregivers

Providing education and training for caregivers forms a crucial part of Evidence-Informed Practices and Programs. These efforts aim to empower caregivers with knowledge, skills, and confidence to provide the best possible care for their loved ones (Gitlin et al., 2020). This might encompass a broad spectrum of topics, ranging from understanding the specifics of a disease or condition and navigating the healthcare system to administering medications and therapies.

A crucial aspect of caregiver education involves teaching techniques for effective communication (Back et al., 2020). Caregivers need to interact efficiently with healthcare providers, the person they're caring for, and other members of the family. They need to understand medical jargon, interpret health information accurately, and communicate the needs and concerns of the person under their care effectively. Training caregivers in these areas can dramatically enhance their caregiving skills and the care recipient's overall well-being.

Caregivers often encounter high levels of stress and emotional challenges, which can adversely affect their mental and physical health over time (Zarit et al., 2014). Therefore, education and training programs also need to focus on strategies for self-care, stress management, and resilience-building. Techniques such as mindfulness, cognitive-behavioral strategies, and relaxation exercises can provide caregivers with the tools they need to manage their stress and prevent burnout (Laver et al., 2020).

EIPs can employ various formats and mediums to deliver education and training for caregivers. Traditional methods might include workshops, seminars, or classes. However, in the digital age, online platforms can also provide resources and learning materials that caregivers can access at their convenience (Powell et al., 2017). These could include webinars, video tutorials, online courses, or interactive learning modules.

Implementing Interventions and Treatments

The implementation of specific interventions or treatments forms the backbone of Evidence-Informed Practices and Programs. The primary objective of these interventions is to promote the best possible outcomes for both the individuals receiving care and their caregivers (Proctor et al., 2011). These interventions could encompass a broad range, such as pharmacological treatments, behavioral therapies, rehabilitative services, or support programs for caregivers.

The interventions incorporated into an EIP should be chosen based on their demonstrated effectiveness in rigorous scientific studies (Melnyk et al., 2019). For instance, a certain medication might be recommended because numerous randomized controlled trials have shown its efficacy in treating a particular condition. Similarly, a specific form of psychotherapy might be suggested because meta-analyses have shown that it effectively addresses certain psychological symptoms.

However, evidence-informed interventions are not one-size-fits-all solutions. They must be customized to the individual's unique needs, preferences, and circumstances (Proctor et al., 2011). For example, a person with a particular medical condition might also have a co-occurring mental health issue, cultural considerations, or personal preferences about treatment. An EIP should take all of these factors into account when deciding which interventions to implement.

The implementation of interventions also requires careful monitoring and evaluation to ensure they are having the desired effects (Powell et al., 2015). This involves regularly reviewing the individual's progress, adjusting the interventions as needed, and being willing to try alternative approaches if the current interventions are not yielding the desired results.

The implementation process should involve clear communication with caregivers, ensuring they understand the reasons behind the chosen interventions and their role in supporting them (Back et al., 2020). This fosters a collaborative environment where caregivers feel empowered and engaged in the care process, promoting better outcomes for everyone involved.

Evidence-Informed Practices and Programs for Caregiver Support

Evidence-Informed Practices and Programs (EIPs) play a significant role in providing caregiver support. Caregivers often find themselves navigating unfamiliar territory, which can result in heightened stress and burden (Zarit et al., 2014). By implementing evidence-informed practices and programs, healthcare professionals can help caregivers better manage their roles, reduce stress, and enhance their caregiving skills (Gitlin et al., 2020).

Firstly, EIPs aim to equip caregivers with the necessary skills and knowledge to provide effective care (Straus et al., 2019). This can include training in performing certain medical procedures, managing medication, and providing physical assistance. These trainings can be offered through various formats like workshops, online courses, or personalized sessions. Further, EIPs can provide resources to educate caregivers about the disease or condition their loved one is dealing with, helping them understand the prognosis, treatment options, and how to manage symptoms effectively.

In addition to equipping caregivers with practical skills, EIPs also focus on promoting caregivers' mental well-being (Back et al., 2020). They may offer psychoeducation about the potential emotional challenges associated with caregiving and provide strategies for stress management and self-care. In some cases, mental health services like counseling or therapy might be offered to help caregivers cope with the emotional burden.

EIPs may also include services that provide respite for caregivers (Chiao et al., 2015). Respite care services allow caregivers to take a temporary break from their responsibilities, helping to reduce burnout and improve their overall well-being. These services could involve home health aides who take over caregiving duties for a few hours, adult daycare centers, or short-term residential care facilities.

Financial support is another crucial aspect of caregiver support EIPs (Reinhard et al., 2019). These can come in the form of subsidies, grants, or financial planning assistance. Caregiving can pose significant financial strains due to lost wages, medical expenses, and other associated costs. By providing financial support, EIPs can help to alleviate some of these strains, making caregiving more manageable.

Connect caregivers with community resources. These can include support groups, legal advice, transportation services, meal programs, and more (Powell et al., 2017). These connections can help caregivers feel less isolated, gain peer support, and access additional help when needed.

Education and Training for Caregivers

Education and training for caregivers serve as cornerstone components in Evidence-Informed Practices and Programs. A comprehensive caregiver support program focuses not only on improving the caregiver's competency in providing care but also on equipping them with skills to maintain their mental well-being and manage stress effectively (Beinart et al., 2012).

In the context of competency enhancement, caregiver training may encompass a range of practical skills, such as administering medication, understanding medical terminology, and using medical equipment. Additionally, training programs can provide caregivers with critical knowledge about the disease or condition their loved one is dealing with. Such knowledge equips caregivers to understand the symptoms, progression, and potential complications of the disease, enabling them to provide care more effectively and take timely action when needed (Cameron et al., 2020).

One of the most critical areas for caregiver education involves communication skills. Efficient and empathetic communication with the care recipient can significantly improve their comfort and overall care quality (Adelman et al., 2014). Also, caregivers often need to communicate effectively with healthcare professionals, interpreting and conveying medical information accurately. Hence, training programs should incorporate elements of effective communication, empowering caregivers to be successful advocates for their loved ones (Reinhard et al., 2020).

The mental well-being of caregivers is equally important. Caregivers often experience high levels of stress, which can lead to burnout and affect their ability to provide care (Adelman et al., 2014). Training programs can incorporate modules focusing on stress management, including relaxation techniques, mindfulness exercises, and cognitive-behavioral strategies (Farran et al., 2013). Such initiatives equip caregivers with skills to manage their stress levels and maintain their mental health.

The delivery of education and training can leverage multiple formats. In-person training sessions, workshops, and seminars provide an interactive learning environment. However, online resources, such as webinars, e-books, and digital courses, offer flexibility and access to a wide range of resources at the caregiver's convenience (Beinart et al., 2012). A blended approach combining both formats could provide an optimal learning environment for caregivers (Cameron et al., 2020).

Support Services for Caregivers

Support services for caregivers form an integral part of Evidence-Informed Practices and Programs. These services can range from counseling services and respite care to financial support and assistance in accessing community resources. The ultimate goal is to alleviate some of the stress and burden associated with caregiving, enhancing the caregiver's capacity to provide care effectively (Adelman et al., 2014).

Counseling services can provide caregivers with a safe and confidential space to discuss their concerns, challenges, and emotions. These services can be crucial in addressing common emotional and mental health issues among caregivers, such as stress, anxiety, and depression (Farran et al., 2013). Counseling can also equip caregivers with coping strategies and resources to manage the emotional challenges of caregiving.

Respite care is another critical support service, providing caregivers with temporary relief from their caregiving duties (Reinhard et al., 2020). This could take the form of home health aides who come to the caregiver's home, adult daycare centers, or short-term residential care facilities. Respite care allows caregivers to rest, recharge, and take care of their personal needs, preventing burnout and maintaining their overall well-being.

Financial support can also be a significant part of EIPs for caregiver support. This can involve providing subsidies or grants to offset the costs associated with caregiving. Financial planning and counseling can help caregivers navigate the financial challenges of caregiving, such as managing medical bills or planning for long-term care costs (Family Caregiver Alliance, 2012).

Connecting caregivers with community resources can significantly enhance their support network. These could include local support groups, legal assistance, transportation services, meal delivery programs, and more (Beinart et al., 2012). By connecting caregivers with these resources, EIPs can help them feel less isolated, provide them with practical assistance, and enhance their ability to provide care.

Specific Programs for Caregiver Support

There are numerous examples of EIPs specifically designed for caregiver support. For example, the Caregiver Support Program (CSP) offered by the Department of Veterans Affairs provides education, training, counseling, and other support services to caregivers of veterans (U.S. Department of Veterans Affairs, 2020).

Similarly, the Dementia Caregiver Support Program (DCSP) offered by the Alzheimer's Association provides comprehensive support to caregivers of individuals with dementia (Alzheimer's Association, 2022). Both of these programs have been shown to improve caregiver well-being and reduce caregiver burden through evidence-based interventions (Nichols et al., 2011).

The goal of EIPs is to provide the best possible care and support for those in need based on the best available evidence. These practices and programs embody the essence of modern healthcare—a careful balance between science and compassion, between evidence and individual needs (Melnyk & Fineout-Overholt, 2019). As such, they serve as a guiding light in our ongoing quest to improve health and well-being for all (Reinhard et al., 2020).

When applied to caregiver support, EIPs can facilitate a greater understanding of their role, provide critical skills training, and offer much-needed support services (Beinart et al., 2012). Examples of such programs include the Caregiver Support Program (CSP) offered by the Department of Veterans Affairs and the Dementia Caregiver Support Program (DCSP) provided by the Alzheimer's Association (U.S. Department of Veterans Affairs, 2020; Alzheimer's Association, 2022). These programs, thoroughly grounded in research, have been shown to significantly improve caregiver well-being and reduce the burden associated with caregiving (Nichols et al., 2011).

Through the use of EIPs, healthcare professionals can ensure that they are providing the best possible care and support to caregivers and their loved ones (Melnyk & Fineout-Overholt, 2019). With ongoing research and refinement, these practices and programs continue to evolve, further enhancing their effectiveness and the positive impacts they have on both caregivers and those they care for.

By embracing an evidence-informed approach, we can strive towards a healthcare system that not only treats illness but also fosters wellness, resilience, and quality of life for caregivers, patients, and their families alike (Reinhard et al., 2020).

1.3: An Integration of Research and Experience in Caregiving

Strategizing Caregiving: A Balance of Empirical Research and Experience

Tackling the multifaceted realm of caregiving mandates a delicate interplay between employing research findings and leveraging firsthand experiences. Caregivers must demonstrate a deep understanding of the needs of the care recipients, coupled with the adaptability to address these demands promptly and adeptly. Recognizing the diversity inherent to caregiving situations, caregivers should assimilate Evidence-Based Practices (EBP) and Evidence-Informed Practices (EIP) to guide their decision-making. This section delves into the importance of integrating these practices into the caregiving decision-making process.

EBP represents the practice of using contemporary, reliable research to guide decision-making and intervention strategies within caregiving. It furnishes caregivers with a robust base of scientifically validated interventions, thereby underpinning caregiving strategies. Nonetheless, caregiving decisions are rarely straightforward, and the subtleties of human experiences and situation-specific dynamics are not always encapsulated within research alone, highlighting the crucial role of EIP (Damianakis & Marziali, 2011).

Understanding Evidence-Based Practices (EBP) in Caregiving

EBP, within the caregiving paradigm, is an organized approach to care-related decisions, informed by the most pertinent research evidence and supplemented by clinical acumen. It converges on three core components: the finest available research evidence, clinical expertise, and patient values and preferences (Sackett et al., 1996). EBP embodies a significant shift from tradition-based decision-making to an evidence-informed model, encouraging the application of high-quality, scientifically validated interventions.

EBP goes beyond mere translation of research into practice. It calls for a critical evaluation of research studies, necessitating caregivers to develop and sharpen skills such as formulating unambiguous clinical questions, searching for relevant research evidence, critically appraising the evidence, and applying the findings to the unique needs, preferences, and circumstances of individual patients (Straus et al., 2018).

Central to EBP is the guarantee that care delivery is rooted in scientific research, offering strategies that have been put through stringent testing and validation. This establishes a standardized basis for intervention strategies used, fostering confidence in their effectiveness (Guyatt et al., 1992).

Notably, EBP is not intended to override the caregiver's clinical judgment or the patient's values and preferences. Instead, it acts as a support tool for clinical decision-making, complementing the caregiver's expertise and the patient's unique circumstances (Sackett et al., 1996).

The Role of EBP in Caregiving

EBP's contribution to caregiving is diverse. Predominantly, it provides caregivers with a structured methodology for informed decision-making pertaining to care. By endorsing the use of scientifically validated interventions, EBP nurtures a culture of excellence and ongoing improvement within caregiving (Melnyk & Fineout-Overholt, 2015).

EBP assists in standardizing caregiving practices. With the plethora of potential interventions in caregiving, it is crucial to ensure that the implemented strategies are both effective and uniform across different caregivers and care settings. EBP offers a shared framework for all caregivers (Melnyk & Fineout-Overholt, 2015).

Moreover, EBP promotes professional growth among caregivers. It inspires caregivers to engage with research, foster critical appraisal skills, and stay updated with the latest findings in the field. This continual learning process enhances their professional knowledge and capability to deliver high-quality care (Straus et al., 2018).

EBP lays the groundwork for performance measurement and quality enhancement within caregiving. By defining what best practice entails, EBP provides a benchmark against which the quality of care can be gauged. It enables the identification of gaps in practice and informs strategies for amelioration (Melnyk & Fineout-Overholt, 2015).

Furthermore, EBP acts as a conduit for communication among caregivers, care recipients, and other healthcare professionals. By offering a shared language and mutual understanding of best practices, EBP encourages collaboration and consensus-building within caregiving (Guyatt et al., 1992).

The Limitations of EBP in Caregiving

Despite its myriad benefits, EBP has certain limitations in caregiving. EBP is premised on research evidence, frequently stemming from randomized controlled trials (RCTs), deemed the gold standard in research design. However, RCTs conventionally test interventions under controlled conditions, which may not always mirror real-world caregiving situations. This often leads to a research-practice gap, posing a challenge for caregivers to translate research findings into everyday practice (Rycroft-Malone, 2007).

EBP's inherent inflexibility can occasionally hinder its application in caregiving. Caregiving requires a dynamic and adjustable approach that can cater to the changing needs of the care recipient. The focus of EBP on adherence to validated interventions can sometimes constrain this flexibility (Holmes et al., 2006).

Moreover, EBP necessitates access to research studies, which may not always be readily accessible to all caregivers. This could hinder some caregivers' ability to engage with EBP. Furthermore, interpreting and applying research findings demands specific skills, such as critical appraisal skills, which caregivers may not always possess (Melnyk & Fineout-Overholt, 2015).

In certain instances, EBP may overlook the significance of individual patient preferences, values, and circumstances. Although EBP integrates these factors into its decision-making process, the focus is often on research evidence. This could result in a one-size-fits-all approach, which may not be suitable for all caregiving situations (Holmes et al., 2006).

Lastly, EBP can unintentionally downplay the experiential knowledge and wisdom accrued from hands-on caregiving. This implicit knowledge, often sidelined in favor of empirical evidence, plays a priceless role in caregiving and should be acknowledged and valued (Rycroft-Malone et al., 2004).

The Importance of Evidence-Informed Practices (EIP) in Caregiving

Evidence-Informed Practice (EIP) in caregiving is a comprehensive approach to decision-making that incorporates various evidence sources (Sackett et al., 1996). Unlike Evidence-Based Practice (EBP), which prioritizes research evidence, EIP appreciates the weight of other types of evidence, like clinical expertise, patient values and preferences, and local context.

EIP provides more flexibility than EBP, acknowledging that research evidence may not always be universally applicable or readily available (Rycroft-Malone et al., 2004). It emphasizes the individual patient's circumstances and preferences, promoting a patient-centered approach to care.

EIP is particularly crucial when research evidence is scarce or inconclusive. In these cases, caregivers can leverage their clinical expertise, patient preferences, and local context to inform decision-making (Greenhalgh et al., 2014). Furthermore, EIP encourages caregivers to continually reflect on their practices, challenge assumptions, and strive for improvement, fostering a culture of inquiry, innovation, and learning.

The Role of Evidence-Based Practice (EBP) in Caregiving

Evidence-Based Practice (EBP) in caregiving is fundamental for optimizing care outcomes (Sackett et al., 1996). EBP leverages current scientific research and empirical evidence to guide caregiving practices, empowering caregivers to make decisions that are both effective and meaningful.

EBP provides caregivers with proven strategies and interventions that have undergone rigorous scientific scrutiny (Straus et al., 2011). The use of such evidence-based methods enhances the caregiver's confidence in their ability to provide care, knowing they are using methods that yield positive results.

Furthermore, EBP standardizes caregiving procedures, ensuring uniform care quality irrespective of the caregiver (Melnyk & Fineout-Overholt, 2015). This standardization is critical in caregiving institutions where multiple caregivers may interact with the same care recipient, ensuring consistent care provision.

However, EBP is not without its limitations. It must be remembered that caregiving is as much an art as a science, and individual nuances, unique circumstances, and caregivers' lived experiences must also be considered (Kitson et al., 2008). This is where the value of Evidence-Informed Practice (EIP) comes to the fore.

The Importance of Evidence-Informed Practices (EIP) in Caregiving

Evidence-Informed Practice (EIP) in caregiving is a comprehensive approach to decision-making that incorporates various evidence sources (Sackett et al., 1996). Unlike Evidence-Based practice (EBP), which prioritizes research evidence, EIP appreciates the weight of other types of evidence, like clinical expertise, patient values and preferences, and local context.

EIP provides more flexibility than EBP, acknowledging that research evidence may not always be universally applicable or readily available (Rycroft-Malone et al., 2004). It emphasizes the individual patient's circumstances and preferences, promoting a patient-centered approach to care.

EIP is particularly crucial when research evidence is scarce or inconclusive. In these cases, caregivers can leverage their clinical expertise, patient preferences, and local context to inform decision-making (Greenhalgh et al., 2014). Furthermore, EIP encourages caregivers to continually reflect on their practices, challenge assumptions, and strive for improvement, fostering a culture of inquiry, innovation, and learning.

The Role of Evidence-Based Practice (EBP) in Caregiving

Evidence-Based Practice (EBP) in caregiving is fundamental for optimizing care outcomes (Sackett et al., 1996). EBP leverages current scientific research and empirical evidence to guide caregiving practices, empowering caregivers to make decisions that are both effective and meaningful.

EBP provides caregivers with proven strategies and interventions that have undergone rigorous scientific scrutiny (Straus et al., 2011). The use of such evidence-based methods enhances the caregiver's confidence in their ability to provide care, knowing they are using methods that yield positive results.

Furthermore, EBP standardizes caregiving procedures, ensuring uniform care quality, irrespective of the caregiver (Melnyk & Fineout-Overholt, 2015). This standardization is critical in caregiving institutions where multiple caregivers may interact with the same care recipient, ensuring consistent care provision.

However, EBP is not without its limitations. It must be remembered that caregiving is as much an art as a science, and individual nuances, unique circumstances, and caregivers' lived experiences must also be considered (Kitson et al., 2008). This is where the value of Evidence-Informed Practice (EIP) comes to the fore.

The Importance of Evidence-Informed Practices (EIP) in Caregiving

Evidence-Informed Practice (EIP) in caregiving offers a different perspective by emphasizing the individuality of each caregiving situation. It highlights the importance of professional expertise, patient preferences, and situational factors when interpreting and implementing evidence (Rycroft-Malone et al., 2004).

EIP values professional expertise derived from practical, on-the-ground experiences as a valuable knowledge source, guiding caregiving practices, especially when research evidence may be unclear, inconclusive, or not fully applicable (Greenhalgh et al., 2014).

Moreover, EIP centers on the preferences and values of the care recipient, recognizing that the most effective care aligns with the care recipient's wishes (Coulter & Collins, 2011). EIP provides the flexibility for caregivers to adapt their strategies to meet these preferences.

Evidence-Based and Evidence-Informed Practices in Caregiving Decision-Making

The integration of Evidence-Based and Evidence-Informed Practices provides a potent tool for caregivers to navigate the myriad decisions involved in caregiving. These practices offer a robust framework for decision-making that is both scientifically sound and tailored to the care recipient's unique needs and circumstances (Melnyk et al., 2014).

Several organizations and programs involved in caregiving are increasingly integrating both EBP and EIP in their frameworks, such as the Department of Veterans Affairs' Caregiver Support Program and the Alzheimer's Association's Dementia Caregiver Support Program (Department of Veterans Affairs, 2020; Alzheimer's Association, 2020).

The synergy of EBP and EIP offers significant impacts on caregiving outcomes. For caregivers, it increases confidence in their caregiving abilities, reduces stress, and improves job satisfaction (Melnyk et al., 2014).

For care recipients, the integration of EBP and EIP translates into better care outcomes, improved health, and higher satisfaction with the care received (Coulter & Collins, 2011).

The Impact of Evidence-Based and Evidence-Informed Practices on Caregiving Outcomes

The amalgamation of evidence-based and evidence-informed practices in caregiving has a profound impact on the outcomes for both the caregiver and the care recipient. The integration of these practices allows for the formation of a versatile caregiving approach that effectively amalgamates empirical research and personal experiences (Rycroft-Malone et al., 2004). This results in a caregiving strategy that is both personalized to meet unique individual needs and rooted in scientifically validated practices (Melnyk et al., 2014).

For the caregiver, this blend allows them to experience a newfound level of confidence in their caregiving skills. This confidence stems from the understanding that their practices are not only backed by solid empirical evidence but are also tailored to the unique needs of their care recipient (Coulter & Collins, 2011). This validation helps in reducing the stress levels experienced by caregivers, often brought on by self-doubt and uncertainty.

Moreover, these evidence-informed practices help caregivers feel more equipped to handle the challenges that come their way. By incorporating their own experiences and adapting practices to meet the needs of their care recipient, caregivers develop a stronger sense of control over their caregiving journey (Rycroft-Malone et al., 2004). This sense of control helps combat feelings of helplessness, often leading to improved mental health and overall well-being for caregivers.

On the other hand, for the care recipient, the integration of EBP and EIP in caregiving can lead to improved health outcomes and quality of life (Melnyk et al., 2014). Care strategies that are backed by empirical evidence have been proven to be effective in bringing about desired health outcomes.

However, by further tailoring these strategies to meet the unique needs and preferences of the care recipient, caregivers can ensure these outcomes are achieved more efficiently and effectively (Coulter & Collins, 2011).

This approach ensures that the care received is not only effective but also humane and respectful. By taking into account the preferences and values of the care recipient, caregivers can ensure that they provide care in a way that respects the care recipient's dignity and autonomy (Rycroft-Malone et al., 2004). This leads to improved satisfaction with the care received, ultimately contributing to improved mental and emotional well-being for the care recipient.

Overall, the integration of evidence-based and evidence-informed practices in caregiving has the potential to significantly improve the caregiving experience for both caregivers and care recipients. By fostering an approach that is both scientifically robust and deeply humane, caregivers can ensure they provide the best possible care for their care recipients.

The Complementary Nature and Potential Setbacks of EBP, EIP, and Field Experience in Caregiving

Evidence-Based Practice (EBP), Evidence-Informed Practice (EIP), and field experience all play crucial roles. Each of these elements comes with its own strengths and limitations, and understanding their interplay can aid caregivers in providing the most effective and personalized care.

EBP, which involves the use of current, high-quality empirical research in decision-making, offers the advantage of reliability (Straus et al., 2011). Since these strategies and interventions have been tested and proven effective, they provide a solid foundation for caregiving. However, EBP may sometimes fail to consider the individualized needs of care recipients, as it is based on generalized findings from research studies (Rycroft-Malone, 2007).

EIP, on the other hand, acknowledges the importance of field experience, patient preferences, and situational factors in implementing caregiving strategies (Rycroft-Malone et al., 2004). It adds a layer of personalization to caregiving, allowing caregivers to adapt their strategies to meet the unique needs of their care recipients. While EIP offers more flexibility than EBP, it might lack the strong evidence base that EBP provides (Greenhalgh et al., 2014).

Field experience brings a wealth of practical knowledge and insights that enrich the caregiving process (Rycroft-Malone et al., 2004). It allows caregivers to handle complex situations effectively, using their hands-on experience to inform their decisions. However, the subjectivity of personal experiences might introduce bias or inconsistency in caregiving strategies.

Despite their individual limitations, EBP, EIP, and field experience can complement each other effectively. EBP provides a robust, scientifically-backed foundation, EIP adds a layer of personalization and flexibility, and field experience brings practical insights and adaptive strategies (Melnyk et al., 2014). Together, these three elements can provide a comprehensive, flexible, and effective approach to caregiving.

However, integrating these elements is not without potential setbacks. For instance, balancing the rigidity of EBP with the flexibility of EIP and field experience can be challenging (Rycroft-Malone, 2007). Caregivers might struggle to decide when to adhere strictly to research evidence and when to deviate based on personal experience or the unique needs of the care recipient. Additionally, the integration of EBP, EIP, and field experience might require additional training and support for caregivers, which can be time-consuming and resource-intensive (Melnyk & Fineout-Overholt, 2015).

Despite these potential setbacks, the integration of EBP, EIP, and field experience offers a promising approach to caregiving. It combines the strengths of each element, creating a holistic, flexible, and effective approach to caregiving (Melnyk et al., 2014). With proper support and training, caregivers can harness the strengths of EBP, EIP, and field experience to provide the best possible care for their care recipients.

Integration of research and experience in caregiving, encapsulated in the blending of EBP and EIP, is a cornerstone of modern caregiving practice. This approach acknowledges the importance of scientific evidence while also recognizing the value of professional expertise, patient preferences, and individual circumstances (Rycroft-Malone et al., 2004).

Caregiving, by its nature, is a complex and multifaceted endeavor. It requires caregivers to make countless decisions, each of which can significantly impact the well-being of the care recipient (Coulter & Collins,

2011). By integrating EBP and EIP, caregivers can make these decisions with confidence, knowing that their strategies are both scientifically sound and uniquely tailored to meet the needs of their care recipients (Melnyk et al., 2014).

Organizations like the Department of Veterans Affairs and the Alzheimer's Association have recognized the value of this integrated approach, offering programs that use EBP and EIP to provide comprehensive support to caregivers (Department of Veterans Affairs, 2020; Alzheimer's Association, 2020). These programs serve as a testament to the power of integrating research and experience in caregiving, highlighting the improved outcomes that can be achieved through this approach.

Ultimately, the integration of EBP and EIP in caregiving represents an evolution in caregiving practice—an evolution towards more effective, personalized, and compassionate care (Rycroft-Malone et al., 2004). By embracing this approach, we can ensure that caregiving is not only a science but also an art, blending the rigor of research with the richness of human experience to provide the best possible care for those in need.

1.4: Practice-Based Evidence in Caregiving: An In-depth Examination

In examining the landscape of caregiving, a striking reality emerges the extensive, often unseen, contributions of informal caregivers. These individuals, typically family members or friends, dedicate significant time and effort to caring for loved ones who are aging, ill, or challenged by disabilities. The breadth of this phenomenon is staggering, with over 40 million people in the United States alone serving as unpaid caregivers (National Alliance for Caregiving, 2020).

Despite the substantial number of individuals engaged in caregiving, this role's unique challenges often remain under-recognized and under-supported. Caregivers frequently grapple with a multifaceted array of difficulties, ranging from the practical to the emotional (Family Caregiver Alliance, 2022). The complexity of these challenges underscores the need for a comprehensive understanding of the caregiving experience and the development of robust, effective support structures to assist caregivers in their vital roles.

In this pursuit, one approach that may provide valuable insights and support is practice-based evidence (PBE). Traditionally, caregiving practices have been informed by evidence-based practice (EBP), a methodology that emphasizes the use of scientific research to guide decision-making (Sackett et al., 1996). However, PBE offers a complementary perspective, one that acknowledges the intrinsic value of the collective wisdom of caregivers themselves (Barker et al., 2016).

PBE is grounded in the recognition that caregiving is a profoundly humanistic endeavor, deeply intertwined with the idiosyncrasies and intricacies of individual lives and their unique challenges. As such, it may elude the confines of traditional research parameters, necessitating a more nuanced, experience-informed approach (Barkham & Mellor-Clark, 2003). This approach considers PBE as a valuable source of knowledge, capturing the compassionate, empathetic, and relational components of caregiving, elements often missed in formal research studies (Barker et al., 2016).

In the following sections, we will delve into the concept of PBE, exploring its potential contributions to caregiving, the challenges it presents, and the ways in which it can be integrated into caregiving practices. We will also examine the impact of caregiving on the physical, emotional, and financial well-being of caregivers themselves and the resources and support structures that can help them navigate their journey.

Understanding Practice-Based Evidence

Practice-based evidence (PBE) is a pivotal concept in the field of caregiving, aiming to shift the narrative from purely research-based evidence to the inclusion of insights drawn from practical experiences (Barker et al., 2016). PBE recognizes the value of practical knowledge that is gleaned from daily interactions, experiences, and direct care. This paradigm recognizes the art of caregiving, emphasizing that it isn't just a clinical or technical endeavor. Instead, it's a practice steeped in humanity, recognizing the intricate weave of individual lives and the complexities that each person presents (Barkham & Mellor-Clark, 2003).

The power of PBE is that it situates the caregiver and their experiences at the center of knowledge creation. In this context, the caregiver isn't just a deliverer of service but is also a contributor to the larger knowledge pool about caregiving (Barker et al., 2016). This is particularly important in caregiving settings where standardized protocols may not fully address or even comprehend the complexities involved. PBE fosters an environment where the insights gained from caregiving are valued, gathered, and utilized to improve practices.

Crucially, PBE acknowledges the intricacies of human life and the individuality of each person under care. It allows caregivers to fine-tune their practices based on the specific needs, preferences, and responses of the person they are caring for. This promotes personalized care – a concept gaining significant momentum in healthcare and social service sectors –

which posits that care should be tailored to each individual rather than implementing a one-size-fits-all approach (Barker et al., 2016).

However, it is essential to understand that PBE does not undermine or reject evidence-based practice (EBP), which is rooted in scientific research and rigorous studies (Sackett et al., 1996). Instead, PBE acts as a complement to EBP, offering a more comprehensive and holistic approach to caregiving. While EBP provides caregivers with reliable and tested techniques and practices, PBE enriches this with insights gained from actual caregiving experiences, creating a more robust and inclusive body of knowledge (Barkham & Mellor-Clark, 2003).

Therefore, the understanding of PBE necessitates a shift in perspective - from viewing caregiving merely as a technical activity based on established rules to recognizing it as a complex, nuanced practice. This shift acknowledges that caregiving is not just about what is clinically or theoretically right but also about what works best in practice, considering the unique needs and circumstances of the individual receiving care (Barker et al., 2016).

The Role of PBE in Caregiving

The use of PBE in caregiving provides a valuable lens through which to view and understand the caregiving process. This lens enables caregivers to illuminate the unexplored complexities of caregiving and bridge the gap between theoretical knowledge and practical application (Barkham & Mellor-Clark, 2003). The value of PBE lies in its recognition of the intimate, compassionate, and relational aspects of caregiving, aspects that cannot be adequately captured by standard research methodologies.

Caregiving, by its very nature, is a deeply humanistic practice that requires a significant amount of compassion, understanding, and empathy. PBE acknowledges these facets of caregiving, which often go unmentioned in formal research studies (Barker et al., 2016). Caregivers' nuanced understanding, developed over time and through interactions with those they care for, can provide an invaluable source of knowledge. PBE highlights this understanding, championing it as a vital contribution to the field.

Another crucial aspect of PBE in caregiving is the sense of community it fosters among caregivers. Through the sharing and pooling of their experiences and insights, caregivers become part of a collective knowledge-making process (Barker et al., 2016). The wisdom of one caregiver, informed by their direct experiences and reflections, can serve as an invaluable resource for another caregiver, enhancing their understanding and practices.

This process of collective knowledge-making can also help to challenge existing norms and conventions in caregiving. As caregivers share their experiences, they bring to light the successes and failures of established practices. This can instigate meaningful discussions and stimulate changes in caregiving practices, pushing the field towards better, more effective, and personalized care strategies (Barkham & Mellor-Clark, 2003).

PBE also offers caregivers a platform to voice their perspectives and experiences. Too often, caregivers' voices are sidelined in favor of more formal, research-based evidence. PBE seeks to rectify this, empowering caregivers by validating and acknowledging their experiences, knowledge, and contributions to the field of caregiving (Barker et al., 2016)

Challenges in Utilizing PBE

Despite the inherent value and potential benefits of PBE, its utilization is not without its challenges. The most significant obstacle lies in the very nature of PBE – its reliance on the reflection and self-evaluation of caregivers (Barkham & Mellor-Clark, 2003). This necessitates a high degree of self-awareness, as well as the ability to critically assess one's experiences, practices, and assumptions.

Caregivers are required to be active participants in their learning process, continually questioning their preconceptions and assumptions. This can be demanding, particularly given the already challenging nature of caregiving (Family Caregiver Alliance, 2022). Maintaining an open mind and being willing to question and change established practices can be emotionally taxing and require significant energy and commitment.

There is also the issue of validating PBE. Unlike traditional evidence, which can be quantified and objectively tested, PBE is highly subjective, rooted in personal experiences and reflections (Barker et al., 2016). This raises questions about the reliability and validity of PBE. How do we ensure that PBE is accurate, consistent, and reliable? How do we standardize the gathering and utilization of PBE, given its inherently individualistic nature?

Another challenge is the potential for bias. Because PBE is based on individual experiences, it's subject to the caregivers' personal biases and subjective interpretations (Barkham & Mellor-Clark, 2003). It can be influenced by a caregiver's beliefs, attitudes, emotions, and perceptions, which may not necessarily be accurate or representative of broader realities.

There is the challenge of integrating PBE into formal training and education for caregivers. Given the importance of standardized, evidence-based education, incorporating PBE can seem daunting (Barker et al., 2016). Balancing the empirical rigor of formal education with the subjective richness of PBE requires careful planning and consideration.

Integrating PBE into Caregiving Practices

Despite these challenges, the integration of PBE into caregiving practices remains essential. Incorporating PBE into caregiving requires the establishment of platforms and opportunities for caregivers to share their experiences and insights (Barker et al., 2016). This could take the form of regular team meetings, reflective practice sessions, or online forums where caregivers can discuss their experiences and learn from one another.

In integrating PBE, organizations should foster a culture that values and respects the knowledge and insights gained from direct caregiving experience (Barkham & Mellor-Clark, 2003). Caregivers should be encouraged to reflect on their experiences, critically analyze their practices, and share their insights with their colleagues. This practice should be nurtured and supported, and caregivers should be provided with the necessary tools and training to effectively engage in reflective practice.

In terms of education and training, PBE should be incorporated into the curriculum alongside evidence-based theories and practices (Barker et al., 2016). This could involve case studies, reflective essays, and group discussions, which allow students to reflect on their experiences and learn from one another. The integration of PBE into education can enhance the learning experience, providing students with a more holistic understanding of caregiving.

Policies and procedures should also reflect the value of PBE (Barkham & Mellor-Clark, 2003). Caregiving organizations can demonstrate their commitment to PBE by integrating it into their policies, procedures, and practice guidelines. This not only legitimizes PBE but also helps to ensure that it is consistently applied across the organization.

The integration of PBE into caregiving practices requires a commitment to fostering a culture of reflective practice, learning, and continuous improvement (Barker et al., 2016). It necessitates an environment where caregivers are empowered to learn from their experiences, question their practices, and contribute to the broader body of knowledge on caregiving.

The Potential Impact of PBE

The potential impact of integrating PBE into caregiving is significant. By acknowledging and valuing the wisdom and experiences of caregivers, PBE has the power to transform caregiving practices (Barkham & Mellor-Clark, 2003). It encourages the development of more nuanced, empathetic, and effective care strategies tailored to the unique needs and circumstances of each individual under care.

In a broader sense, PBE also has the potential to transform the caregiving field as a whole (Barker et al., 2016). By valuing the wisdom distilled from lived experiences, it can contribute to a more comprehensive and holistic understanding of caregiving. This can lead to the development of new theories, models, and practices that reflect the realities of caregiving, enhancing the effectiveness and quality of care.

On an individual level, PBE can empower caregivers. By recognizing their experiences and insights as valuable sources of knowledge, PBE can help caregivers to feel seen, heard, and valued (Barkham & Mellor-Clark, 2003). This can enhance their confidence and satisfaction in their role, reducing caregiver burnout and improving their well-being.

For the individuals under care, the impact of PBE can also be significant. Care strategies informed by PBE are likely to be more personalized, considerate, and effective, leading to improved care outcomes (Barker et al., 2016). The individual under care is likely to feel more understood and valued, leading to improved satisfaction and quality of life.

The potential impact of PBE is extensive. It holds the promise of improved care outcomes, more satisfied and empowered caregivers, and a more comprehensive understanding of caregiving (Barkham & Mellor-Clark, 2003). As such, PBE represents a valuable tool in the caregiving toolkit, one that warrants further exploration and integration into caregiving practices.

1.5: The Integration of Empirical Evidence and Professional Expertise in Caregiving: A Comprehensive Approach

Caregiving is a multifaceted endeavor, one that demands the integration of various forms of knowledge and expertise. The uniqueness of each caregiving situation, combined with the humanistic nature of the role, requires an approach that can effectively navigate this complexity. By integrating empirical evidence, professional expertise, and personal caregiving insights, caregivers are better equipped to provide the best possible care to their loved ones (Pearson et al., 2007).

One approach to this integration is through the use of practice-based evidence (PBE) and evidence-informed practice (EIP) in caregiving decision-making. These approaches recognize the importance of blending the insights gained from research with the wisdom distilled from lived experience (Greenhalgh et al., 2014). By doing so, they offer a more comprehensive and nuanced understanding of caregiving, one that is responsive to the unique needs and circumstances of each care recipient.

Evidence-based practice (EBP) has long been a cornerstone of caregiving, guiding decision-making based on the best available evidence from systematic research (Sackett et al., 1996). However, it is not always possible to rely solely on formal research studies, which may not fully capture the unique needs and circumstances of care recipients. This is where PBE comes in, filling in the gaps left by formal research studies and allowing caregivers to tailor interventions to meet the unique needs of care recipients (Barkham & Mellor-Clark, 2003).

Evidence-informed practice (EIP), on the other hand, complements EBP by integrating personal caregiving insights with objective research findings (Rycroft-Malone et al., 2004). This blending of EBP and EIP equips caregivers with a comprehensive toolkit for decision-making, enabling them to navigate the complexities of human experiences and individualized care situations.

In the following sections, we will delve into the process of integrating empirical evidence, professional expertise, and personal caregiving insights in caregiving. We will examine the role of PBE and EIP, explore examples of evidence-informed programs, and discuss innovative methodologies for translating evidence-based programs into real-world settings.

The Role of Practice-Based Evidence and Evidence-Informed Practice

Understanding Practice-Based Evidence

Practice-based evidence (PBE) is an innovative approach that acknowledges the importance of caregiver wisdom in shaping effective care strategies (Barkham & Mellor-Clark, 2003). Rather than relying strictly on a traditional research paradigm, PBE seeks to harness the insights and practical knowledge gleaned from on-the-ground caregiving experiences. This form of evidence often illuminates overlooked dimensions of caregiving, such as the psychological and emotional toll it takes on caregivers or the intricate dynamics of a patient-caregiver relationship.

PBE doesn't attempt to dilute caregiving experiences into quantifiable metrics or standardized procedures. Instead, it champions the authenticity and richness of real-world caregiving experiences (Barker et al., 2016). The value of PBE lies in its capacity to capture and honor the complexity of caregiving realities, acknowledging that each caregiver's journey is unique and deeply personal. This includes the personal struggles, triumphs, learned skills, and acquired wisdom that define each caregiver's experience.

Fundamentally, PBE challenges the notion that caregiving best practices can be solely derived from abstracted, population-level studies (Barkham & Mellor-Clark, 2003). It recognizes that caregiving is an inherently human enterprise grounded in the nuances of individual personalities, histories, and relationships. It understands that effective caregiving strategies are often borne out of the crucible of direct experience, refined over time through trial, error, resilience, and adaptive learning.

However, acknowledging the value of PBE doesn't necessitate the wholesale rejection of traditional research methodologies. On the contrary, it encourages a symbiotic relationship between practice and research, where each informs the other in a continual cycle of growth and refinement (Greenhalgh et al., 2014). PBE can thus be seen as an invitation to broaden the horizons of caregiving knowledge, promoting a more inclusive and holistic understanding of what it means to provide care.

In a world that is increasingly data-driven, there's a risk that the human element of caregiving can be overlooked in favor of more quantifiable metrics (Barkham & Mellor-Clark, 2003). However, PBE serves as a crucial counterbalance to this trend, championing the primacy of lived experience and the nuanced wisdom it engenders. It underscores the idea that while data and research are invaluable resources, they are not the sum total of what it means to provide effective, compassionate care.

The Importance of PBE in Caregiving

The importance of PBE in caregiving cannot be overstated. It provides a unique perspective that augments formal research studies by offering insights into the complex, nuanced realities of providing care (Barkham & Mellor-Clark, 2003). These insights, derived from the lived experiences of caregivers themselves, illuminate the human side of caregiving—the joys, frustrations, triumphs, and challenges that define the caregiving journey.

Moreover, PBE can serve as a guide to navigating the often unpredictable and uncertain landscape of caregiving (Barker et al., 2016). As caregivers grapple with the daily realities of providing care, they develop a wealth of practical knowledge and wisdom that can be invaluable to other caregivers navigating similar situations. This collective wisdom can provide guidance and support, helping caregivers feel less isolated and more equipped to handle the challenges of caregiving.

PBE also holds the potential to enrich our understanding of the emotional aspects of caregiving (Barkham & Mellor-Clark, 2003). It acknowledges the deeply emotional nature of providing care, recognizing that caregiving is not simply a set of tasks to be performed but a profoundly human endeavor marked by empathy, compassion, and connection. It illuminates the emotional challenges that caregivers often face, from feelings of stress and burnout to the sense of fulfillment and purpose that can come from providing care.

Furthermore, PBE allows for the exploration of the relational components of caregiving (Barker et al., 2016). It emphasizes the interpersonal dynamics between caregivers and care recipients, acknowledging the reciprocal nature of caregiving relationships. It provides insights into how these relationships can evolve and change over time, shaped by the shared experiences and emotional bonds between caregivers and care recipients.

The importance of PBE lies in its capacity to bridge the gap between theory and practice (Greenhalgh et al., 2014). While evidence-based practice provides valuable guidelines and frameworks for caregiving, PBE complements these by illuminating the realities of caregiving in practice. It grounds caregiving knowledge in the lived experiences of caregivers, making it more relevant and applicable to the daily challenges of providing care.

Understanding Evidence-Informed Practice

Evidence-informed practice (EIP) is an approach that integrates the best available research evidence with clinical expertise and patient values and preferences to make decisions about care (Melnyk & Fineout-Overholt, 2019). EIP acknowledges that while empirical research provides important insights into best practices, it does not have all the answers for complex care situations. Caregiving is as much an art as it is a science; thus, the experiential knowledge of practitioners is equally vital (Rycroft-Malone et al., 2004). This recognition helps caregivers navigate unpredictabilities and respond effectively to patients' unique needs.

EIP considers caregivers' clinical judgment gained through experience as complementary to research findings. Caregivers develop an in-depth understanding of patients that enriches the care process when incorporated into decision-making (Clyne et al., 2013). EIP also acknowledges the socio-cultural context of caregiving. It recognizes that caregiving is influenced by cultural values, social norms, and personal beliefs of both the caregiver and patient and integrates these factors to promote culturally sensitive care (Kirmayer, 2012).

EIP promotes continuous learning and adaptation in caregiving. It encourages caregivers to stay updated on research, learn from experience, and adapt practices as needed. This makes EIP a dynamic, evolving approach capable of responding to the changing realities of caregiving (Titler, 2018).

The Role of EIP in Caregiving

EIP plays multiple roles in caregiving by integrating research and practice insights to respond effectively to patients' circumstances. EIP facilitates personalized care by tailoring interventions to each patient's unique needs and preferences, resulting in improved quality of care (Sidani & Braden, 2011).

EIP empowers caregivers by validating their experiential wisdom, boosting confidence, and enhancing competence. This can lead to greater job satisfaction and improved mental health among caregivers (Janssen et al., 2011). EIP also promotes resilience in caregivers by providing coping strategies for caregiving challenges, enabling them to better handle stress and avoid burnout (Sherman et al., 2013).

EIP advances caregiving knowledge and practice by integrating research and practice insights to develop effective strategies, policies, and programs, improving the overall quality of care (Melnyk et al., 2020).

The Synergy of PBE and EIP

The constructive collaboration of practice-based evidence (PBE) and EIP offers a comprehensive, balanced approach to caregiving. PBE values the wisdom from caregiving experiences, while EIP integrates it with research findings (Breckenridge-Sproat et al., 2012). This allows caregivers to utilize diverse knowledge to enhance care quality.

This synergistic approach enables personalized, adaptive care by considering patients' unique needs and integrating caregiver insights. This alignment of care with the patient's circumstances can optimize outcomes (Spiri & MacPhee, 2020).

The PBE and EIP integration also promotes informed decision-making by providing a holistic understanding of caregiving that equips caregivers to make appropriate choices and feel empowered (Pearson et al., 2005).

Additionally, the constructive interaction contributes to advancing knowledge by elucidating caregiving complexities and sparking effective innovations in strategies and policies (Holmes et al., 2006). Ultimately, this underscores the multifaceted nature of quality caregiving requiring the integration of science and compassion (Eraut, 2000).

Evidence-Informed Programs in Caregiving

The Role of Evidence-Informed Programs

Evidence-informed programs serve a vital function in caregiving by providing caregivers with valuable resources to deliver effective and personalized care to patients (Burgio et al., 2009). Programs such as the Department of Veterans Affairs Caregiver Support Program integrate the latest empirical research findings with insights gained from real-world caregiving practice. This allows them to address the complex multidimensional realities involved in caregiving. Rather than focusing only on the technical skills needed for caregiving, these programs provide comprehensive support that also tackles the significant emotional, social, psychological, and practical challenges that caregivers routinely face (Dam et al., 2016).

These programs highlight the importance of holistic, person-centered care. They recognize that caregiving involves much more than just providing basic physical care to patients. Effective caregiving requires providing emotional support, facilitating social engagement, managing healthcare needs, and assisting with activities of daily living. By making resources and support available across all these areas, evidence-based caregiving programs enable caregivers to take an integrated approach that enhances the overall physical, mental, and social well-being of care recipients (Gitlin et al., 2010).

In addition, the programs empower caregivers by equipping them with state-of-the-art knowledge, skills, and resources to confidently navigate the caregiving process. This empowerment can boost caregivers' self-efficacy, resilience, and caregiving capabilities. It allows them to provide higher-quality care while also effectively coping with the challenges and stresses inherent in the caregiving role (Burgio et al., 2009).

These programs also actively contribute to the ongoing development of evidence-informed best practices in the caregiving field. By continually integrating emerging research findings with evolving real-world caregiving insights, they enable a more nuanced, comprehensive understanding of effective caregiving. This fosters ongoing improvements, sparking further advancements and innovations in practical caregiving strategies, policies, and programs (Burgio et al., 2001).

The Impact of CSP and DCSP

The Caregiver Support Program offered by the Department of Veterans Affairs (CSP) and the Alzheimer's Association's Dementia Caregiver Support Program (DCSP) have made significant contributions and impacted countless caregivers and care recipients through the evidence-based resources they provide. These include offerings such as specialized education and training tailored to caregiving needs, one-on-one counseling, support groups focused on sharing practical and emotional coping strategies, and respite care relief services to temporarily relieve caregivers from duties (Judge et al., 2011; Mittelman et al., 2006).

Numerous studies have shown that caregivers participating in these programs report decreased stress and feelings of being overwhelmed, increased confidence in their caregiving abilities, improved caregiving skills, higher engagement levels, and greater satisfaction with the types of support received through these programs. Such improvements among caregivers translate directly into enhanced daily caregiving practices and interactions, resulting in better health, safety, and quality of life outcomes for care recipients (Gitlin et al., 2003; Henriksson et al., 2012).

In addition to their direct impacts on individual caregivers and care recipients, the CSP and DCSP serve a valuable role in the broader caregiving ecosystem. They have emerged as models that other governmental, non-profit, and private sector organizations look to when seeking to develop or enhance their own caregiver support programs. In this way, the CSP and DCSP help promote the expanded adoption of evidence-based and empirically validated best practices throughout the caregiving field (Van Houtven et al., 2011).

However, it is important to note that even well-designed programs like the CSP and DCSP cannot act as a rigid, one-size-fits-all solution. Caregiving is an inherently complex and multifaceted process that must account for a diverse array of individual needs and circumstances. These programs recognize this reality and thus strive to provide a wide range of resources, support mechanisms, and intervention strategies that can be tailored and personalized to match the unique needs profile of each caregiver and care recipient (Burgio et al., 2009).

The Importance of Tailoring Interventions

The ability to tailor interventions and resources to match the specific needs and circumstances of individual caregivers and care recipients represents a foundational pillar underlying the success of evidence-based caregiving support programs. This recognition of the diversity of needs and the importance of individualization enables caregivers to selectively utilize the strategies and resources likely to be most beneficial and relevant for their situation. Being able to access the "right fit" resources for their needs enhances intervention effectiveness and the caregiver's sense of empowerment (Samus et al., 2014).

One way tailoring is achieved is through conducting comprehensive assessments of each caregiver and care recipient. This allows for a detailed understanding of their unique risk factors, challenges, needs, resources, and circumstances. Based on assessment findings, an individualized care plan can be collaboratively developed that provides targeted recommendations of specific strategies, services, and resources matched to the caregiver's needs profile and designed to enhance their capabilities. This personalized approach also improves caregiver engagement and adherence to the jointly developed care plan (Elliott et al., 2010).

Tailoring also recognizes that care recipients have diverse needs, backgrounds, preferences, and abilities that impact care. Effective care strategies must account for these individual differences rather than take a one-size-fits-all approach. Tailored interventions that consider the unique care recipient profile led to more personalized and higher-quality care (Burgio et al., 2001).

Moreover, tailored approaches can help optimize the efficient allocation of available resources and avoid wasting efforts on ineffective interventions. By focusing on the specific strategies demonstrated to work best for an individual's needs, resources can be concentrated where they will have the biggest impact (Van Houtven et al., 2011).

The Role of Support in Evidence-Informed Programs

Providing comprehensive support across practical, emotional, and social domains represents a fundamental element woven through evidence-based caregiving programs. Their resources and services aim to address the diverse sources of stress and challenges that caregivers routinely encounter in an effort to enhance coping capabilities and empower effective caregiving (Chien et al., 2011).

Practical forms of support include education and training focused on building caregiving knowledge and hands-on skills, providing equipment and technologies that facilitate care tasks, and offering respite care services that temporarily relieve the caregiver and provide a much-needed break from constantly being "on call." Enhancing these practical competencies and resources helps caregivers feel more confident in their abilities to provide care safely and effectively (Dam et al., 2018).

Emotional forms of support are also crucial, given that caregiving can be mentally and emotionally draining. Counseling services, caregiving support groups, and peer networks create a safe space for caregivers to openly share their experiences, express feelings, exchange coping strategies, and gain emotional validation and encouragement. This facilitates emotional processing and enhances coping capacities to help navigate stressful situations (Williams et al., 2019).

Facilitating social connections and community engagement provides another layer of invaluable support. This helps reduce feelings of isolation, creates meaningful social roles, and connects caregivers with additional resources and networks that can further enhance knowledge, skills, and support. Strengthening social bonds and community integration promotes resilience and emotional well-being, enabling caregivers to deliver higher-quality care (Dam et al., 2018).

Comprehensive support is a cornerstone woven through evidence-informed caregiving programs. Addressing intertwined practical, emotional, and social needs allows programs to alleviate caregiver burden across multiple dimensions, fosters empowerment, and enables caregivers to deliver individualized, high-quality care tailored to the specific needs of each care recipient (Burgio et al., 2009).

Evidence-Informed Programs: A Path Forward

Evidence-informed programs represent a promising approach to enhancing caregiver support and improving outcomes for care recipients. By seamlessly integrating empirical research evidence, the professional expertise of practitioners, and experiential knowledge gained from hands-on caregiving, these programs provide a comprehensive, holistic framework for delivering impactful caregiver support (Burgio et al., 2009).

The development and implementation of such programs underscore the vital importance of taking an evidence-informed approach to caregiving.

This goes beyond simply applying research findings directly into practice. It involves an iterative, dynamic process of continuous learning and adaptation, recognizing the multifaceted complexities inherent in real-world caregiving contexts and the diversity of needs among caregivers and care recipients. This enabling approach empowers caregivers to actively incorporate new research findings into their practices aligned with their personal experiences and insights (Rycroft-Malone et al., 2004).

Furthermore, well-designed, evidence-based programs provide an ideal platform for promoting ongoing learning and continuous improvement in caregiving. These programs can evolve and adapt by regularly integrating emerging research findings, implementation feedback from caregivers, and lessons learned from real-world applications. This fosters the development of increasingly effective, personalized caregiving strategies, enhanced support resources for caregivers, and improved health and wellness outcomes for care recipients (Titler, 2018).

Implementing robust evidence-informed programs also underscores the importance of fostering multidisciplinary collaboration in caregiving. Caregiving encompasses a broad spectrum of interconnected disciplines, including nursing, medicine, social work, psychology, rehabilitation sciences, and more. Bringing together stakeholders across these disciplines can catalyze innovation and result in more comprehensive, holistic, and higher-impact caregiver support programs (Chien et al., 2011).

Additionally, well-designed programs recognize caregivers as active collaborative partners rather than passive care recipients. They aim to empower caregivers by equipping them with state-of-the-art knowledge, skills, resources, and technologies tailored to their needs. This enables caregivers to optimize their contributions and enhance their effectiveness, improving care experiences and outcomes for care recipients (Burgio et al., 2009).

Translating Evidence-Based Programs into Real-World Settings

Innovative Methodologies for Translation

Translating evidence-based programs designed in controlled research settings into messy, complex real-world caregiving contexts presents multifaceted challenges. However, innovative implementation science methodologies offer promising solutions to bridge this translational gap. They provide pathways for caregivers to successfully apply empirically supported knowledge in their unique settings.

One translational methodology for gaining recognition involves proactively adapting interventions to optimize fit with real-world contexts. This approach appreciates real-world caregiving's inherent variability and dynamics and aims to ensure interventions are flexible and responsive to local needs (Chambers et al., 2013). Carefully adapting programs to align with the caregiving context enhances relevance, feasibility, and sustainability, enabling more practical application of evidence-based knowledge.

Another methodology is to directly study the implementation process itself. This involves elucidating how evidence-based interventions are applied in real-world settings, systematically identifying barriers and facilitators that influence implementation success, and developing tailored strategies to enhance implementation effectiveness (Damschroder et al., 2009). These implementation insights can directly inform the optimization of evidence-based program design and delivery.

Participatory research methods that actively engage caregivers as partners in the research process have also proven valuable for translation. Tapping into caregiver perspectives and insider insights helps ensure interventions are well-aligned with their needs and values (Jagosh et al., 2012). This fosters greater relevance, satisfaction, and sustained use of programs.

Additionally, utilizing structured implementation science frameworks can promote success. These frameworks offer systematic approaches for catalyzing change in specific settings. They provide a multidimensional perspective spanning individual, organizational, and broader system levels to guide effective translation (Tabak et al., 2012).

The Impact of Real-World Adaptations

Adapting evidence-based interventions to optimize fit with highly variable real-world caregiving contexts can profoundly impact enhancing their effectiveness. Tailoring programs to align with local needs, perspectives, and resources enables caregivers to apply knowledge more successfully in practical and meaningful ways (Chambers et al., 2013). This, in turn, empowers improved caregiving practices and enhances care recipient health, safety, and quality of life.

Real-world adaptations can take many forms across multiple dimensions. This includes modifying program content, adjusting delivery formats and channels, altering timing and dosage, and changing implementation strategies. Regardless of adaptation type, the overarching goal remains responsively aligning programs to the living realities of caregivers and care recipients (Wiltsey Stirman et al., 2019).

Importantly, real-world adaptation underscores the fundamental nature of caregiving as a dynamic, nonlinear process requiring constant learning and agility to evolving circumstances. Providing caregivers with flexible interventions fosters resilience and sustained effectiveness amidst ever-changing demands (Rycroft-Malone et al., 2004).

Additionally, real-world adaptations contribute to intervention sustainability. Ensuring programs deliver value for caregivers enhances satisfaction, engagement, and continued use, leading to enduring impact and return on investment (Chambers et al., 2013).

Furthermore, studying real-world adaptations provides integral learning opportunities to advance the science of caregiving. Elucidating when, why, and how interventions are adapted informs future research, program design, and implementation optimization (Wiltsey Stirman et al., 2019).

Studying the Implementation Process

Intentionally studying the real-world implementation process represents a pivotal undertaking enabling the successful translation of evidence-based interventions into practice. A deepening understanding of how programs are applied in messy clinical contexts provides invaluable insights to inform translation optimization (Tabak et al., 2012).

Elucidating contextual factors influencing successful implementation allows the identification of key barriers undermining effectiveness, such as insufficient caregiver training or lack of leadership support, along with vital facilitators enhancing success, like caregiver engagement and organizational alignment (Damschroder et al., 2009). Developing tailored strategies to address barriers while leveraging facilitators is key to implementation success.

Studying real-world applications sheds light on what works, for whom, and under what conditions. These insights enable the design of effective implementation strategies adapted to the caregiving context and optimized for sustainability. This empowers the successful translation of evidence-based programs, elevating caregiving practices (Chambers et al., 2013).

The My Journey Program

The My Journey program represents an inspiring example of an evidence-based intervention thoughtfully translated into an impactful real-world caregiving context. This program provides adolescent students a safe space to explore their evolving cultural identity and develop skills to support healthy choices and behaviors (Moran & Reaman, 2002).

Culturally relevant activities like decorating medicine wheels, creating winter counts pictographs, and tribal storytelling engage students' strengths and perspectives. The program promotes the development of self-knowledge, cultural pride, relational values, and purpose to guide positive decision-making. Students are empowered to express their cultural identity and wisdom through their personal choices and actions (Moran & Reaman, 2002).

The success of My Journey demonstrates the immense potential of collaboratively translating evidence-based programming into real-world settings when done in a manner aligned with community needs, values, and culture. It provides inspiration and guidance for enhancing future translation efforts across myriad caregiving contexts.

Evidence-Informed Programs: A Path Forward

Evidence-informed caregiving programs integrated with implementation science approaches hold immense promise for tangibly enhancing caregiver support and improving health outcomes for care recipients. When rooted in firm empirical evidence, professional expertise, and caregiving experience, they can provide impactful real-world solutions (Burgio et al., 2009).

Moving forward, optimizing structures and processes for collaborative translation focused on adaptable, contextually aligned implementation will be key to actualizing this promise at scale. While translation is multifaceted, the payoff of empowering caregivers with practical, evidence-based strategies and resources that enable them to provide higher quality, personalized care is well worth the effort (Rycroft-Malone et al., 2004).

The translation process itself generates invaluable opportunities for stakeholder learning, field advancement, and cross-pollination of insights from research, practice wisdom, and lived caregiver experience. This strengthening of the connections across caregiving system components fosters continuous iterative improvements in caregiving programs, practices, and policies (Titler, 2018).

By embracing the complexity and continuously learning together, researchers, caregivers, practitioners, and others can co-create the future of caregiving. Although the path forward holds challenges, it is filled with immense possibilities to tangibly transform care experiences and outcomes through meaningful collaboration and groundbreaking innovation. The potential for positive impact is boundless.

The Potential of Translating Evidence-Based Programs

The breadth of potential benefits from translating evidence-based caregiving programs into real-world practice is immense. Effective translation can provide caregivers with practical, rigorously evaluated strategies and resources that empower them to optimize care quality and outcomes (Burgio et al., 2009). For this potential to be realized, however, keen attention must be devoted to thoughtfully adapting programs to align with the messy complexities of authentic caregiving contexts, needs, and values.

It is vital to recognize that simple, linear transfer of research findings into varied clinical settings is unrealistic. Rather, ethical, empowering translation is a dynamic, iterative process requiring a deep understanding of caregiving realities, human needs, and the nuances of catalyzing real change (Rycroft-Malone et al., 2004). Creativity, flexibility, and unwavering persistence are essential to the process.

The fruits of this arduous translational labor are well worth the required effort. Effective translation can provide caregivers with the empirically supported knowledge, skills, and tools needed to optimize care provision. This contributes to improved caregiver support, enhanced care recipient health and well-being, more robust implementation evidence, and the accelerated advancement of caregiving science (Burgio et al., 2009).

Importantly, studying the translation process itself generates invaluable knowledge about implementation mechanics in real-world settings. Evaluating evidence-based program outcomes and dynamics within authentic caregiving contexts provides key insights to inform the optimization of future research, intervention development, and implementation processes (Chambers et al., 2013).

Finally, the collaborative translation journey serves as a catalyst for transformational multi-stakeholder learning. By working closely together, researchers, caregivers, clinicians, and others gain key skills and build critical connections across disciplines to drive continuous improvement. This propels the integrated evolution of caregiving research, practice, policy, and education (Titler, 2018).

Translating evidence-based programs into real clinical settings, although complex, holds immense potential to tangibly improve caregiving through innovation. Guided by empathy, wisdom, and an empowering implementational approach, we can co-create a brighter caregiving future. This path promises boundless opportunities to enhance lives through purposeful collective action.

1.6: Unearthing the Potential of Fusion: Integrating Empirical Evidence and Professional Expertise in Caregiving

The multifaceted practice of caregiving requires a flexible, comprehensive approach that integrates various knowledge sources, including empirical research evidence, professional expertise gained from experience, and personal caregiving insights (Eraut, 2000). This fusion of perspectives can significantly enhance caregiving practices and improve outcomes for both caregivers and recipients (Rycroft-Malone et al., 2004).

Evidence-based programs like the VA Caregiver Support Program provide valuable research-informed resources to aid caregivers (Van Houtven et al., 2011). However, empirical evidence alone is insufficient. It must be complemented by the nuanced clinical judgment honed through years of direct practice experience, which offers a unique understanding of person-centered, individualized care (Clyne et al., 2013).

Integrating empirical knowledge and professional expertise creates a multifaceted lens to address complex caregiving needs holistically across physical, psychological, social, and spiritual domains (Chien et al., 2011). For instance, the My Journey program successfully fuses evidence and expertise to support healthy adolescent development (Moran & Reaman, 2002). This fusion also has the potential to mitigate caregiver stress and burnout by providing tailored support to navigate caregiving demands (Williams et al., 2019).

In the following sections, we explore the transformative synergistic power of integrating empirical and professional knowledge in caregiving, the myriad benefits of this fusion, and its immense potential for elevating caregiving programs and practices.

The Transformative Power of Fusion

Understanding the Fusion

The fusion of empirical evidence and professional expertise creates an impactful combination that significantly enhances the efficiency and effectiveness of caregiving practices. Empirical evidence derived from rigorous research provides a robust foundation for decision-making, informing caregivers about scientifically validated interventions (Melnyk & Fineout-Overholt, 2019).

Meanwhile, professional caregiving expertise encapsulates the nuanced practical expertise accrued through years of hands-on experience across diverse contexts and challenges. This helps caregivers exercise effective real-time judgment to balance standardized practices with individualized care (Eraut, 2000).

Together, these complementary domains offer caregivers an expansive, multifaceted understanding to address care recipients varied biopsychosocial needs and preferences. This fusion brings together the strengths of each, with empirical research providing the overarching framework and professional expertise filling in the intricate details reflecting care recipients' unique needs and values (Rycroft-Malone et al., 2004).

Within caregiving support programs, fusion enhances versatility and adaptability. Empirical evidence grounds interventions in rigorous research promoting proven best practices (Melnyk & Fineout-Overholt, 2019).

Concurrently, professional expertise ensures these practices are implemented in nuanced, personalized ways aligned with caregivers' and recipients' contexts and needs (Clyne et al., 2013).

This fusion becomes even more impactful when underpinned by a commitment to continuous learning and improvement. As caregivers integrate empirical and professional knowledge, they can develop a learning mindset characterized by curiosity, humility, and dedication to excellence (Eraut, 2000). This mindset fuels the ongoing enhancement of caregiving practices.

The Role of Fusion in Caregiving Support Programs

Fusion is crucial for elevating the relevance and efficacy of caregiving support programs. Bridging empirical evidence and professional expertise ensures programs provide research-informed support that aligns with practice realities, thereby meeting diverse caregiver and recipient needs more responsively (Rycroft-Malone et al., 2004).

Fusion enriches program content and methods by combining research-based knowledge offering insights into effective interventions, with practice wisdom imparting real-world nuance and applicability (Eraut, 2000). This robust integration enhances program quality and utility.

Additionally, fusion boosts program accessibility and applicability. Grounding in empirical evidence establishes program credibility, while professional expertise ensures relatability to lived experiences, increasing engagement and use of strategies (Melnyk & Fineout-Overholt, 2019).

Fusion also promotes program adaptability and sustainability. Empirical evidence provides an evolving, relevant basis, while professional expertise enables contextual responsiveness to be evolving needs, ensuring enduring impact (Rycroft-Malone et al., 2004).

Moreover, fusion facilitates stakeholder partnership and co-creation of programs integrating research and practice insights. This collaboration can optimize intervention relevance, acceptability, and efficacy (Clyne et al., 2013).

Benefits of Fusion in Caregiving

Integrating empirical research evidence with professional caregiving expertise yields numerous impactful benefits, including enhanced decision-making, reduced caregiver stress, improved care quality, enriched support resources, and promotion of individualized, person-centered care (Rycroft-Malone et al., 2004).

By blending rigorous research knowledge with nuanced insights from experience, caregivers are empowered to make better-informed decisions tailored to each care recipient's unique needs and preferences. This enables more personalized, effective care strategies that optimize well-being (Clyne et al., 2013).

Additionally, this multifaceted integration provides caregivers with evidence-based stress management techniques and seasoned guidance on applying them amidst caregiving challenges. This holistic support fosters resilience, helping mitigate burnout risks (Williams et al., 2019).

Furthermore, combining empirical best practices with practical wisdom cultivated through care delivery ensures caregiving approaches are simultaneously research-driven and experientially attuned. This drives improvements in care quality and recipient outcomes across physical, psychological, and social domains (Rycroft-Malone et al., 2004).

Also, incorporating professional perspectives into research-based support programs enhances relevance and comprehensiveness in addressing caregivers' real-world needs. This strengthens interventions, empowering caregivers' capacities, and well-being (Eraut, 2000).

Moreover, fusing empirical findings and clinical judgment promotes individually tailored, compassionate, person-centered care focused on each recipient's unique priorities and preferences, supporting their dignity (Clyne et al., 2013).

Unleashing the Potential of Fusion in Caregiving Support Programs

Strategically integrating empirical and professional knowledge sources holds immense potential for optimizing caregiving support programs through responsiveness to evolving demands, sparking meaningful innovations, and elevating the field. Realizing this potential requires concerted efforts.

Cultivating a culture of dynamic learning and improvement is fundamental, with investment in regular skills training incorporating the latest research alongside experiential insights from seasoned caregivers.

Developing ongoing feedback loops leveraging both knowledge spheres to inform program adaptations is also key (Titler, 2018).

Likewise, facilitating diverse stakeholder collaboration across caregiver, healthcare, research, policy, and community roles is crucial for gaining a holistic, empathetic understanding of caregiving realities to collaboratively develop impactful solutions (Chien et al., 2011).

Equally vital is promoting rigorous caregiving research and effective translation into practice while prioritizing professional caregiver perspectives and lived experiences as complementary knowledge sources to enrich studies (Melnyk & Fineout-Overholt, 2019).

Advocacy for inclusive policies integrating empirical evidence and practice insights can heighten support for caregivers while advancing care quality (Rycroft-Malone et al., 2004).

Helping caregivers build resilience through research-backed self-care strategies enriched with experiential nuance is imperative for sustaining effective practices and upholding caregiver wellness (Williams et al., 2019).

The Role of Fusion in Caregiving Support Programs

Fusion plays an invaluable role in caregiving support programs, enabling the provision of multifaceted, nuanced, person-centered care while promoting responsiveness, learning, collaboration, advocacy, and caregiver support (Rycroft-Malone et al., 2004).

Integrating empirical best practices with practical expertise enhances program quality, effectiveness, and care personalization, improving recipient and caregiver well-being (Clyne et al., 2013).

Additionally, fusion facilitates continuous improvement through feedback loops informed by both knowledge spheres to evaluate programs and identify enhancement opportunities (Titler, 2018).

Fusion also fosters collaboration across diverse caregiving stakeholders, bringing together researchers, practitioners, policymakers, and community members. This catalyzes the co-creation of comprehensive solutions to emerging care challenges (Chien et al., 2011).

Furthermore, fusion enables programs to inform policymaking by advocating for inclusive caregiving policies reflecting research evidence and practice insights (Rycroft-Malone et al., 2004).

Fusion equips caregivers with multifaceted support to manage demands, prevent burnout, and uphold their invaluable well-being and resilience (Williams et al., 2019).

Examples of Fusion in Practice

The My Journey student caregiver support program powerfully demonstrates the real-world impacts of integrating empirical knowledge and clinical expertise grounded in the latest developmental and mental health research while incorporating educators' experiential insights on student needs (Moran & Reaman, 2002).

This fusion is clearly evidenced in the peer mentoring component, which empirical findings indicate is crucial for youth mental health. Concurrently, mentor training and support systems reflect professional expertise ensuring appropriate guidance and oversight (Moran & Reaman, 2002).

Additionally, My Journey leverages both research and practical knowledge in technology-based support innovations that effectively engage youth by aligning with their digital preferences. This exemplifies how fusion can drive impactful caregiving innovations (Moran & Reaman, 2002).

Significantly improved participant mental well-being and caregiving confidence highlight My Journey's success in applying fusion. This underscores the immense potential of integrating empirical and professional knowledge to build responsive, effective, innovative caregiving support programs that optimize outcomes (Moran & Reaman, 2002).

The Impact of Fusion on Caregiving Support Programs

The impact of integrating empirical evidence and professional expertise in caregiving support programs is multifaceted and significant. By combining these complementary knowledge sources, programs can continually evolve and innovate to respond effectively to the changing needs of caregivers and care recipients over time.

One major dimension of this impact is enhanced program effectiveness. When caregiving support programs are firmly grounded in robust empirical evidence from research studies yet also enriched by the nuanced, practical insights gained from seasoned caregivers' years of direct hands-on experience, they can deliver more personalized, high-quality support. This leads to improved outcomes and enhanced well-being for both caregivers and care recipients, supporting their physical, psychological, and social health (Rycroft-Malone et al., 2004).

Another key impact is the promotion of meaningful innovation. The fusion of empirical data and clinical expertise fosters a dynamic culture of learning, experimentation, and forward momentum within caregiving support programs. This encourages programs to actively explore new and emerging approaches, technologies, and solutions to address arising caregiving challenges. Ongoing innovation enables programs to continue evolving and providing state-of-the-art support over time (Titler, 2018).

Additionally, the integration of research findings and practice-based wisdom fosters inclusivity within programs. It enables programs to be more holistic and responsive to the diverse needs of varied caregivers and care recipients. This can lead to more inclusive programs that respect the individuality of each person involved and actively seek to accommodate a wide spectrum of needs and preferences (Chien et al., 2011).

Furthermore, by comprehensively incorporating empirical insights and clinical perspectives, caregiving support programs can significantly inform and influence policy-making processes. They can advocate strongly for the development of more supportive and responsive policies and regulations governing the caregiving field. This advocacy can drive positive changes leading to improved environments for caregivers and upgraded quality across the spectrum of caregiving (Rycroft-Malone et al., 2004).

Moreover, the fusion of scientific evidence and experiential nuance strengthens caregiver resilience. It equips them with effective self-care strategies, helps prevent burnout, and enables them to sustain their invaluable work over the long term. Prioritizing caregiver wellness enhances their capacity to provide quality care as well as their overall health and well-being (Eraut, 2000).

The Future of Fusion in Caregiving Support Programs

The integration of empirical evidence and professional expertise within caregiving support programs must be viewed as an ongoing journey rather than a fixed destination. As knowledge continues advancing, our programs must also adapt and evolve apace. Embracing the fusion of complementary research and clinical perspectives is key for ensuring programs remain relevant, responsive, and impactful over time (Rycroft-Malone et al., 2004).

One likely trajectory for the future entails increased incorporation of technology solutions guided by empirical findings and professional insights. This can enable programs to meet more effectively the diverse and changing needs of caregivers and recipients in the digital era (Eraut, 2000).

Another important trajectory will involve deeply integrating the fusion approach within caregiver education and training programs. Equipping caregivers with knowledge grounded in both research and practical wisdom can enrich competency development, preparing them for multifaceted roles (Eraut, 2000).

Additionally, the development of supportive policies and regulatory frameworks can serve as catalysts to further accelerate fusion integration. Policy initiatives promoting research, innovation, collaboration, and professional development will foster environments where fusion can thrive (Titler, 2018).

Cultivating organizational cultures within programs that embrace continuous learning, creativity, innovation, and a willingness to evolve will also be instrumental. This provides fertile ground for fusion to take root and flourish over the long term (Rycroft-Malone et al., 2004).

Finally, finding ways to strengthen the caregiver's voice and integrate their lived experiences and insights alongside empirical and professional knowledge sources will promote more inclusive, person-centered programs (Chien et al., 2011).

The Promise of Fusion

The fusion of scientific research and clinical caregiving expertise holds great promise for transforming caregiving support programs now and in the years ahead. It provides a path forward grounded in the interplay of evidence-based practices and real-world pragmatic insights. By fully embracing fusion's potential, programs can be elevated and optimized to meet emerging challenges (Rycroft-Malone et al., 2004).

One area of immense promise is fusion's potential to catalyze the evolution of caregiving programs into learning systems capable of constantly adapting and innovating. The synergistic integration of empirical findings and professional perspectives creates a culture of continuous improvement through ongoing learning and responsiveness (Titler, 2018).

Additionally, fusion holds promise for amplifying program effectiveness. Empirical evidence ensures interventions are scientifically validated, while clinical expertise enables customized applications to match individual circumstances and preferences. This multifaceted approach can significantly enhance care quality and outcomes (Clyne et al., 2013).

Furthermore, by accommodating diverse insights, fusion promises to make programs more holistic, inclusive, and able to address the full spectrum of user needs respectfully (Chien et al., 2011).

Moreover, equipped with empirical data and practice-based wisdom, programs can more effectively inform caregiving policies, advocate for positive reforms, and influence decision-making to create supportive environments (Rycroft-Malone et al., 2004).

The promise of fusion is a future where caregiving support programs integrate knowledge from research, practice, and lived experience fluidly. This enables continuous evolution to proactively meet emerging needs through responsive, effective, compassionate, evidence-based approaches that uplift and empower all those involved in the sacred caregiving journey.

1.7: The Role of Contextual Factors in Caregiving Support Programs: A Comprehensive Examination

Caregiving support programs play a crucial role in enhancing the lives of both caregivers and care recipients. However, these programs do not operate in isolation. They are deeply intertwined with the broader socio-cultural, economic, and political context in which they are embedded. This context can significantly shape the programs' effectiveness, sustainability, and overall impact, influencing everything from the availability of resources to cultural norms and values.

Understanding these contextual factors is therefore essential for the design, implementation, and management of effective caregiving support programs. These factors refer to the unique circumstances, environments, and socio-cultural aspects that interact with caregiving support programs. By acknowledging and incorporating these contextual factors, caregiving support programs can better meet the unique needs and circumstances of caregivers and care recipients.

A study published in the Journal of Health Services Research and Policy underscored the significant role that contextual factors play in shaping the effectiveness of healthcare quality improvement initiatives. In the realm of caregiving support programs, similar dynamics are at play. Contextual factors such as cultural norms and values, the availability and accessibility of resources, support from healthcare systems, and the economic and political climate can all affect the success of these programs.

One example of a program that effectively incorporates contextual factors is the My Journey program. This program integrates evidence-based practices and professional expertise, considering caregivers' unique needs and circumstances to promote healthy decision-making. By integrating contextual factors into its design and implementation, My Journey effectively bridges the gap between theory and practice.

In the following sections, we will delve into the role of contextual factors in caregiving support programs. We will explore how these factors influence the success of these programs, the importance of integrating contextual factors, and the potential for enhancing caregiving support programs by acknowledging and incorporating these factors.

The Influence of Contextual Factors

Understanding Contextual Factors

Contextual factors refer to the unique circumstances, environments, and socio-cultural aspects that intertwine with caregiving support programs. These factors can shape the effectiveness, sustainability, and overall impact of these programs. They can influence everything from the availability of resources to the acceptance of the program within different cultural norms and values (Brewer et al., 2021).

These factors can vary from one situation to another. They can include the caregiver's and care recipient's socioeconomic status, health conditions, cultural background, and personal beliefs, as well as the broader environment in which the caregiving takes place (Chapin et al., 2022). For example, a caregiver living in a rural area may have different resources and face different challenges than a caregiver living in an urban area (Skufca & Fouts, 2022).

Understanding these contextual factors is crucial in designing and implementing effective caregiving support programs. By acknowledging the specific circumstances and environments in which caregiving occurs, we can develop interventions that are more likely to resonate with caregivers and, therefore, be more effective (Samus et al., 2018).

It is important to remember that contextual factors are not static – they can change over time (Martindale-Adams et al., 2016). As a result, the effectiveness of caregiving support programs may also need to be re-evaluated and adjusted over time. This underscores the need for ongoing monitoring and evaluation of these programs to ensure they continue to meet the needs of caregivers and care recipients (Montgomery et al., 2017).

Contextual factors can also interact with one another in complex ways, further shaping the caregiving experience (McLennon et al., 2022). For instance, a caregiver's socioeconomic status can influence their access to resources, while cultural norms and values can shape their attitudes towards caregiving. Understanding these interactions is key to developing a nuanced understanding of caregiving and designing effective support programs (Chee et al., 2021).

The Role of Contextual Factors in Caregiving Support Programs

In caregiving support programs, contextual factors play a crucial role in shaping the effectiveness of these initiatives. Factors such as cultural norms and values, the availability and accessibility of resources, support from healthcare systems, and the economic and political climate can all affect the implementation and management of these programs (Van Houtven et al., 2021).

Cultural norms and values can heavily influence the acceptance and effectiveness of caregiving support programs. In cultures where caregiving is seen as a personal or family responsibility, caregivers may be less likely to seek outside support (Sharma et al., 2021). In contrast, in cultures where caregiving is seen as a shared responsibility, support programs may be more readily embraced (Chui et al., 2021).

The availability and accessibility of resources can also shape the effectiveness of caregiving support programs. In areas where resources are scarce, support programs may struggle to meet the needs of caregivers and care recipients (Reinhard et al., 2019). Conversely, in areas where resources are abundant, support programs may be able to offer a broader range of services and supports (Bergen et al., 2022).

Support from healthcare systems can significantly influence the success of caregiving support programs. In healthcare systems that recognize and value the role of caregivers, support programs may receive more funding, resources, and institutional backing (Family Caregiver Alliance, 2022).

This can enhance the capacity of these programs to support caregivers and care recipients effectively.

The economic and political climate can affect the operation and impact of caregiving support programs. In times of economic downturn or political instability, these programs may face funding cuts or other challenges (Gleckman, 2021). This underscores the need for advocacy and policy support to ensure the sustainability of these vital programs (Reinhard et al., 2019).

The Impact of Contextual Factors on Program Success

The impact of contextual factors on the success of caregiving support programs is significant. These factors can influence the extent to which programs are able to meet the needs of caregivers and care recipients, the sustainability of programs, and their ability to make a lasting impact (Dam et al., 2021). Understanding and considering these contextual factors is therefore crucial for the design, implementation, and management of effective caregiving support programs.

For example, a program designed to support caregivers in a high-income, urban area may not work as effectively in a low-income, rural area due to differences in resource availability (Skufca & Fouts, 2022). Similarly, a program that works well in a culture where caregiving is seen as a shared responsibility may struggle in a culture where caregiving is seen as a private family matter (Sharma et al., 2021).

The sustainability of caregiving support programs can also be affected by contextual factors. For instance, in regions where there is a lack of consistent funding or resources, programs may struggle to maintain their services over the long term (Reinhard et al., 2019). This can leave caregivers without the support they need, undermining the effectiveness of the program.

The ability of a caregiving support program to make a lasting impact can also be shaped by contextual factors. If a program is well-aligned with the cultural norms, values, and circumstances of its target audience, it is more likely to be accepted and adopted, leading to lasting changes in caregiving practices and outcomes (Van Houtven et al., 2021).

Conversely, if a program does not consider these factors, it may struggle to gain traction and make a lasting impact. This highlights the importance of integrating a deep understanding of the local context into the design and implementation of caregiving support programs (Dam et al., 2021).

The Importance of Acknowledging Contextual Factors

Acknowledging contextual factors is an essential part of developing and implementing effective caregiving support programs. By recognizing the unique circumstances, environments, and socio-cultural aspects that interact with these programs, we can develop interventions that resonate with caregivers and care recipients and that are responsive to their unique needs and circumstances (Brewer et al., 2021).

Acknowledging contextual factors can help ensure that caregiving support programs are accessible to all who need them. For example, if a program only offers support in English, it may not reach caregivers who speak other languages. By taking language diversity into account, the program can ensure it is accessible to a broader range of caregivers (Ngwakongnwi et al., 2021).

Furthermore, acknowledging contextual factors can help support programs better meet the needs of diverse caregivers and care recipients. For instance, a program that acknowledges the unique challenges faced by caregivers of people with dementia may be able to offer more targeted and effective support (Samus et al., 2018).

In addition, acknowledging these factors can enhance the credibility and acceptance of support programs. If a program is seen as sensitive to and respectful of the local context, it is more likely to be trusted and embraced by caregivers and care recipients (Van Houtven et al., 2021).

Acknowledging contextual factors can contribute to the sustainability of caregiving support programs. If a program is well-aligned with the local context, it is more likely to be supported by local stakeholders, including funding bodies, healthcare providers, and the community at large (Bergen et al., 2022). This can enhance the program's sustainability and its ability to make a lasting impact.

The Role of Contextual Factors in Program Design and Implementation

Contextual factors play a crucial role in the design and implementation of caregiving support programs. By incorporating these factors into program design and implementation, we can ensure that programs are relevant, responsive, and effective (Dam et al., 2021). This includes considering factors such as cultural norms and values, the availability and accessibility of resources, and the broader economic and political climate.

When designing a caregiving support program, it is crucial to consider the specific needs and circumstances of the target audience. This might involve conducting needs assessments, holding focus groups, or interviewing caregivers to gain insights into their challenges, needs, and preferences (Van Houtven et al., 2021). These insights can inform the design of the program, ensuring it is tailored to the specific context in which it will be implemented.

When implementing a caregiving support program, it is equally important to consider contextual factors. This might involve providing training for staff on cultural competency, ensuring services are accessible to people with diverse abilities, or engaging with local stakeholders to build support for the program (Ngwakongnwi et al., 2021). By considering these factors, the program can ensure it is responsive to the unique needs and circumstances of the caregivers it aims to support.

Continual evaluation and adaptation based on contextual factors are also important. As the context changes, so must the program (Martindale-Adams et al., 2016). This might involve regularly monitoring program outcomes, seeking feedback from caregivers and care recipients, or conducting periodic reviews to identify areas for improvement

(Montgomery et al., 2017). By doing so, the program can continue to evolve and improve, ensuring it remains effective and relevant.

Incorporating contextual factors into program design and implementation can help build the sustainability of caregiving support programs. By aligning the program with the local context, it is more likely to be supported by local stakeholders and sustainable over the long term (Bergen et al., 2022). This can ensure that caregivers continue to receive the support they need, even as the context changes.

Integrating Contextual Factors in Caregiving Support Programs

The Need for Integration

Integrating contextual factors into caregiving support programs is vital. Understanding the unique circumstances, environments, and socio-cultural aspects that intertwine with caregiving can help tailor programs to meet the specific needs of caregivers and care recipients. This can lead to more effective, sustainable, and impactful programs (Brewer & Watson, 2015; Sörensen et al., 2002).

The integration of contextual factors into caregiving support programs involves understanding and incorporating the unique circumstances, environments, and socio-cultural aspects that intersect with caregiving. This can range from understanding the social and cultural norms that shape caregiving attitudes and behaviors to acknowledging the influence of economic conditions and available resources on caregiving (Goins et al., 2021; Pinquart & Sörensen, 2005).

The integration of contextual factors can result in programs that are more tailored to the unique needs and circumstances of caregivers. By considering the specific contexts in which caregivers operate, these programs can provide more personalized support, ranging from emotional and psychological support to practical assistance with caregiving tasks (Carretero et al., 2009; Healy et al., 2020).

This integration can also lead to programs that are more sustainable. By aligning with the local context, programs can gain greater acceptance and support from local stakeholders, including caregivers, healthcare providers, and policymakers. This can help ensure the ongoing availability of support for caregivers (Chadiha et al., 2011; Sörensen & Pinquart, 2005).

The Impact of Integration

The integration of contextual factors can significantly enhance the effectiveness of caregiving support programs. By considering these factors, programs can better respond to the unique needs and circumstances of those they aim to support. This can lead to improved outcomes for both caregivers and care recipients, enhancing their quality of life and overall well-being (Ducharme et al., 2007; Gitlin et al., 2006).

By aligning programs with the specific contexts in which caregiving occurs, we can increase their relevance and acceptability. For example, a program designed for caregivers in urban areas might not be as effective for caregivers in rural areas due to differences in resource availability, healthcare infrastructure, and social norms (Chadiha et al., 2011). By integrating these contextual factors, programs can ensure they are relevant to their intended audience.

Integration can also enhance the efficiency of programs. By tailoring services to the unique needs and circumstances of caregivers, programs can avoid a one-size-fits-all approach that may waste resources. Instead, they can deliver targeted support that directly addresses the specific challenges faced by caregivers, resulting in more effective use of resources (Gitlin et al., 2010).

In addition, integration can enhance the sustainability of programs. Programs that are well-aligned with their context are more likely to be supported by local stakeholders and to secure ongoing funding and resources. This can ensure that support for caregivers is sustained over time rather than being a temporary or one-off initiative (Sörensen & Pinquart, 2005).

Integrating contextual factors can enhance the impact of caregiving support programs. By addressing the unique needs and circumstances of caregivers and care recipients, programs can lead to improved outcomes, ranging from better mental health for caregivers to improved quality of care for care recipients (Belle et al., 2006; Sörensen et al., 2002).

Examples of Successful Integration: The REACH II Program

The REACH II program is a prime example of the successful integration of contextual factors in caregiving support programs. By incorporating evidence-based practices and professional expertise while considering caregivers' unique needs and circumstances, the program promotes healthy decision-making among caregivers. The success of REACH II is a testament to the power of contextual integration in enhancing caregiving support programs (Belle et al., 2006).

The REACH II program begins with a thorough assessment of the caregiver's needs and circumstances, which includes understanding their social, cultural, and economic context. This information is used to tailor the support provided, ensuring it is relevant and effective for each individual caregiver (Elliott et al., 2010).

The program also provides ongoing support and monitoring, recognizing that the caregiving journey is dynamic, and that caregivers' needs and circumstances can change over time. By regularly reassessing caregivers' situations and adjusting support as needed, the program remains responsive to the evolving context of caregiving (Burgio et al., 2009).

The success of the REACH II program lies in its ability to deliver personalized, responsive support that is well-aligned with the unique needs and circumstances of caregivers. By integrating contextual factors into its design and implementation, the program has been able to improve the well-being of caregivers, enhance their caregiving capabilities, and reduce caregiver stress (Belle et al., 2006; Gitlin et al., 2003).

The REACH II program serves as an inspiring example of what can be achieved when contextual factors are effectively integrated into caregiving support programs. Its success highlights the power of contextual integration in enhancing the effectiveness, sustainability, and impact of these vital programs (Elliott et al., 2010).

The Role of Contextual Factors in Tailoring Interventions

Contextual factors can play a crucial role in tailoring interventions to meet the unique needs and circumstances of caregivers and care recipients. By understanding and considering these factors, caregiving support programs can develop interventions that are relevant, personalized, and effective. This can lead to improved outcomes for caregivers and care recipients and a more rewarding caregiving experience (Ducharme et al., 2011; Sörensen et al., 2002).

Understanding the unique needs and circumstances of caregivers and care recipients involves considering a range of contextual factors. These can include socio-cultural norms, available resources, and the broader socio-economic and political climate. By taking these factors into account, caregiving support programs can ensure that interventions are tailored to the specific needs and circumstances of those they serve (Elliott et al., 2010; Montgomery & Kosloski, 2013).

The tailoring of interventions can enhance their effectiveness. By delivering support that is relevant and personalized, programs can better meet the unique needs of caregivers and care recipients. This can lead to improved outcomes, such as improved mental health for caregivers and improved quality of care for care recipients (Gitlin et al., 2010).

Tailoring interventions can also enhance the sustainability of caregiving support programs. By aligning interventions with the local context, programs can gain greater acceptance and support from local stakeholders. This can help to ensure the ongoing availability of support for caregivers (Sörensen & Pinquart, 2005).

Tailoring interventions to the unique needs and circumstances of caregivers and care recipients can make caregiving a more rewarding experience. By receiving support that is relevant and personalized, caregivers can feel more understood and supported, leading to increased satisfaction and resilience in their caregiving roles (Carretero et al., 2009).

Moving Forward: The Potential of Contextual Integration

The integration of contextual factors holds great potential for enhancing caregiving support programs. By acknowledging and incorporating these factors, we can develop programs that are not only effective but also sustainable and impactful. As we move forward, it is crucial to continue to recognize the importance of contextual factors and integrate them into the core framework of caregiving support programs (Brewer & Watson, 2015).

As our understanding of caregiving evolves, so too must our support programs. Future programs should prioritize the integration of contextual factors to ensure that they are responsive to the dynamic and complex nature of caregiving. By doing so, we can contribute to a future where caregiving support programs are more effective, sustainable, and impactful (Montgomery & Kosloski, 2013).

Continuing to recognize the importance of contextual factors is crucial. These factors can shape everything from the needs and circumstances of caregivers to the sustainability and impact of caregiving support programs. By prioritizing the integration of these factors, we can ensure that our programs are not only evidence-based but also contextually relevant (Goins et al., 2021).

Integrating contextual factors into the core framework of caregiving support programs is essential. This can involve everything from conducting thorough assessments of caregivers' needs and circumstances to considering contextual factors in the design and implementation of interventions. By integrating these factors, we can develop programs that are grounded in the realities of caregiving (Ducharme et al., 2011).

The potential of contextual integration is immense. It offers a path forward that is both informed by research and grounded in the realities of caregiving. By unleashing the potential of contextual integration, we can propel caregiving support programs toward new frontiers of innovation and evolution (Sörensen & Pinquart, 2005).

The Importance of Contextual Integration

Contextual integration is essential for the success of caregiving support programs. By acknowledging the unique circumstances, environments, and socio-cultural aspects that intertwine with caregiving, we can develop interventions that resonate with caregivers on a personal level and meet their unique needs (Hiel et al., 2015).

The integration of contextual factors allows for the creation of support programs that are personalized and relevant. Rather than adopting a one-size-fits-all approach, programs can consider the unique circumstances, environments, and socio-cultural aspects that intertwine with caregiving. This leads to the development of programs that are more effective and impactful, as they are grounded in the realities of caregiving (Bourke-Taylor et al., 2020).

Integration also enables the development of programs that are more sustainable. By aligning with the local context, programs can secure greater support from local stakeholders, such as healthcare providers, policymakers, and the community. This support can ensure the ongoing availability of resources and services for caregivers (Brown et al., 2004).

Contextual integration also allows for the tailoring of interventions. By considering the unique needs and circumstances of caregivers and care recipients, programs can develop interventions that are personalized and effective. This can lead to improved outcomes for both caregivers and care recipients, enhancing their quality of life and overall well-being (Samus et al., 2014).

The importance of contextual integration cannot be overstated. By acknowledging and incorporating the unique circumstances, environments, and socio-cultural aspects that intertwine with caregiving, we can develop caregiving support programs that are effective, sustainable, and impactful (Bourke-Taylor et al., 2020).

The Role of Contextual Integration in Enhancing Program Impact

Contextual integration plays a significant role in enhancing the impact of caregiving support programs. It allows these programs to better serve caregivers and care recipients by aligning interventions with the realities of the caregiving landscape. As such, contextual integration can lead to improved outcomes for both caregivers and care recipients (Gitlin et al., 2006).

An enhanced program impact can be seen in terms of improved health outcomes for caregivers and care recipients. By tailoring interventions to the unique needs and circumstances of these individuals, programs can deliver more effective support. This can lead to better physical and emotional health, increased resilience, and improved overall well-being for caregivers and care recipients (Hoffmann et al., 2016).

Beyond health outcomes, contextual integration can also enhance the quality of care. By delivering interventions that resonate with the unique circumstances, environments, and socio-cultural aspects that intertwine with caregiving, programs can provide care that is more personalized and meaningful. This can lead to increased satisfaction and improved quality of life for caregivers and care recipients (Bekhet, 2013).

Furthermore, the enhanced impact of contextual integration extends to the sustainability of caregiving support programs. By acknowledging and aligning with the local context, programs can secure the necessary resources and support to ensure their ongoing operation. This is crucial for maintaining the availability of support for caregivers and care recipients (Brown et al., 2004).

The integration of contextual factors has the potential to significantly enhance the impact of caregiving support programs. It holds the promise of improved health outcomes, better quality of care, and enhanced sustainability for these programs (Bekhet, 2013).

Examples of Successful Contextual Integration: Patient-Centered Medical Home Models

One successful example of contextual integration in caregiving support programs is the Patient-Centered Medical Home (PCMH) model. The PCMH model emphasizes the importance of contextual factors in shaping healthcare delivery. It aims to provide comprehensive, coordinated, accessible, and patient-centered care, taking into account the unique needs and circumstances of patients and their caregivers (Jackson et al., 2013).

The PCMH model integrates various contextual factors into its approach. These include the socio-cultural aspects of patient's lives, the unique challenges and circumstances faced by caregivers, and the wider healthcare and community environment. By considering these factors, the PCMH model is able to provide care that is relevant, personalized, and effective (Abramson et al., 2014).

The impact of the PCMH model has been widely recognized. It has been associated with improved patient satisfaction, better health outcomes, and reduced healthcare costs. Its success demonstrates the potential of contextual integration in enhancing the effectiveness and impact of caregiving support programs (Jackson et al., 2013).

Moreover, the PCMH model highlights the importance of considering contextual factors in the design and implementation of interventions. By acknowledging and responding to these factors, the model is able to tailor its interventions to the specific needs and circumstances of patients and their caregivers. This underscores the potential of contextual integration in enhancing the delivery of care (Abramson et al., 2014).

The success of the PCMH model provides a promising example of how contextual integration can enhance caregiving support programs. It offers valuable insights into the potential of this approach in improving health outcomes, enhancing the quality of care, and ensuring the sustainability of these programs (Jackson et al., 2013).

The Future of Contextual Integration

Looking forward, the continued integration of contextual factors holds great promise for the future of caregiving support programs. As we continue to learn more about the complex and dynamic nature of caregiving, it is crucial that we adapt our support programs to reflect these realities. By continuing to integrate contextual factors, we can ensure that our programs are responsive, effective, and sustainable (Bekhet, 2013).

The future of contextual integration will involve further research and innovation. This includes deepening our understanding of the various contextual factors that impact caregiving and developing innovative approaches to integrate these factors into our programs. By doing so, we can enhance the effectiveness of our interventions and ensure that they are relevant and responsive to the unique needs and circumstances of caregivers and care recipients (Samus et al., 2014).

The future will also see the continued integration of contextual factors into the core framework of caregiving support programs. This will ensure that these programs are grounded in the realities of caregiving and can provide support that is personalized, meaningful, and effective. This approach will not only improve the outcomes for caregivers and care recipients but also enhance the sustainability and impact of these programs (Hiel et al., 2015).

Moreover, the future of contextual integration holds the potential for greater collaboration. By acknowledging and incorporating the unique circumstances, environments, and socio-cultural aspects that intertwine with caregiving, we can foster partnerships between various stakeholders, such as healthcare providers, policymakers, and the community. This can lead to more comprehensive and coordinated support for caregivers and care recipients (Brown et al., 2004).

The continued integration of contextual factors holds great potential for the future of caregiving support programs. By acknowledging and responding to the complex realities of caregiving, we can enhance the effectiveness, sustainability, and impact of these programs (Bekhet, 2013).

The Promise of Contextual Integration

The integration of contextual factors into caregiving support programs holds great promise. It offers a path forward that is both informed by research and grounded in the realities of caregiving. By recognizing and responding to the unique circumstances, environments, and socio-cultural aspects that intertwine with caregiving, we can develop support programs that are effective, sustainable, and impactful (Bourke-Taylor et al., 2020).

The promise of contextual integration is rooted in its potential to improve health outcomes for caregivers and care recipients. By delivering interventions that are tailored to the unique needs and circumstances of these individuals, we can provide support that leads to better physical and emotional health, increased resilience, and improved overall well-being (Hoffmann et al., 2016).

The promise of contextual integration also extends to the quality of care. By providing care that is relevant, personalized, and meaningful, we can enhance the caregiving experience for both caregivers and care recipients. This can lead to increased satisfaction and improved quality of life for these individuals (Bekhet, 2013).

Furthermore, the promise of contextual integration lies in its potential to enhance the sustainability of caregiving support programs. By acknowledging and aligning with the local context, we can ensure that these programs continue to operate and provide support for caregivers and care recipients (Brown et al., 2004).

The promise of contextual integration holds great potential for the future of caregiving support programs. It represents a path forward that is informed by research, grounded in the realities of caregiving, and centered on improving outcomes for caregivers and care recipients. By embracing this approach, we can ensure that our programs are not only effective and sustainable but also impactful (Bekhet, 2013).

Chapter 2: Essential Competencies for Caregivers

2.1: Prioritizing Self-Care in Caregiving: A Holistic Approach

The role of caregiving, while rewarding, can be demanding and draining. Caregivers, often considered the unsung heroes of our society, dedicate their time and energy to the needs of others. However, this intense focus on others can lead caregivers to neglect their own needs, resulting in significant physical and mental health issues. The importance of self-care in caregiving cannot be overstated—it is a critical component of effective caregiving and a key determinant of caregivers' overall well-being (Acton, 2002).

Self-care in caregiving is about more than just maintaining physical health. It encompasses a holistic approach to well-being, addressing not just physical needs but also emotional, social, spiritual, and intellectual needs. By prioritizing self-care, caregivers can avoid burnout, cope with stress more effectively, and continue to provide quality care to their loved ones (Acton, 2002).

Despite the importance of self-care, caregivers often struggle to prioritize their own needs. Societal norms and expectations can exacerbate this problem, with women disproportionately affected due to gendered expectations around caregiving roles (Hill et al., 2019). To address these challenges, caregiving support programs must integrate empirical evidence and professional expertise to provide comprehensive support and facilitate effective self-care strategies (Zarit et al., 2014).

Understanding Self-Care in Caregiving

Understanding self-care in the context of caregiving begins with acknowledging that caregiving while rewarding, can also be physically, emotionally, and mentally demanding. Caregivers often prioritize the needs of those they are caring for above their own, which can lead to a neglect of personal health and well-being (Hill et al., 2019).

Self-care in caregiving involves more than just maintaining physical health. It also entails nurturing emotional, social, spiritual, and intellectual needs. This holistic approach ensures that all aspects of the caregiver's well-being are addressed, helping them to manage stress, avoid burnout, and continue to provide effective care (Wong et al., 2022).

Emotional self-care might involve strategies such as stress management techniques, psychological counseling, or engaging in hobbies and activities that bring joy and relaxation. This helps caregivers to manage the emotional demands of their role and fosters a sense of balance and personal fulfillment (Henriksson & Andershed, 2007).

Social self-care could include maintaining relationships with friends and family, seeking out support groups, or enlisting help from others. This allows caregivers to maintain a sense of connection and support, reducing feelings of isolation and overload (Zarit et al., 2014).

Spiritual and intellectual self-care may involve practices such as meditation, prayer, reading, or learning new skills. These activities can provide a sense of purpose, growth, and inner peace, helping caregivers to cope with the challenges of their role (Henriksson & Andershed, 2007).

The Impact of Neglecting Self-Care

The impact of neglecting self-care in caregiving can be severe, often leading to a range of physical and mental health problems. Research has shown that caregivers are at a higher risk of experiencing stress-related conditions, such as cardiovascular disease and impaired immune function (Vitaliano et al., 2003).

In addition to physical health issues, neglecting self-care can also lead to mental health problems, such as depression, anxiety, and feelings of overwhelm. These mental health issues can, in turn, further exacerbate physical health problems, creating a vicious cycle of deteriorating health and well-being (Hill et al., 2019).

Neglecting self-care can also lead to a decrease in the quality of care provided. As caregivers' health and well-being deteriorate, their ability to effectively care for their loved ones may also diminish. They may experience decreased patience, increased irritability, and a lack of energy, all of which can affect their caregiving (Cheung et al., 2015).

Caregivers who neglect self-care may also find themselves experiencing caregiver burnout. This is a state of physical, emotional, and mental exhaustion caused by the prolonged and intense stress of caregiving. Symptoms of burnout can include feelings of overwhelm, chronic fatigue, decreased interest in previously enjoyed activities, and difficulty concentrating (Hill et al., 2019).

The risks associated with neglecting self-care underscore the crucial importance of implementing self-care strategies. By taking time to address their own needs, caregivers can enhance their health and well-being, improve their ability to provide care and mitigate the risk of burnout (Cheung et al., 2015).

The Role of Self-Care in Preventing Burnout

The role of self-care in preventing caregiver burnout is critical. Burnout often results from chronic stress and neglect of personal well-being, making effective self-care strategies an essential tool for prevention (Hill et al., 2019).

By ensuring they take regular breaks, caregivers can rest and rejuvenate, mitigating the risk of burnout. These breaks provide much-needed time for relaxation and personal pursuits, helping caregivers maintain a sense of balance and personal fulfillment (Cheung et al., 2015).

Asking for help when needed is another essential self-care strategy for preventing burnout. By delegating tasks and seeking support, caregivers can reduce their workload and stress levels. This also enables them to spend more time on self-care activities (Henriksson & Andershed, 2007).

Nurturing mental and physical health is another important aspect of self-care for preventing burnout. This includes practices such as regular exercise, maintaining a balanced diet, ensuring adequate sleep, and engaging in stress management techniques. By promoting their physical and mental well-being, caregivers can enhance their resilience and ability to cope with stress (Wong et al., 2022).

Simplifying schedules and setting healthy boundaries can also help to prevent burnout. By reducing unnecessary tasks and commitments and setting limits on caregiving duties, caregivers can ensure they have sufficient time and energy for self-care (Zarit et al., 2014).

Self-Care as a Key Component of Effective Caregiving

Self-care is not only beneficial for the caregivers themselves but also plays a crucial role in effective caregiving. When caregivers take care of their own health and well-being, they are better equipped to provide high-quality, compassionate care to their loved ones (Cheung et al., 2015).

Self-care supports physical energy and resilience, allowing caregivers to meet the physical demands of their role. This might include tasks such as lifting or moving the care recipient, managing medical equipment, or dealing with emergencies (Wong et al., 2022).

Emotionally, self-care helps caregivers to manage the stress and emotional demands of their role. It provides them with strategies to cope with difficult emotions, maintain a positive outlook, and foster an emotional connection with their care recipient (Henriksson & Andershed, 2007).

Intellectually, self-care supports decision-making and problem-solving abilities, which are critical skills in caregiving. By taking time to rest and recharge, caregivers can maintain their cognitive function and effectively address the challenges of their role (Zarit et al., 2014).

Spiritually, self-care can provide a sense of purpose and resilience, helping caregivers to find meaning in their role and to cope with the challenges of caregiving. This can promote a sense of fulfillment and personal growth, which can, in turn, enhance the quality of care provided (Henriksson & Andershed, 2007).

The Importance of Holistic Self-Care

Holistic self-care, which addresses all aspects of the caregiver's well-being, is particularly important in caregiving. By nurturing their physical, emotional, social, spiritual, and intellectual needs, caregivers can enhance their resilience, manage stress more effectively, and provide better care to their loved ones (Acton, 2002).

Physical self-care involves activities such as regular exercise, maintaining a balanced diet, ensuring adequate sleep, and managing medical needs. This supports the caregiver's physical health and resilience, allowing them to meet the physical demands of caregiving (Wong et al., 2022).

Emotional self-care might involve strategies such as stress management techniques, psychological counseling, or engaging in activities that bring joy and relaxation. This helps caregivers to manage the emotional demands of their role and fosters a sense of emotional well-being (Henriksson & Andershed, 2007).

Social self-care could include maintaining relationships with friends and family, seeking out support groups, or enlisting help from others. This allows caregivers to maintain a sense of connection and support, which can help to reduce feelings of isolation and overload (Zarit et al., 2014).

Spiritual self-care may involve practices such as meditation, prayer, or spending time in nature. These activities can provide a sense of purpose, peace, and connection, helping caregivers to find meaning in their role and cope with its challenges (Henriksson & Andershed, 2007).

Intellectual self-care might involve activities such as reading, learning new skills, or problem-solving exercises. These can provide mental stimulation, promote personal growth, and help caregivers to maintain their cognitive function and problem-solving abilities (Zarit et al., 2014).

Challenges in Prioritizing Self-Care

The Struggles of Prioritizing Self-Care

The Struggles of Prioritizing Self-Care

Caregiving, by its very nature, is a role that requires immense dedication, compassion, and patience. However, these very qualities can often result in caregivers neglecting their own needs. It's not uncommon for caregivers to find themselves completely absorbed by the needs and demands of those they care for, leading them to overlook the importance of their own self-care. Consequently, caregivers may experience significant physical and mental health issues, from stress and anxiety to physical exhaustion and chronic health conditions (Hill et al., 2019).

The struggle to prioritize self-care is also rooted in the challenge of finding a balance between caregiving duties and personal life. Caregivers often juggle multiple roles and responsibilities, and carving out time for self-care can seem like an impossible task. As a result, self-care tends to take a backseat, with caregivers choosing to dedicate what little free time they have to rest or catch up on other duties (Cheung et al., 2015).

Another significant challenge in prioritizing self-care is the unpredictability inherent in caregiving. The health and needs of care recipients can fluctuate dramatically and unexpectedly, leaving caregivers constantly on alert. This constant state of high alert can make it difficult for caregivers to disconnect and take time for self-care (Zarit et al., 2014).

Additionally, many caregivers experience feelings of guilt when they take time for themselves. They may feel that they are neglecting their care recipients, or they may worry about what could happen in their absence. These feelings of guilt can serve as a significant barrier to self-care, adding emotional stress to an already challenging situation (Hill et al., 2019).

Some caregivers may lack awareness or understanding of the importance of self-care. They may underestimate the impact of caregiving on their health and well-being, or they may not know how to effectively engage in self-care. This lack of knowledge can further impede the prioritization of self-care (Henriksson & Andershed, 2007).

The Influence of Societal Norms and Expectations

The societal norms and expectations around caregiving can greatly influence how caregivers approach self-care. Often, there is a societal expectation that caregivers, particularly those providing care for family members, should be selfless and fully devoted to the needs of their care recipients. This narrative can create feelings of guilt and conflict when caregivers try to take time for themselves (Hill et al., 2019).

These societal norms and expectations can be even more pronounced in cultures where family caregiving is highly valued and expected. In these contexts, the caregiver role may be seen as a duty or obligation, and self-care may be seen as a luxury or even a selfish act. This can create additional barriers to self-care, with caregivers feeling pressured to live up to these expectations at the expense of their own well-being (Losada et al., 2010).

In addition, the media and popular culture often romanticize the role of the caregiver, presenting it as a noble and selfless endeavor. While caregiving can indeed be fulfilling and meaningful, this narrative can be damaging by minimizing the challenges and struggles that caregivers face, including the difficulty of prioritizing self-care (Hill et al., 2019).

Caregivers themselves may internalize these societal norms and expectations, leading them to set unrealistic standards for themselves. They may feel that they must be available and attentive to their care recipient at all times, and they may struggle with feelings of inadequacy or failure if they are unable to live up to these standards (Cheung et al., 2015).

Challenging these societal norms and expectations is crucial in promoting self-care among caregivers. It's important to acknowledge the challenges and sacrifices involved in caregiving and to validate the importance of self-care in maintaining the caregiver's health and well-being (Losada et al., 2010).

The Disproportionate Impact on Women

The challenge of prioritizing self-care in caregiving often disproportionately affects women. Due to societal norms and expectations, women are frequently expected to take on caregiving roles, particularly within families. This expectation is rooted in traditional gender roles that associate women with nurturing and caregiving tasks (Hill et al., 2019).

This disproportionate burden of caregiving can compound the challenges women face in prioritizing self-care. In addition to caregiving, women often shoulder a variety of other responsibilities, including household chores, childcare, and paid work. This multiple-role occupancy can leave women with little time and energy for self-care and can exacerbate feelings of stress and exhaustion (Cheung et al., 2015).

Moreover, societal norms and expectations around femininity and caregiving can exacerbate feelings of guilt and conflict when women attempt to prioritize self-care. Women may feel that they are neglecting their caregiving duties or failing to live up to societal expectations if they take time for themselves (Losada et al., 2010).

The intersectionality of gender with other social identities can further compound these challenges. For example, women of color or women with lower socio-economic status often face additional barriers to self-care, including limited access to resources, discrimination, and additional caregiving or work responsibilities (Hill et al., 2019).

In addressing the challenge of self-care in caregiving, it's crucial to consider the unique experiences and challenges faced by women and to implement strategies and interventions that are sensitive to these challenges (Cheung et al., 2015).

The Risk of Burnout

Neglecting self-care can lead to caregiver burnout, a state of physical, emotional, and mental exhaustion caused by the prolonged and intense stress of caregiving. Burnout can have severe implications for the caregiver's health and well-being, as well as their ability to provide care (Cheung et al., 2015).

Burnout is characterized by a variety of symptoms, including fatigue, loss of interest in previously enjoyed activities, feelings of helplessness and hopelessness, irritability, and changes in appetite or sleep patterns. If left unaddressed, burnout can lead to more severe health issues, including depression, anxiety, and chronic health conditions (Hill et al., 2019).

In addition to the personal toll it takes, burnout can also affect the caregiver's ability to provide care. They may become less patient, less attentive, or less able to handle the physical demands of caregiving. This can compromise the quality of care provided, potentially affecting the care recipient's health and well-being (Zarit et al., 2014).

Burnout can also impact the caregiver's relationships with others, including the care recipient and other family members or friends. Feelings of irritability and hopelessness can strain these relationships, potentially leading to conflict and further stress (Cheung et al., 2015).

Given these risks, it's crucial for caregivers to prioritize self-care and seek support when needed. By recognizing the signs of burnout and taking proactive steps to manage stress and maintain well-being, caregivers can reduce their risk of burnout and ensure they are able to continue providing care (Hill et al., 2019).

The Need for Support in Prioritizing Self-Care

Given the challenges caregivers face in prioritizing self-care, it's clear that they often need support in this area. This support can come in many forms, from formal support services to informal networks of family and friends (Zarit et al., 2014).

Healthcare professionals can play a crucial role in providing this support. They can educate caregivers about the importance of self-care, provide strategies and resources for self-care, and offer referrals to support services. They can also provide emotional support and validation, helping caregivers to manage feelings of guilt or conflict around self-care (Cheung et al., 2015).

Family and friends can also provide invaluable support. They can offer practical assistance with caregiving tasks, giving the caregiver a break and freeing up time for self-care. They can also provide emotional support, offering a listening ear and words of encouragement (Zarit et al., 2014).

Caregiving support programs are another crucial source of support. These programs can provide a range of services to assist caregivers, including respite care, counseling, support groups, and educational resources. By accessing these services, caregivers can gain the knowledge, skills, and resources they need to effectively manage their roles and prioritize self-care (Cheung et al., 2015).

Caregivers can also seek support from other caregivers through support groups or online communities. These spaces can offer a sense of community and understanding, providing an outlet for caregivers to share their experiences, learn from others, and gain emotional support (Hill et al., 2019).

Strategies for Enhancing Self-Care Among Caregivers

Understanding the Importance of Self-Care Strategies

Implementing effective self-care strategies is a critical step for caregivers to manage the stress and demands of their role. These strategies can vary widely based on the individual's needs and preferences but generally involve activities that promote physical, emotional, and mental well-being (Zarit et al., 2014).

One of the first steps in implementing self-care strategies is understanding their importance. Caregivers need to recognize that self-care is not a luxury but a necessity for their health and well-being. This shift in perspective can help to mitigate feelings of guilt or conflict around self-care and can motivate caregivers to dedicate time and effort to self-care activities (Cheung et al., 2015).

Next, caregivers need to identify what self-care activities work best for them. These activities can range from physical exercise and healthy eating to hobbies, relaxation techniques, and social activities. What matters most is that the activities are enjoyable and beneficial to the caregiver's well-being (Wong et al., 2022).

Developing a regular self-care routine can also be beneficial. By scheduling self-care activities into their daily or weekly routines, caregivers can ensure that they regularly take time for themselves. This routine can also create a sense of stability and control, which can help to mitigate the stress and unpredictability of caregiving (Zarit et al., 2014).

Caregivers should be encouraged to be flexible with their self-care strategies. What works one day may not work the next, and that's okay. The goal is not to create a rigid self-care regime but to cultivate a toolbox of self-care strategies that can be adapted based on the caregiver's needs and circumstances (Cheung et al., 2015).

The Role of Positive Psychology, Mindfulness, and Cognitive-Behavioral Approaches

Positive psychology, mindfulness, and cognitive-behavioral approaches can all be effective tools for enhancing self-care among caregivers. These approaches can help caregivers to manage stress, improve mood, and maintain a positive outlook, contributing to better self-care and overall well-being (Lloyd et al., 2016).

Positive psychology focuses on cultivating positive experiences, emotions, and character traits. For caregivers, this might involve seeking out positive interactions with their care recipient, finding meaning and fulfillment in their role, or practicing gratitude. Research has shown that such positive psychology interventions can reduce caregiver stress and improve well-being (Lloyd et al., 2016).

Mindfulness, the practice of being fully present and engaged in the current moment, can also be beneficial for caregivers. Mindfulness can help to mitigate the stress and emotional turmoil of caregiving and can enhance feelings of calm and well-being. Mindfulness techniques might include meditation, deep breathing exercises, or simply taking a few moments each day to be present and aware (Wong et al., 2022).

Cognitive-behavioral approaches, which focus on identifying and changing unhelpful thought patterns, can be another effective tool for caregivers. These approaches can help caregivers to challenge feelings of guilt, inadequacy, or overwhelm that can interfere with self-care. Cognitive-behavioral therapy, either through individual counseling or self-help resources, can be particularly beneficial (Lloyd et al., 2016).

These approaches offer caregivers a set of tools to enhance their mental and emotional well-being, supporting more effective self-care and resilience in the face of caregiving challenges (Wong et al., 2022).

The Importance of Regular Breaks and Setting Boundaries

Taking regular breaks and setting boundaries are two critical self-care strategies for caregivers. These strategies not only provide caregivers with time to rest and rejuvenate but also help to prevent overcommitment and burnout (Zarit et al., 2014).

Regular breaks are essential for caregivers to rest and rejuvenate. These breaks can be as simple as a few minutes of quiet time, a short walk, or a relaxing bath. Longer breaks, such as respite care, can also be beneficial, giving caregivers an opportunity to rest, recharge, and engage in enjoyable activities (Cheung et al., 2015).

Setting boundaries is also crucial for caregivers. This involves setting limits on what caregivers are willing and able to do and communicating these limits to others. Boundaries might involve specific times for rest, saying no to additional responsibilities, or delegating tasks to others (Zarit et al., 2014).

Both of these strategies require caregivers to prioritize their own needs and well-being, which can be challenging. However, with support and practice, caregivers can learn to integrate regular breaks and boundaries into their routines, enhancing their resilience and ability to provide care (Cheung et al., 2015).

The Role of Physical Health in Self-Care

Physical health plays a crucial role in self-care for caregivers. Maintaining good physical health can enhance caregivers' resilience, energy levels, and overall well-being, supporting their ability to provide care (Wong et al., 2022).

One key aspect of physical health is ensuring adequate rest. Caregivers often face disrupted sleep due to the demands of their role, which can lead to fatigue and other health problems. Therefore, implementing strategies for good sleep hygiene, such as maintaining a regular sleep schedule, creating a restful sleep environment, and avoiding caffeine and electronics before bed, is crucial (Cheung et al., 2015).

Regular exercise is another important aspect of physical health. Exercise can help to manage stress, boost mood, and enhance physical resilience. Caregivers should be encouraged to find an exercise routine that fits into their schedule and is enjoyable to them, whether that's walking, yoga, swimming, or any other form of physical activity (Wong et al., 2022).

Eating a balanced diet is also important for maintaining physical health. Caregivers may be tempted to skip meals or resort to fast food due to time constraints, but this can lead to health problems in the long run. Instead, caregivers should aim for a diet rich in fruits, vegetables, whole grains, lean proteins, and healthy fats (Zarit et al., 2014).

Preventative healthcare, such as regular check-ups and screenings, is an important part of physical self-care. Caregivers often neglect their own healthcare due to the demands of their role, but this can lead to serious health problems. Regular medical care can help to identify and address health issues early, promoting better health and well-being (Cheung et al., 2015).

The Importance of Emotional and Social Self-Care

Emotional and social self-care is critical for caregivers. These aspects of self-care involve acknowledging and healthily expressing feelings, practicing self-compassion, nurturing relationships outside of the caregiving role, seeking and accepting help from others, and joining support groups (Zarit et al., 2014).

Emotional self-care involves acknowledging and healthily expressing feelings. Caregiving can elicit a range of emotions, including stress, frustration, guilt, and sadness. It's important for caregivers to allow themselves to feel these emotions, rather than suppressing them, and to express them in healthy ways, such as through journaling, art, or talking to a trusted friend or therapist (Cheung et al., 2015).

Practicing self-compassion is another crucial aspect of emotional self-care. This involves treating oneself with kindness and understanding rather than harsh self-criticism. It also involves recognizing that all caregivers face challenges and make mistakes and that it's okay to not be perfect (Wong et al., 2022).

Social self-care involves nurturing relationships outside of the caregiving role. While caregiving can be consuming, it's important for caregivers to maintain connections with friends, family, and other loved ones. These relationships can provide emotional support, a sense of identity outside of the caregiving role, and a much-needed outlet for relaxation and enjoyment (Zarit et al., 2014).

Seeking and accepting help from others is another important aspect of social self-care. This can involve delegating caregiving tasks, seeking advice, or simply having someone to talk to. Accepting help can reduce the burden of caregiving and provide emotional support (Cheung et al., 2015).

Joining support groups, whether in person or online, can provide caregivers with a community of individuals who understand their experiences. These groups can offer emotional support, practical advice, and a sense of camaraderie, reducing feelings of isolation and providing a valuable resource for self-care (Zarit et al., 2014).

The Need for Contextual Integration in Caregiving Support Programs

Understanding Contextual Integration

Contextual integration in caregiving support programs requires a nuanced understanding of the individual and collective factors that shape the caregiving experience. This approach recognizes that caregiving is embedded in a complex web of social, cultural, political, and economic systems that influence caregivers' experiences, resources, and needs (Eifert et al., 2015).

This complexity necessitates an interdisciplinary approach to support program design and implementation. Caregiving support programs must draw from various fields of knowledge, including psychology, social work, healthcare, and public policy, to create comprehensive and effective interventions. By doing so, programs can respond to the multi-faceted challenges faced by caregivers (Trukeschitz et al., 2013).

Contextual integration also involves understanding the specificities of the caregiving context. Caregivers' experiences vary widely depending on factors such as the health condition of the care recipient, the caregiver's relationship with the care recipient, the availability of other forms of support, and the caregiver's individual strengths and resources. This understanding can guide the design of flexible and adaptable programs that cater to a diverse range of caregiving scenarios (Eifert et al., 2015).

The process of contextual integration is dynamic and ongoing. As societal norms, policies, and healthcare practices evolve, so too should caregiving support programs. This requires a commitment to continuous learning, reflection, and adaptation (Brewer & Watson, 2015).

Contextual integration seeks to bridge the gap between theory and practice in caregiving support. By grounding support programs in the realities of the caregiving context, contextual integration ensures that interventions are not only theoretically sound but also practically applicable, relevant, and effective (Eifert et al., 2015).

The Role of Contextual Integration in Enhancing Program Impact

Integrating contextual factors into the design and implementation of caregiving support programs can enhance their impact in several ways. For one, it ensures that interventions resonate with caregivers' lived experiences. This increases the relevance of support programs, making it more likely that caregivers will engage with them and benefit from their resources and services (Brewer & Watson, 2015).

Moreover, contextual integration can improve the sustainability of caregiving support programs. By aligning with the existing systems and structures within which caregivers operate, these programs can become a natural extension of caregivers' support networks. This integration makes it easier for caregivers to access and utilize support services on a regular basis, contributing to the long-term impact of these programs (Eifert et al., 2015).

Contextual integration also fosters a sense of empowerment among caregivers. By acknowledging and addressing the unique challenges and needs of caregivers, support programs can validate caregivers' experiences and promote self-efficacy. This empowers caregivers to take charge of their well-being and improve their caregiving skills, enhancing their resilience and their ability to provide care (Brewer & Watson, 2015).

Contextual integration can enhance the scalability of caregiving support programs. By considering factors such as cultural norms, resource availability, and public policy, these programs can develop strategies and resources that are adaptable to different contexts and populations. This allows for the broader dissemination and impact of these programs (Eifert et al., 2015).

By integrating contextual factors, caregiving support programs can contribute to the wider recognition and validation of caregiving as a societal responsibility. This can lead to greater public awareness, policy support, and resources for caregiving, further enhancing the impact of these programs on caregivers and care recipients (Brewer & Watson, 2015).

The Influence of Cultural Norms and Values

Culture plays a significant role in shaping caregiving experiences and should be an integral part of contextual integration in caregiving support programs. Different cultures have different norms and values related to caregiving, and these can greatly influence caregivers' perceptions and experiences of their role (Losada et al., 2017).

For example, in many cultures, caregiving is seen as a familial obligation. This can influence how caregivers perceive their role and how they approach the task of caregiving. It can also impact their willingness to seek help, with some caregivers feeling that they should shoulder the burden of care themselves without outside assistance (Losada et al., 2017).

In other cultures, certain beliefs about illness and care can shape caregiving practices. For instance, cultural beliefs about the cause of illness can influence how caregivers respond to the care recipient's symptoms and needs. These beliefs can also affect caregivers' openness to using certain forms of support or treatment (Eifert et al., 2015).

Moreover, cultural norms can impact the dynamics within the caregiving relationship. For example, in cultures where respect for elders is highly valued, caregivers may feel more pressure to provide care, even at the expense of their own well-being (Losada et al., 2017).

Therefore, caregiving support programs should seek to understand and respect these cultural norms and values. By doing so, they can develop interventions that align with caregivers' cultural beliefs and practices, increasing their acceptance and effectiveness (Eifert et al., 2015).

The Role of Healthcare Systems and Public Policy

Healthcare systems and public policy play a pivotal role in determining the resources, recognition, and support available for family caregivers. Policy and system-level changes are imperative to enable more comprehensive, sustainable caregiving support programs (Brewer & Watson, 2015).

At the healthcare system level, the infrastructure to identify and engage caregivers is lacking but sorely needed. Provider training in assessing caregiver needs, electronic health record enhancements to document caregiver data, and reimbursement for caregiver support are some improvements required (Reinhard et al., 2019). Healthcare systems must also strengthen care coordination and integration between patients, caregivers, and providers across treatment settings. Navigational assistance and care transition support would aid caregivers immensely in these areas (Family Caregiver Alliance, 2022).

Expanding eligibility and access to respite care through Medicare, Medicaid, and other insurance is another priority healthcare system change. Currently, limited eligibility criteria exclude many family caregivers who could benefit from temporary relief (Park et al., 2022). Payment and coverage policies must evolve to enable healthcare facilities to provide these caregiver supports. Partnering with community-based organizations can further augment healthcare systems' capacity for delivering caregiver services through local networks (Reinhard et al., 2019).

At the public policy level, legislative measures to financially support family caregivers are critical. These include tax credits for caregiving costs, Social Security credits for lost wages, and compensation for family medical leave (Redfoot et al., 2022). Such policies help offset the tremendous economic impacts of caregiving. Workplace policies like paid family leave are also essential to alleviate caregiver strain and enable labor force participation (Feinberg, 2022).

Caregiver assessments and care plans, embedded in broader care coordination efforts, should also be formalized through policy. Standardizing these processes across healthcare settings would streamline caregiver identification and support (Redfoot et al., 2022). Other public health policies around home and community-based services, affordable senior housing, and transportation access would also tangibly aid caregivers (Family Caregiver Alliance, 2022).

The voices of family caregivers must directly steer policy-making through representation and advocacy. Their lived expertise is invaluable in strengthening public programs and systems to better promote caregiver health, financial security, and well-being (Redfoot et al., 2022).

With engaged advocacy, thoughtful partnerships, and pioneering policies, healthcare and public systems can be transformed into robust sources of caregiver support. But truly actualizing this requires recognizing caregiving as a shared social responsibility, not just an individual burden. Policy, system, and culture change must intersect to elevate family caregivers and the invaluable care they provide (Brewer & Watson, 2015).

Unlocking the Transformative Power of Caregiving Support Programs

The Potential of Caregiving Support Programs

Caregiving support programs, when appropriately designed and implemented, have the potential to significantly enhance the quality of life of both caregivers and care recipients. They can provide much-needed resources, guidance, and support, easing the burden of caregiving and empowering caregivers to provide the best care possible. Through such programs, caregivers can learn how to manage stress, maintain their well-being, and effectively navigate the caregiving journey (Beach et al., 2022).

Furthermore, these programs can also help create a supportive community for caregivers. The isolation often experienced in caregiving can be reduced as caregivers interact and share experiences with others in similar situations. In this way, caregiving support programs foster social connectedness, a crucial component of mental and emotional well-being (Ploeg et al., 2022).

In addition, these programs can also contribute to improving care recipients' health and quality of life. Better-supported caregivers are more likely to provide better care and may feel more confident and competent in their role, thus indirectly benefiting the care recipient (Beach et al., 2022).

More broadly, successful caregiving support programs can raise awareness of the importance of caregiving and help to establish caregiving as a shared societal responsibility. They can contribute to policy dialogues, advocating for systemic changes to better support caregivers and care recipients alike (Ploeg et al., 2022).

Caregiving support programs, especially those that are evidence-based, can contribute to our understanding of what works in caregiving support. They can help identify effective strategies and interventions, shaping future research and informing the development of future programs (Beach et al., 2022).

The Role of Contextual Integration in Unlocking This Potential

The transformative potential of caregiving support programs can be fully realized through contextual integration. This involves acknowledging the unique circumstances, environments, and socio-cultural aspects that intertwine with caregiving, ensuring that programs are not just theoretically sound but also practically applicable and culturally relevant (Brewer & Watson, 2015).

Understanding the specific challenges and needs of individual caregivers is the first step in this process. This could involve assessing caregivers' levels of stress, their coping strategies, the nature and extent of their caregiving responsibilities, and the resources they have at their disposal (Ploeg et al., 2022).

Next, it is crucial to consider the broader socio-cultural context in which caregiving takes place. This could include societal attitudes towards caregiving, cultural norms around care and support, and the availability and accessibility of resources within the community (Brewer & Watson, 2015).

Incorporating these contextual factors into the design and implementation of caregiving support programs can enhance their relevance and effectiveness. It can ensure that programs are tailored to the unique needs and circumstances of caregivers, increasing their resonance and impact (Ploeg et al., 2022).

Moreover, contextual integration can help ensure that caregiving support programs are sustainable. Programs that fit well within their context, both in terms of individual caregiver needs and broader socio-cultural factors, are more likely to be adopted and maintained over time (Brewer & Watson, 2015).

Contextual integration is a powerful strategy for enhancing the effectiveness, relevance, and sustainability of caregiving support programs, unlocking their transformative potential, and maximizing their impact on caregivers' and care recipients' lives (Ploeg et al., 2022).

Examples of Successful Contextual Integration

One example of successful contextual integration is the Resources for Enhancing Alzheimer's Caregiver Health (REACH) program, an evidence-based multicomponent psychosocial intervention for dementia caregivers (Belle et al., 2006).

The program starts with a thorough assessment of the caregivers' needs, resources, and caregiving context. It then provides tailored interventions designed to enhance caregivers' coping, social support, and management of care recipient behaviors. These interventions include education, skills training, stress management, and telephone support (Belle et al., 2006).

The REACH program also incorporates regular reassessments and modifications to the interventions over time to remain responsive to caregivers' evolving needs. This adaptability is a key aspect of contextual integration, allowing the program to provide effective support as dementia caregiving progresses (Belle et al., 2006).

The program's demonstrated success highlights the power of contextual integration in meeting caregivers' unique needs and improving their well-being and coping (Belle et al., 2006).

The Future of Caregiving Support Programs

The future of caregiving support programs lies in the continued integration of empirical evidence, professional expertise, and contextual factors. As our understanding of caregiving evolves, so too must our support programs. By embracing the complexities and intricacies of the caregiving landscape, we can create programs that are not only theoretically sound but also practically relevant and impactful (Beach et al., 2022).

Emerging trends, such as the increasing use of technology in caregiving, present both challenges and opportunities for caregiving support programs. On the one hand, technology can enhance the accessibility and reach of these programs, but on the other, it may also create new challenges and stressors for caregivers (Ploeg et al., 2022).

Continued research is crucial to navigate these evolving landscapes. By continually assessing the needs and experiences of caregivers and by rigorously evaluating the effectiveness of various interventions, we can ensure that our caregiving support programs remain relevant and impactful (Beach et al., 2022).

In addition to research, collaboration, and advocacy are also key. Collaboration between researchers, healthcare providers, policymakers, and caregivers themselves can lead to the development of more comprehensive and effective programs. Advocacy can help raise awareness of the importance of caregiving, influencing public policy and societal attitudes toward caregiving (Ploeg et al., 2022).

The future of caregiving support programs is one of continued evolution and innovation. Through contextual integration, we can create programs that are not only effective in reducing caregiver stress and enhancing well-being but also transformative in their impact on caregivers, care recipients, and society as a whole (Beach et al., 2022).

The Promise of Contextual Integration

The integration of contextual factors into the design and implementation of caregiving support programs holds great promise for enhancing their impact and effectiveness. By acknowledging the complex realities of caregiving, we can create programs that are not just effective on paper but in practice as well (Brewer & Watson, 2015).

Contextual integration allows us to tailor our interventions to the unique needs and circumstances of caregivers, ensuring their relevance and resonance. It recognizes that there is no one-size-fits-all solution to caregiving support and that successful programs must be flexible and adaptable (Ploeg et al., 2022).

Furthermore, contextual integration can also enhance the sustainability of caregiving support programs. By aligning with the cultural norms and societal attitudes of the communities they serve, these programs can gain greater acceptance and integration, ensuring their long-term sustainability (Brewer & Watson, 2015).

Finally, contextual integration holds promise for advancing our understanding of what works in caregiving support. By evaluating the effectiveness of contextually-integrated interventions, we can identify best practices and successful strategies, informing future research and program development (Beach et al., 2022).

The promise of contextual integration lies in its potential to enhance the relevance, effectiveness, and sustainability of caregiving support programs. By grounding our programs in the realities of caregiving, we can unlock their transformative potential, propelling them toward new frontiers of innovation and impact (Ploeg et al., 2022).

2.2: Stress Management Techniques for Caregivers: A Comprehensive Approach

Caregiving, while rewarding, can be an immensely challenging role that requires significant emotional, physical, financial, and social investment. The stress associated with caregiving is a complex issue that encompasses biological, psychological, and social dimensions. Managing this stress effectively requires a comprehensive understanding of these dimensions and the implementation of evidence-based techniques and interventions aimed at building resilience (Beach et al., 2022).

From a biological perspective, caregiver stress can lead to physical manifestations such as elevated stress hormones, impaired immune function, and an increased risk of chronic diseases. Psychologically, this stress can result in anxiety, depression, feelings of frustration, grief, loneliness, and social isolation.

Financially, caregivers often face the challenge of balancing the costs associated with caregiving with the potential loss of income due to reduced work hours or early retirement. Socially, caregivers can feel overwhelmed by the coordination of care across multiple healthcare professionals and family members, often at the expense of personal relationships and leisure activities (Ploeg et al., 2022).

To manage this intricate web of stress, caregivers need to implement effective stress management techniques. These techniques, which include mindfulness, self-care, cognitive restructuring, and time management, can empower caregivers to build resilience and cope more effectively with the demands of their role (Beach et al., 2022).

Building Resilience: Evidence-Based Stress Management Techniques for Caregivers

The Role of Mindfulness in Stress Management

Mindfulness is a stress management technique that has been increasingly recognized for its mental health benefits. Rooted in Buddhist traditions, mindfulness involves paying non-judgmental attention to experiences in the present moment. For caregivers, mindfulness can provide a space of calm and tranquility amidst the potential turmoil of their caregiving responsibilities (Wong et al., 2018).

One way mindfulness can assist caregivers is by activating the body's parasympathetic nervous system, which helps to reduce stress and foster relaxation. Regular practice of mindfulness has been associated with reductions in blood pressure, heart rate, and levels of the stress hormone cortisol. By fostering a state of physiological relaxation, mindfulness can help to counteract the harmful effects of chronic stress on the body (Wong et al., 2018).

Furthermore, mindfulness can also improve psychological well-being. By helping individuals to stay focused on the present, mindfulness can prevent ruminative thinking about the past or worry about the future, reducing feelings of stress and anxiety. Additionally, mindfulness encourages acceptance and compassion towards oneself, which can help caregivers to manage the emotional challenges associated with their role (Beach et al., 2022).

Mindfulness-based interventions tailored for caregivers, such as Mindfulness-Based Stress Reduction (MBSR), have been found to increase quality of life, self-efficacy, and subjective well-being. They often include practices such as mindful breathing, body scan exercises, and mindful movement, providing caregivers with a range of techniques that they can incorporate into their daily routines (Wong et al., 2018).

The practice of mindfulness offers significant potential for managing caregiver stress. By promoting both physiological relaxation and psychological well-being, mindfulness can enhance caregivers' overall quality of life and their ability to provide care (Beach et al., 2022).

The Importance of Self-Care in Stress Management

Self-care plays a critical role in caregiver stress management. It involves activities and practices that individuals engage in on a regular basis to maintain and enhance their health and well-being. For caregivers, who often put the needs of their care recipients before their own, self-care can be particularly important for managing stress and avoiding burnout (Cheung et al., 2015).

One aspect of self-care involves setting healthy boundaries. This means recognizing and honoring one's own limitations and needs, even while caring for others. By setting boundaries, caregivers can ensure they have enough energy and resources for self-care, reducing the risk of burnout (Ploeg et al., 2022).

Another key component of self-care is engaging in leisure activities. Leisure activities, such as hobbies, exercise, or socializing with friends, can provide caregivers with a much-needed respite from their caregiving responsibilities. They can also foster feelings of joy, relaxation, and fulfillment, counteracting the effects of stress (Cheung et al., 2015).

Ensuring adequate rest and nutrition is also a crucial part of self-care. Sleep deprivation and poor nutrition can exacerbate stress and reduce caregivers' ability to cope. By prioritizing good sleep hygiene and a healthy diet, caregivers can foster their physical well-being and resilience to stress (Ploeg et al., 2022).

Lastly, seeking support is an important self-care strategy. This can involve reaching out to friends or family, joining a caregiver support group, or seeking professional help, such as counseling or respite care services. By seeking support, caregivers can alleviate some of the burdens of caregiving, reduce feelings of isolation, and gain valuable insights and coping strategies (Cheung et al., 2015).

Self-care is a critical strategy for managing caregiver stress. By practicing self-care, caregivers can improve their well-being, avoid burnout, and continue to provide compassionate care to their loved ones (Ploeg et al., 2022).

Cognitive Restructuring: Reframing Thoughts for Stress Management

Cognitive restructuring is a technique derived from cognitive-behavioral therapy (CBT), a form of psychotherapy that focuses on changing negative thought patterns to improve emotional regulation and coping skills. For caregivers, cognitive restructuring can be a powerful tool for managing stress and enhancing well-being (Lloyd et al., 2016).

The process of cognitive restructuring involves several steps. First, caregivers are taught to identify their automatic thoughts—those immediate, reflexive thoughts that occur in response to a situation. Often, these automatic thoughts are negative and may exacerbate feelings of stress or overwhelm (Lloyd et al., 2016).

Once these automatic thoughts have been identified, the next step in cognitive restructuring involves challenging these thoughts. This might involve examining the evidence for and against the thought, considering alternative explanations, or assessing the potential implications of the thought (Lloyd et al., 2016).

After challenging their automatic thoughts, caregivers can then reframe or replace these thoughts with more positive or realistic ones. For example, a caregiver might replace the thought "I can't handle this" with "I'm doing the best I can, and it's okay to ask for help when I need it." (Beach et al., 2022).

Cognitive restructuring is a skill that can be learned and practiced independently, offering a cost-effective and accessible tool for managing caregiver stress. It can also be taught as part of a structured CBT program or with the assistance of a mental health professional (Lloyd et al., 2016).

Cognitive restructuring can help caregivers identify and challenge cognitive distortions that exacerbate stress. By reframing their thoughts, caregivers can regain a sense of control and self-efficacy, reducing their stress levels and enhancing their ability to cope (Beach et al., 2022).

Time Management for Stress Management

Effective time management is a crucial aspect of caregiver stress management. With the myriad tasks and responsibilities involved in caregiving, managing one's time effectively can reduce feelings of overwhelm and enhance feelings of control and self-efficacy (Ploeg et al., 2022).

One key aspect of time management involves maintaining a calendar or schedule. This can provide a visual representation of the caregiver's responsibilities and help to ensure that tasks are not forgotten. Additionally, it can provide a sense of structure and predictability, which can reduce stress (Cheung et al., 2015).

Delegating tasks is another important time management strategy. Caregivers often feel the need to do everything themselves, but this can lead to overwhelm and burnout. By delegating tasks to other family members, friends, or professional caregivers, they can reduce their workload and stress levels (Ploeg et al., 2022).

Setting boundaries around responsibilities is also crucial. This might involve saying no to additional tasks or responsibilities or setting aside certain times for relaxation or self-care. By setting boundaries, caregivers can protect their own well-being and ensure they have the energy and resources needed to provide care (Cheung et al., 2015).

Finally, scheduling relaxation or leisure activities can also enhance time management. These activities can provide a respite from caregiving duties and foster relaxation and well-being. They can also provide caregivers with something to look forward to, which can improve mood and motivation (Ploeg et al., 2022).

Effective time management is crucial for managing caregiver stress. This involves maintaining a calendar, delegating tasks appropriately, setting boundaries around responsibilities, and scheduling relaxation activities. By managing their time effectively, caregivers can balance their caregiving responsibilities with their own needs, reducing stress and enhancing their well-being (Cheung et al., 2015).

The Role of Stress Management Techniques in Building Resilience

Building resilience—the ability to adapt positively in the face of adversity—can play a critical role in managing caregiver stress. Caregivers often face significant challenges and stressors, and building resilience can help them navigate these challenges effectively (Ploeg et al., 2022).

One way to build resilience is through the consistent practice of stress management techniques. Techniques such as mindfulness, self-care, cognitive restructuring, and effective time management can provide caregivers with the tools they need to manage stress and foster resilience (Beach et al., 2022).

Resilience is characterized by several key traits, including equanimity, self-efficacy, social connectedness, and an optimistic yet realistic outlook. By practicing stress management techniques, caregivers can foster these traits and build their resilience (Ploeg et al., 2022).

Equanimity, or the ability to stay calm and balanced in the face of stress, can be fostered through techniques such as mindfulness and self-care. Self-efficacy, or the belief in one's ability to handle challenges, can be enhanced through techniques like cognitive restructuring and time management (Beach et al., 2022).

Social connectedness is another key aspect of resilience. Caregivers can foster social connectedness by seeking support from others, such as friends, family, or support groups. An optimistic yet realistic outlook can also be beneficial. This involves maintaining a positive attitude while also acknowledging and preparing for potential challenges (Ploeg et al., 2022).

Through consistent practice of these stress management techniques, caregivers can build resilience. Resilience, characterized by equanimity, self-efficacy, social connectedness, and an optimistic yet realistic outlook, enables positive adaptation in the face of adversity. By building resilience, caregivers can improve their quality of life and their ability to provide care (Beach et al., 2022).

The Intricate Web of Caregiver Stress: A Biopsychosocial Perspective

Biological Dimensions of Caregiver Stress

From a biological perspective, caregiver stress can have significant physical manifestations. Chronic stress can lead to the overproduction of stress hormones like cortisol, which can have detrimental effects on the body. Understanding these biological manifestations is crucial for managing caregiver stress and maintaining caregivers' physical health (Aschbrenner et al., 2019).

Chronic stress can impair immune function, making caregivers more susceptible to illnesses. It can also increase the risk of chronic diseases such as heart disease, diabetes, and depression. By understanding these biological effects of stress, caregivers can take steps to manage their stress and protect their physical health (Aschbrenner et al., 2019).

Furthermore, chronic stress can also impact sleep and nutrition. Caregivers under stress may struggle with insomnia or other sleep disturbances, which can further exacerbate stress and impair health. Stress can also impact appetite and eating habits, potentially leading to malnutrition or weight problems (Beach et al., 2022).

Research in psychoneuroimmunology, the study of how psychological factors can influence the nervous system and immune systems, has provided valuable insights into the biological effects of caregiver stress. This research suggests that effective stress management can reduce the production of stress hormones, improve immune function, and protect against the harmful effects of stress on the body (Aschbrenner et al., 2019).

From a biological perspective, caregiver stress can manifest physically through elevated levels of stress hormones like cortisol, which can impair immune function and increase the risk of chronic diseases. Understanding these biological manifestations is crucial for managing caregiver stress and maintaining caregivers' physical health (Beach et al., 2022).

Psychological Dimensions of Caregiver Stress

Psychologically, caregiver stress can involve a range of emotions and cognitive processes. Caregivers may experience feelings of anxiety, depression, frustration, grief, and loneliness. They may also struggle with cognitive distortions or inaccurate thought patterns that exacerbate stress, such as catastrophizing (assuming the worst-case scenario) or overgeneralizing (applying one negative experience to all situations) (Lloyd et al., 2016).

Understanding these psychological dimensions of caregiver stress can help caregivers and their support networks to develop effective coping strategies. For instance, cognitive-behavioral interventions can be particularly effective in addressing cognitive distortions. These interventions can teach caregivers to identify, challenge, and reframe their automatic negative thoughts, reducing stress and enhancing well-being (Lloyd et al., 2016).

Feelings of grief and loss are also common among caregivers, particularly those caring for individuals with progressive conditions such as Alzheimer's disease or cancer. It's important to acknowledge and validate these feelings and to seek support as needed. Grief counseling or support groups can be valuable resources (Beach et al., 2022).

Depression and anxiety are also common among caregivers. These conditions are serious and require professional treatment. Caregivers experiencing symptoms of depression or anxiety, such as persistent sadness, loss of interest in activities, excessive worry, or changes in sleep or appetite, should seek help from a healthcare provider (Ploeg et al., 2022).

Psychologically, caregiver stress often involves feelings of anxiety, depression, frustration, grief, and loneliness. Caregivers may also experience cognitive distortions that exacerbate stress, such as catastrophizing or overgeneralizing. Addressing these psychological dimensions is key to enhancing caregivers' mental health and well-being (Lloyd et al., 2016).

Social Dimensions of Caregiver Stress

Caregiving, while often rewarding, can also present social challenges that contribute to caregiver stress. For example, caregivers often need to coordinate care among various healthcare professionals, which can be confusing and time-consuming. Communication with healthcare providers and family members about the care recipient's condition and needs can also be stressful (Chen et al., 2015).

Moreover, caregiving duties can lead to social isolation. Caregivers may find themselves having less time to engage in social activities or maintain personal relationships. This lack of social interaction can exacerbate feelings of loneliness and stress. It's important for caregivers to find ways to stay socially connected, such as by joining support groups or staying in touch with friends and family through technology (Chen et al., 2015).

Some caregivers may also experience changes in their relationships with the care recipient or other family members. These changes can bring about emotional stress. For example, a spouse caring for their partner may grieve the loss of their traditional relationship dynamics. It's crucial to communicate these feelings and seek professional help if necessary (Beach et al., 2022).

The role of a caregiver often comes with certain expectations and social pressures, which can further contribute to stress. Society often expects caregivers to provide care without complaining or seeking help, which can make caregivers feel guilty or inadequate if they're struggling. It's important for caregivers to challenge these societal norms and acknowledge that it's okay to seek help and support (Ploeg et al., 2022).

Addressing the social dimensions of caregiver stress involves recognizing and managing the challenges associated with coordinating care, communication, social isolation, relationship changes, and societal expectations. By addressing these social factors, caregivers can enhance their social well-being and improve their caregiving experience (Chen et al., 2015).

Financial Dimensions of Caregiver Stress

Caregiving can also have significant financial implications. The costs of medical care, home modifications, assistive devices, and other care-related expenses can quickly add up. Moreover, caregivers often need to balance these financial responsibilities with their own personal financial needs and goals (Redfoot et al., 2022).

For caregivers who need to reduce their work hours or leave the workforce entirely to provide care, the loss of income can be a significant source of stress. Financial stress can exacerbate the other dimensions of caregiver stress, leading to a vicious cycle. It's crucial for caregivers to seek financial advice and explore all available resources to help manage these financial challenges (Redfoot et al., 2022).

It's also important for caregivers to plan for the future. This can include setting up a budget, saving for retirement, and considering the financial implications of different care options. Financial planning can provide a sense of control and reduce financial stress (Ploeg et al., 2022).

Caregivers should also be aware of the financial resources available to them. This can include government benefits, insurance coverage, nonprofit assistance programs, and tax credits for caregivers. By accessing these resources, caregivers can alleviate some of the financial stress associated with caregiving (Redfoot et al., 2022).

Caregivers should not hesitate to seek professional financial advice. Financial advisors who specialize in elder care can provide valuable advice on managing the costs of care, preserving assets, and planning for the future. By seeking professional advice, caregivers can navigate the financial challenges of caregiving more effectively (Ploeg et al., 2022).

The Importance of a Biopsychosocial Understanding of Caregiver Stress

A comprehensive understanding of the biopsychosocial dimensions of caregiver stress is crucial for effective stress management. The biopsychosocial model recognizes that biological, psychological, and social factors all play a role in human health and illness. In the context of caregiving, these factors can interact to influence caregivers' stress levels and overall well-being (Beach et al., 2022).

By considering the biological dimensions of caregiver stress, caregivers can better understand the physical manifestations of stress and take steps to protect their physical health. This can include activities such as regular exercise, adequate nutrition, and proper sleep, which can all help to mitigate the physical effects of stress (Aschbrenner et al., 2019).

Addressing the psychological dimensions of caregiver stress involves understanding and managing the cognitive distortions and emotional challenges associated with caregiving. Psychological interventions, such as cognitive-behavioral therapy, can be particularly effective in managing these dimensions (Lloyd et al., 2016).

The social dimensions of caregiver stress highlight the importance of social support and effective communication in managing caregiver stress. By maintaining social connections, seeking support when needed, and communicating effectively with healthcare providers and family members, caregivers can improve their social well-being and caregiving experience (Chen et al., 2015).

Lastly, the financial dimensions of caregiver stress underscore the importance of financial planning and resources in managing caregiver stress. By seeking financial advice, planning for the future, and accessing available resources, caregivers can alleviate financial stress and focus more on the essential task of providing care (Redfoot et al., 2022).

A comprehensive understanding of the biopsychosocial dimensions of caregiver stress is crucial for developing holistic and effective stress management strategies (Beach et al., 2022).

The Transformative Power of Stress Management Techniques

Fostering Growth and Empowerment Through Stress Management

Stress management techniques can foster personal growth and empowerment in caregivers. By gaining the skills to manage their own stress, caregivers can cultivate a sense of control over their own mental and emotional state. This can protect against feelings of helplessness and hopelessness, often associated with high-stress roles such as caregiving (Beach et al., 2022).

Having a strong repertoire of stress management techniques can also promote self-efficacy. Self-efficacy is an individual's belief in their ability to succeed in specific situations or accomplish a task. In the context of caregiving, this means believing in their ability to provide care while maintaining their own well-being. Developing self-efficacy can lead to a more positive self-concept, further fostering personal growth (Bandura, 1977).

Stress management techniques also allow caregivers to take proactive steps toward maintaining their mental health. Instead of being reactive—merely dealing with stressors as they arise—caregivers can become proactive, employing these techniques regularly to manage stress levels and prevent burnout (Beach et al., 2022).

By fostering personal growth and empowerment, stress management techniques can also improve the caregiver's capacity to provide care. An empowered caregiver is likely to be more engaged, patient, and empathetic, improving the quality of care provided (Bandura, 1977).

Through the consistent practice of stress management techniques, caregivers can foster growth and empowerment, enhancing their well-being, their resilience, and their ability to provide care (Beach et al., 2022).

Therapeutic Approaches to Stress Management

Therapeutic approaches to stress management, such as cognitive-behavioral therapy (CBT) and mindfulness-based interventions, can be highly beneficial for caregivers. CBT, for example, teaches individuals how to identify, challenge, and change maladaptive thoughts and behaviors. This can help caregivers manage the stress and negative emotions that often accompany the caregiving role (Lloyd et al., 2016).

Mindfulness-based interventions, on the other hand, focus on cultivating present-moment awareness and acceptance. By practicing mindfulness, caregivers can learn to stay present and focused rather than getting caught up in worrying thoughts about the past or future. This can reduce stress and enhance overall well-being (Wong et al., 2018).

Both CBT and mindfulness-based interventions can also enhance emotional regulation, the ability to manage and respond to emotional experiences in a healthy way. By improving emotional regulation, these therapeutic approaches can help caregivers manage the emotional challenges of caregiving, such as frustration, grief, and worry (Lloyd et al., 2016).

In addition, these therapeutic approaches can be learned and practiced independently, providing caregivers with accessible, cost-effective tools for managing stress. Many resources are available online, including guided mindfulness meditations and CBT self-help guides (Wong et al., 2018).

Therapeutic approaches to stress management can provide caregivers with the skills and strategies they need to manage stress effectively. These approaches can help caregivers to challenge cognitive distortions, manage their thoughts and emotions, and stay present and focused, reducing stress and enhancing their ability to cope (Lloyd et al., 2016).

The Role of Resilience in Stress Management

Resilience plays a crucial role in caregiver stress management. By definition, resilience is the process of adapting well in the face of adversity, trauma, tragedy, threats, or significant sources of stress. It's the ability to "bounce back" from difficult experiences and carry on with life (Ploeg et al., 2022).

In the context of caregiving, resilience can be thought of as the caregiver's ability to maintain their well-being and continue providing care, despite the inherent challenges and stresses of the role. Resilient caregivers are not just able to survive these challenges but to learn, grow, and find meaning in them (Ploeg et al., 2022).

Building resilience often involves developing effective coping strategies, enhancing emotional intelligence, and cultivating a positive outlook. These attributes allow caregivers to navigate the stress and challenges of caregiving with strength and grace (Beach et al., 2022).

Resilience can also be fostered through self-care, social support, and therapeutic interventions. Taking time for oneself, seeking support from others, and learning stress management techniques can all enhance resilience (Ploeg et al., 2022).

By building resilience, caregivers can enhance their mental and emotional strength, improve their coping skills, and maintain their well-being in the face of the challenges associated with caregiving (Beach et al., 2022).

Finding Meaning and Satisfaction in Caregiving

Beyond merely managing stress, stress management techniques can also help caregivers find meaning and satisfaction in their caregiving journey. By managing stress effectively and building resilience, caregivers can shift their perspective on their role, finding personal growth and fulfillment in their caregiving duties (Beach et al., 2022).

Caregiving, despite its challenges, offers numerous opportunities for personal growth and satisfaction. It can deepen relationships, foster empathy and compassion, and provide a sense of purpose and fulfillment. By managing stress effectively, caregivers can be more open to and aware of these positive aspects of caregiving (Ploeg et al., 2022).

Moreover, finding meaning and satisfaction in caregiving can serve as a buffer against the negative effects of stress. Research has shown that individuals who find their work meaningful and satisfying are more resilient to stress and less likely to experience burnout (Arnold et al., 2007).

The practices of mindfulness and cognitive reframing, often used in stress management, can be particularly helpful in finding meaning and satisfaction in caregiving. Mindfulness encourages present-moment awareness and acceptance, allowing caregivers to fully experience and appreciate their caregiving journey. Cognitive reframing helps individuals to see situations from a different perspective, which can reveal hidden opportunities for growth and satisfaction (Beach et al., 2022).

Beyond managing stress, these techniques can help caregivers find meaning and satisfaction in their caregiving journey. By managing stress effectively and building resilience, caregivers can shift from merely surviving to thriving, finding personal growth and fulfillment in their role (Ploeg et al., 2022).

The Promise of Stress Management Techniques

Stress management techniques hold great promise for enhancing the caregiving experience. They offer a proactive approach to managing stress, allowing caregivers to maintain their well-being and continue providing care effectively (Beach et al., 2022).

By integrating stress management techniques into their daily lives, caregivers can manage their stress in real time, preventing it from accumulating and leading to burnout. This can help caregivers maintain their physical, mental, and emotional health, enhancing their ability to provide care (Ploeg et al., 2022).

Stress management techniques can also foster personal growth and empowerment, leading to a more positive caregiving experience. By learning and practicing these techniques, caregivers can develop a sense of mastery and control over their stress, enhancing their self-esteem and resilience (Beach et al., 2022).

Moreover, the skills learned through stress management techniques can be beneficial beyond the caregiving context. Techniques such as mindfulness, cognitive reframing, and emotional regulation can improve the overall quality of life, fostering well-being and resilience in various life areas (Wong et al., 2018).

Stress management techniques hold great promise for enhancing the caregiving experience. By integrating these techniques into their daily lives, caregivers can manage stress, build resilience, and improve their well-being, enhancing their ability to provide compassionate, effective care to their loved ones (Ploeg et al., 2022).

2.3: Evidence-Based Approaches to Medication Management for Caregivers: A Comprehensive Guide

Medication management is a vital role that caregivers often assume. This responsibility involves handling complex medication regimens, which requires pharmaceutical knowledge, meticulous organization, and constant vigilance to ensure safety and adherence (Elliott & Marriott, 2009). Despite the complexity of this role, caregivers can effectively navigate this multifaceted task with the aid of evidence-based approaches.

Understanding the pharmacokinetics, mechanism of action, dosage, intended effects, potential adverse effects, precautions, and contraindications of each medication is crucial. This comprehensive understanding allows caregivers to make informed administration decisions, monitor for interactions and side effects, and promptly seek medical advice when necessary (Elliott & Marriott, 2009).

Promoting medication regimen adherence is another essential aspect of medication management. Non-adherence, often due to complex regimens, forgetfulness, side effects, cost issues, or lack of understanding of therapeutic benefits, can undermine treatment outcomes. Therefore, it's important for caregivers to employ effective interventions to promote adherence (Zarit et al., 2014).

Ensuring medication safety is a fundamental responsibility of caregivers. This involves following strict protocols for medication preparation, dosage calculation, administration, and documentation, as well as monitoring for side effects and allergic reactions and properly storing and disposing of medications (Elliott & Marriott, 2009).

Comprehending Medication Pharmacology and Therapeutic Effects

The Importance of Dosage and Intended Effects

Understanding the prescribed dosage and intended effects of each medication is crucial for caregivers. Dosage is determined by the doctor based on a variety of factors, including the patient's age, weight, overall health status, and the specific condition being treated. By understanding the dosage, caregivers can accurately administer the medication and avoid potential over or under-dosing (Elliott & Marriott, 2009).

Awareness of the intended effects of the medication can guide caregivers in observing and monitoring the patient's response. This can involve changes in physical symptoms, mental status, and overall health condition. If the medication is intended to control pain, for instance, the caregiver should observe whether the patient's pain levels decrease after the medication is taken (Reinhard et al., 2019).

Knowing the intended effects of the medication also aids in identifying if the medication is not working as it should. If the intended effects are not seen after a period of taking the medication, it may indicate that the dosage needs adjustment or that the medication is not effective for the patient's condition (Elliott & Marriott, 2009).

Understanding the intended effects of medication also allows caregivers to have informed discussions with healthcare providers. They can provide feedback about the medication's effectiveness, express concerns, and ask relevant questions. This can contribute to the ongoing assessment and adjustment of the patient's medication regimen, promoting more personalized and effective care (Reinhard et al., 2019).

Understanding the dosage and intended effects of each medication enhances the caregiver's role in medication management, leading to more effective care and better health outcomes for the patient (Elliott & Marriott, 2009).

Recognizing potential adverse effects and precautions associated with each medication is another essential aspect of medication management for caregivers. Adverse effects, or side effects, are unintended, often undesirable effects that may occur with drug use. Precautions refer to specific actions or care that should be taken to prevent or manage potential side effects (Elliott & Marriott, 2009).

For each medication, caregivers should understand what the potential side effects are and how they might present in the patient. Some side effects, such as nausea or dizziness, may be relatively common and manageable. Others, however, like breathing difficulty or severe allergic reactions, can be serious and require immediate medical attention (Reinhard et al., 2019).

Understanding precautions is equally important. For some medications, this may involve taking the medication with food to minimize stomach upset or avoiding certain activities, like driving or operating machinery, due to potential drowsiness. Knowing these precautions allows caregivers to plan medication administration accordingly and help patients manage potential side effects effectively (Elliott & Marriott, 2009).

In addition, recognizing when to seek medical attention is critical. Caregivers should know which side effects are potentially dangerous and require immediate medical intervention. This knowledge allows for prompt action in emergency situations, enhancing patient safety (Reinhard et al., 2019).

Knowledge about potential adverse effects and precautions enables caregivers to manage medications more safely and effectively, promote patient comfort, and contribute to overall patient safety (Elliott & Marriott, 2009).

Understanding contraindications, or situations in which medication should not be used because it may be harmful to the patient, is essential for caregivers. Contraindications can be absolute, indicating a medication should never be used under certain circumstances, or relative, indicating a medication should be used with caution under certain circumstances (Elliott & Marriott, 2009).

Caregivers should be aware of any contraindications associated with each medication the patient is taking. This could involve certain health conditions, allergies, or potential interactions with other medications or substances. For instance, medication may be contraindicated in patients with liver disease or in combination with certain other medications (Reinhard et al., 2019).

Knowing contraindications can help caregivers avoid harmful situations. For instance, if a patient is prescribed a new medication that is contraindicated based on their current medication regimen or health status, an informed caregiver can bring this to the attention of the healthcare provider (Elliott & Marriott, 2009).

Understanding contraindications also involves knowing what to do if a contraindicated situation arises. This might involve seeking immediate medical attention or withholding the medication and contacting the healthcare provider (Reinhard et al., 2019).

In short, understanding contraindications enhances the caregiver's role in ensuring medication safety, promoting patient well-being, and preventing potential harm (Elliott & Marriott, 2009).

Reliable sources of information are crucial for caregivers in understanding and managing medications. These sources can provide accurate, comprehensive, and up-to-date information about medications, enhancing the caregiver's knowledge and competence (Reinhard et al., 2019).

Drug monographs, or detailed written studies of individual medications, are excellent sources of information. They provide detailed information about the medication, including its uses, dosage, side effects, contraindications, and precautions. Most medications come with a patient information leaflet that provides a simplified version of the drug monograph (Elliott & Marriott, 2009).

Medical literature, such as medical textbooks, journal articles, and clinical guidelines, can provide more in-depth information about medications and their uses. This can be particularly useful for understanding the scientific rationale behind medication regimens or for learning about new medications or treatment approaches (Reinhard et al., 2019).

Healthcare providers, including doctors, pharmacists, and nurses, are invaluable sources of information. They can provide personalized advice and education about medications, answer questions, and clarify any confusion or concerns. Regular communication with healthcare providers can enhance caregivers' understanding and management of medications (Elliott & Marriott, 2009).

Leveraging reliable sources of information allows caregivers to develop a comprehensive understanding of each medication, enhancing their ability to manage medications safely and effectively and contributing to the overall quality of patient care (Reinhard et al., 2019).

Promoting Medication Regimen Adherence

Understanding the Challenges of Medication Adherence

Medication adherence refers to the degree to which a person follows the prescribed dosage, timing, and frequency of their medications. Unfortunately, non-adherence is a common issue, with potential ramifications on the care recipient's health status and overall quality of care (Lam & Fresco, 2015). Understanding the challenges of medication adherence is the first step in promoting adherence in a caregiving setting.

Several factors can contribute to non-adherence. These can range from complex medication regimens that are difficult to manage to simple forgetfulness. Other issues may include medication side effects that may discourage the care recipient from taking their medications as prescribed or a lack of understanding about why the medication is necessary. It's important to recognize that adherence can be a challenge even for the most dedicated caregivers and care recipients (Reinhard et al., 2019).

Socioeconomic factors can also pose challenges to medication adherence. For example, the cost of medications can sometimes be prohibitive, leading to skipped doses or unfilled prescriptions. Additionally, care recipients with limited health literacy may not fully understand the importance of their medication regimen, leading to non-adherence (Lam & Fresco, 2015).

Behavioral and psychological factors can also impact medication adherence. For instance, care recipients who are depressed or anxious may be less likely to adhere to their medication regimen. Furthermore, some care recipients may have beliefs or attitudes about medications that deter them from taking their medications as prescribed (Reinhard et al., 2019).

Given these challenges, promoting medication adherence requires a multifaceted approach that includes clear communication, support from healthcare professionals, the use of adherence aids, and ongoing education and motivation (Lam & Fresco, 2015).

The Role of Clear Instructions and Reminders

One of the primary ways to promote medication adherence is through the provision of clear, simple instructions. When caregivers provide clear instructions about when and how to take each medication, it reduces confusion and increases the likelihood that the care recipient will take their medications correctly (Elliott & Marriott, 2009).

Reminders are another effective tool for promoting medication adherence. This could be as simple as setting alarms or reminders on a smartphone or using a daily checklist or calendar. Some caregivers find it helpful to associate medication times with routine daily activities, like meals or bedtime, as these natural cues can serve as effective reminders (Reinhard et al., 2019).

In addition to verbal reminders, visual aids can also be helpful. This could involve using a chart or diagram to illustrate the medication schedule or color-coding medications according to the time of day they should be taken. Visual aids can be particularly beneficial for care recipients with cognitive impairments, as they provide a tangible reminder of when to take each medication (Elliott & Marriott, 2009).

Another effective strategy is to use pill organizers. These devices, which have compartments for each day of the week, and sometimes different times of the day, can help ensure that the care recipient takes the right medications at the right times. They can also provide a visual reminder of whether a dose has been taken, reducing the likelihood of missed or double doses (Reinhard et al., 2019).

Caregivers should aim to establish a routine for medication administration. By administering medications at the same times each day, caregivers can help establish a habit that promotes consistent adherence. This routine can also make it easier for caregivers to remember when each medication should be given, reducing the likelihood of errors (Elliott & Marriott, 2009).

The Importance of Pill Organizers and Medication Dispensers

Pill organizers and medication dispensers play a crucial role in promoting medication regimen adherence. These tools can greatly simplify the task of managing multiple medications, making it easier for both caregivers and care recipients to ensure that each medication is taken at the correct time (Reinhard et al., 2019).

Pill organizers are typically small, portable devices with compartments for each day of the week. Some organizers have separate compartments for different times of the day, making it easy to keep track of multiple daily doses. By filling out the organizer at the start of each week, caregivers can ensure that all medications are accounted for and easily accessible (Elliott & Marriott, 2009).

Medication dispensers are slightly more complex devices that can dispense the right dose of medication at the right time. Some dispensers can even provide auditory or visual alerts when it's time to take a medication, making them a valuable tool for promoting adherence (Reinhard et al., 2019).

Both pill organizers and medication dispensers can reduce the risk of medication errors, such as taking the wrong medication or taking the wrong dose, by having a visual confirmation of what medication should be taken and when, caregivers and care recipients can be more confident in their medication management (Elliott & Marriott, 2009).

These tools can also alleviate stress for caregivers. Instead of needing to remember complex medication schedules or handle multiple medication bottles, caregivers can rely on the organizer or dispenser to ensure that each medication is taken correctly. This can free up mental resources for other caregiving tasks and reduce the risk of caregiver burnout (Reinhard et al., 2019).

Pill organizers and medication dispensers can facilitate communication with healthcare professionals. By bringing the organizer or dispenser to medical appointments, caregivers can show healthcare providers exactly what medications are being taken and how they are being managed. This can foster more informed, collaborative decision-making and ensure that the medication regimen is optimal for the care recipient's needs (Elliott & Marriott, 2009).

Motivational Interviewing and Ongoing Education

Motivational interviewing is a client-centered counseling approach that can be used to enhance medication adherence. It involves exploring and resolving ambivalence to change, with the aim of motivating the care recipient to adhere to their medication regimen. This approach recognizes that the care recipient is the expert on their own life and experiences and seeks to guide them towards positive change rather than imposing it (Joosten et al., 2008).

In the context of medication adherence, motivational interviewing could involve exploring the care recipient's beliefs and attitudes towards their medications, understanding their concerns or fears, and working together to find solutions to any barriers to adherence. For example, if a care recipient is concerned about side effects, the caregiver could provide reassurance, seek advice from a healthcare professional, or explore alternative medications or dosages (Reinhard et al., 2019).

Ongoing education is another key aspect of promoting medication adherence. By continually educating the care recipient about their medications and the importance of adherence, caregivers can ensure that they understand why each medication is necessary and how it contributes to their health. Education can also help dispel any misconceptions or fears about medications, which can improve adherence (Elliott & Marriott, 2009).

Education should be tailored to the care recipient's needs and understanding. It should be provided in clear, simple language and should involve active discussion and participation rather than just lecturing. Visual aids, handouts, or demonstrations can also be used to enhance understanding (Reinhard et al., 2019).

Caregivers should continually reinforce the importance of adherence and the consequences of non-adherence. This could involve regularly reviewing the medication regimen, discussing the benefits of each medication, and reminding the care recipient of the progress they have made. By reinforcing these messages, caregivers can help motivate the care recipient to adhere to their medication regimen (Elliott & Marriott, 2009).

The Role of Collaboration and Support

Collaboration and support from healthcare professionals is crucial in promoting medication adherence. By working closely with doctors, pharmacists, and other healthcare providers, caregivers can ensure that the care recipient's medication regimen is manageable, effective, and safe (Reinhard et al., 2019).

Doctors and pharmacists can provide valuable advice on how to manage complex medication regimens, deal with side effects, and enhance adherence. They can also simplify medication regimens, if possible, by recommending combination medications, adjusting dosing times to fit with the care recipient's routine, or prescribing long-acting medications that need to be taken less frequently (Elliott & Marriott, 2009).

Prescription assistance programs can also provide support for caregivers and care recipients who are struggling to afford their medications. These programs, which are often sponsored by pharmaceutical companies, government agencies, or non-profit organizations, can provide financial assistance, discounted medications, or even free medications for eligible individuals. By leveraging these resources, caregivers can ensure that cost is not a barrier to adherence (Reinhard et al., 2019).

In addition to these external supports, caregivers can also seek support from other caregivers. Caregiver support groups, online forums, and community resources can provide valuable advice, encouragement, and resources for managing medications. By connecting with others who are in a similar situation, caregivers can gain new insights and feel less alone in their caregiving journey (Lam & Fresco, 2015).

Promoting medication regimen adherence is a multifaceted task that involves understanding the challenges of adherence, providing clear instructions and reminders, utilizing adherence aids like pill organizers and medication dispensers, employing techniques like motivational interviewing, providing ongoing education, and seeking collaboration and support from healthcare professionals. With these strategies, caregivers can enhance medication adherence and ensure that care recipients receive the full benefits of their medication regimens (Reinhard et al., 2019).

Ensuring Medication Safety

Following Strict Protocols for Medication Management

Ensuring medication safety is a paramount responsibility for caregivers. This involves following strict protocols for medication preparation, dosage calculation, administration, and documentation. These protocols are designed to prevent medication errors and ensure medication safe and effective administration (Elliott & Marriott, 2009).

Medication preparation involves correctly identifying the medication, checking the expiration date, and preparing the correct dose. Caregivers should always verify the medication against the care recipient's medication list or prescription before preparing it. This can prevent errors such as administering the wrong medication or an expired medication (Reinhard et al., 2019).

Dosage calculation is another critical aspect of medication safety. Caregivers must accurately calculate the correct dose of each medication, taking into account factors such as the care recipient's weight, age, and kidney function. This requires a good understanding of dosage calculations and the ability to use tools such as dosing calculators or nomograms (Elliott & Marriott, 2009).

Medication administration involves giving the medication to the care recipient in the correct manner. This could involve administering the medication orally, topically, via inhalation, or via injection, depending on the medication. Caregivers must be familiar with the correct administration techniques for each medication and should always check the care recipient's identity before administering a medication (Reinhard et al., 2019).

Finally, documentation involves recording each medication administration in the care recipient's medication administration record (MAR). This includes recording the date and time of administration, the medication and dose, and any observations or side effects. Accurate documentation can help prevent medication errors, facilitate communication with healthcare professionals, and provide a record of the care recipient's medication history (Elliott & Marriott, 2009).

Adhering to these strict protocols, caregivers can ensure medication safety, prevent medication errors, and enhance the quality of care (Reinhard et al., 2019).

Verifying Medications and Adhering to Prescribed Timing

Verification of medications is a crucial aspect of ensuring medication safety. Before administering medication, caregivers should always verify the medication against the care recipient's MAR. This involves checking the medication name, dose, route, and timing against the MAR to ensure that the correct medication is being given at the correct time (Elliott & Marriott, 2009).

Verification also involves checking the medication's expiration date. Expired medications may not be as effective and could potentially be harmful. By always checking the expiration date, caregivers can ensure that the care recipient is receiving effective, safe medication (Reinhard et al., 2019).

Adherence to the prescribed timing of doses is another crucial aspect of medication safety. Some medications need to be taken at specific times of the day or at specific intervals to be effective. Others may need to be taken with or without food or at a certain distance from other medications. By adhering to these instructions, caregivers can ensure the medication's effectiveness and prevent potential complications (Elliott & Marriott, 2009).

Finally, verification should be a double-check process. Even if a caregiver is confident in their knowledge and abilities, they should still verify each medication before administering it. This double-check process can catch potential errors and ensure that each medication is administered safely and correctly (Reinhard et al., 2019).

By verifying medications and adhering to prescribed timing, caregivers can ensure medication safety, enhance the effectiveness of medications, and provide optimal care to the care recipient (Elliott & Marriott, 2009).

Monitoring for Side Effects and Allergic Reactions

Monitoring for side effects and allergic reactions is another critical aspect of ensuring medication safety. After administering a medication, caregivers should observe the care recipient closely for any signs of side effects or allergic reactions. This allows for prompt identification and management of any adverse reactions, minimizing potential harm to the care recipient (Reinhard et al., 2019).

Side effects can range from mild, such as drowsiness or stomach upset, to severe, such as breathing difficulties or severe skin reactions. Caregivers should be familiar with the common side effects of each medication and should inform the care recipient of these potential side effects so they can also monitor their own reactions (Elliott & Marriott, 2009).

Allergic reactions to medications can be serious and potentially life-threatening. Signs of an allergic reaction may include hives, swelling of the face or throat, difficulty breathing, or a sudden drop in blood pressure. If an allergic reaction is suspected, caregivers should seek medical help immediately (Reinhard et al., 2019).

In addition to observing for side effects and allergic reactions, caregivers should also monitor the effectiveness of each medication. This could involve observing the care recipient for improvements in symptoms, monitoring their vital signs, or using other objective measures of medication effectiveness. If a medication does not appear to be effective, or if the care recipient experiences significant side effects, the caregiver should consult with a healthcare professional (Elliott & Marriott, 2009).

Through vigilant monitoring, caregivers can ensure the safe and effective use of medications, promptly identify and manage side effects or allergic reactions, and contribute to the overall quality of care (Reinhard et al., 2019).

Proper Storage and Disposal of Medications

Proper storage and disposal of medications are also important for ensuring medication safety. Medications should be stored in a secure location, out of reach of children or unauthorized individuals. They should also be stored in their original containers, with clear labels, to prevent mix-ups (Elliott & Marriott, 2009).

Many medications need to be stored in specific conditions to maintain their effectiveness. For example, some medications need to be stored at room temperature, while others need to be refrigerated. Caregivers should be familiar with the storage requirements of each medication and should check these requirements each time a new medication is prescribed (Reinhard et al., 2019).

When a medication is no longer needed or has expired, it should be disposed of properly to prevent misuse or accidental ingestion. Many communities have medication take-back programs that allow for the safe disposal of unused medications. If such a program is not available, caregivers should follow the disposal instructions on the medication label or consult with a pharmacist (Elliott & Marriott, 2009).

By properly storing and disposing of medications, caregivers can prevent medication errors, ensure the effectiveness of medications, and contribute to the safety of the care recipient and the community (Reinhard et al., 2019).

Recognizing the Limits of the Caregiver Role and the Need for Professional Consultation

Finally, caregivers must recognize the limits of their role and the need for professional consultation. While caregivers play a crucial role in medication management and safety, they are not healthcare professionals and should not hesitate to seek professional advice when needed (Reinhard et al., 2019).

If a caregiver is unsure about a medication, they should consult with a pharmacist or doctor. Pharmacists and doctors can provide valuable advice on medication use, side effects, interactions, and other medication-related issues. They can also provide advice on managing complex medication regimens and improving medication adherence (Elliott & Marriott, 2009).

If a caregiver notices a concerning reaction in the care recipient, such as a severe side effect or an allergic reaction, they should seek medical help immediately. Quick action can prevent serious harm and ensure that the care recipient receives appropriate treatment (Reinhard et al., 2019).

Caregivers should also consult with healthcare professionals on a regular basis to review the care recipient's medication regimen. Regular reviews can catch potential problems, such as medication interactions or ineffective medications, and can ensure that the care recipient's medications are still appropriate and effective (Elliott & Marriott, 2009).

Recognizing the limits of their role and seeking professional consultation, caregivers can enhance medication safety, provide optimal care to the care recipient, and contribute to the overall quality of care (Reinhard et al., 2019).

The Transformative Power of Evidence-Based Approaches to Medication Management

Building Confidence in Medication Management

Building confidence in medication management is crucial for caregivers. The ability to confidently and accurately manage medications can significantly enhance the quality of care provided. With proper training and the use of evidence-based practices, caregivers can gain confidence in managing even the most complex medication regimens (Reinhard et al., 2019).

Confidence in medication management begins with education. Caregivers must have a solid understanding of the medications they are administering, including their purposes, proper dosages, potential side effects, and interactions with other drugs or foods. This understanding not only enables accurate administration but also empowers caregivers to answer questions, address concerns, and explain the importance of medication adherence to care recipients (Elliott & Marriott, 2009).

Evidence-based practices provide a framework for effective medication management. These practices, which are informed by scientific research and clinical expertise, can guide caregivers in managing medications accurately and efficiently. By following these practices, caregivers can ensure that they are providing the best possible care and reduce the likelihood of medication errors (Reinhard et al., 2019).

Regular practice is also crucial for building confidence. The more caregivers practice medication management, the more familiar and comfortable they become with the process. Even when faced with complex medication regimens, caregivers who regularly practice these skills can remain calm, competent, and confident (Elliott & Marriott, 2009).

Caregivers can further enhance their confidence by seeking support and feedback. This could involve consulting with healthcare professionals, participating in caregiver support groups, or seeking out additional training or resources. Through continuous learning and improvement, caregivers can steadily build confidence in their medication management abilities (Reinhard et al., 2019).

Enhancing the safety and efficacy of care is a core goal of medication management. Proper medication management can significantly reduce the risk of medication errors, adverse drug events, and non-adherence, thereby improving the safety and effectiveness of care (Elliott & Marriott, 2009).

Understanding medication pharmacology is crucial for enhancing safety and efficacy. This involves understanding how the medication works, its potential side effects, and its interactions with other medications or foods. This knowledge can help caregivers anticipate and prevent problems, ensuring that care recipients receive the full benefits of their medication regimens (Reinhard et al., 2019).

Promoting medication adherence is another key aspect of enhancing safety and efficacy. Non-adherence can lead to poor health outcomes, hospitalizations, and increased healthcare costs. Caregivers can promote adherence by explaining the importance of taking medications as prescribed, setting up medication reminders, and addressing any barriers to adherence, such as forgetfulness or difficulty swallowing pills (Elliott & Marriott, 2009).

Ensuring medication safety involves careful attention to medication administration, storage, and disposal. This involves administering the correct medication at the correct dose and time, storing medications properly to maintain their potency and prevent misuse, and disposing of expired or unused medications safely (Reinhard et al., 2019).

Continuous monitoring and assessment are also crucial for ensuring safety and efficacy. Caregivers need to monitor for side effects, changes in health status, or signs of non-adherence. By regularly assessing the effectiveness of the medication regimen and responding promptly to any issues, caregivers can ensure the safety and efficacy of care (Elliott & Marriott, 2009).

Promoting Caregiver Empowerment

Promoting caregiver empowerment is an often-overlooked aspect of medication management. However, it is a crucial element of effective caregiving. Empowered caregivers feel more in control of their caregiving responsibilities, are more resilient in the face of challenges, and are more likely to provide high-quality care (Beach et al., 2022).

Empowerment begins with education. By learning about medications, their uses, and how to manage them effectively, caregivers can gain the knowledge and skills they need to handle their responsibilities confidently. This knowledge empowers them to make informed decisions, answer questions, and advocate for the care recipient's needs (Reinhard et al., 2019).

Evidence-based practices can further empower caregivers by providing a clear, proven framework for medication management. These practices provide reassurance that the caregiver is doing the right thing, reduce uncertainty and stress, and enhance the caregiver's sense of competence (Elliott & Marriott, 2009).

Empowerment also involves developing problem-solving skills. As caregivers navigate the challenges of medication management, they have opportunities to develop their problem-solving abilities. This not only improves their effectiveness in managing medications but also enhances their overall caregiving abilities (Beach et al., 2022).

Empowerment involves taking care of one's own well-being. Caregiving can be stressful and demanding, and it's important for caregivers to take care of their own physical and mental health. This could involve taking breaks, practicing self-care, seeking support, or using stress management techniques. By prioritizing their well-being, caregivers can sustain their caregiving efforts and avoid caregiver burnout (Reinhard et al., 2019).

Facilitating Collaboration with Healthcare Professionals

Effective medication management involves close collaboration with healthcare professionals. Doctors, pharmacists, and other healthcare providers have expert knowledge and can provide invaluable support and guidance to caregivers (Elliott & Marriott, 2009).

Regular communication with doctors is crucial. Doctors can provide detailed information about the care recipient's medication regimen, explain any changes, and answer any questions the caregiver may have. They can also provide advice on managing side effects, promoting adherence, and monitoring for changes in health status (Reinhard et al., 2019).

Pharmacists are also an invaluable resource. They can provide detailed information about each medication, including its purpose, proper dosage, potential side effects, and interactions. They can also provide advice on medication storage, administration, and disposal and can answer any questions or concerns the caregiver may have (Elliott & Marriott, 2009).

Other healthcare professionals, such as nurses or social workers, can also provide support. They can provide education, training, and resources, assist with problem-solving, and provide emotional support. They can also liaise with doctors and pharmacists on the caregiver's behalf, ensuring that all members of the healthcare team are working together to provide the best possible care (Reinhard et al., 2019).

Fostering close collaboration with healthcare professionals, caregivers can stay informed, gain confidence, and ensure they are providing the best possible care (Elliott & Marriott, 2009).

Cultivating Resilience and Growth in Caregiving

The challenges of medication management can provide opportunities for resilience and personal growth among caregivers. Despite the difficulties, these challenges can provide valuable learning experiences, enhance problem-solving skills, and foster a sense of accomplishment and personal growth (Ploeg et al., 2022).

Resilience in caregiving involves the ability to adapt to challenges, maintain a positive outlook, and bounce back from setbacks. In the context of medication management, this could involve adjusting to changes in the medication regimen, finding solutions to adherence problems, or dealing with side effects or medication errors. By facing these challenges head-on and learning from them, caregivers can enhance their resilience and their ability to handle future challenges (Ploeg et al., 2022).

Personal growth involves learning, skill development, and self-improvement. Caregivers can experience personal growth by learning about medications and their management, developing problem-solving skills, and improving their communication and advocacy abilities. This growth not only improves their effectiveness as caregivers but also enhances their self-confidence and personal satisfaction (Beach et al., 2022).

Overcoming challenges can also foster a sense of accomplishment. Successfully managing complex medication regimens, solving problems, and seeing improvements in the care recipient's health can all provide a sense of achievement. This sense of accomplishment can motivate caregivers to continue their efforts, even when faced with new challenges (Ploeg et al., 2022).

By cultivating resilience and personal growth, caregivers can enhance their caregiving experience. They can find joy and satisfaction in their role, reduce their risk of burnout, and provide high-quality care. With resilience, personal growth, and a positive outlook, caregivers can navigate the challenges of medication management and find fulfillment in their role (Beach et al., 2022).

2.4: Developing Critical Problem-Solving Skills for Caregivers: A Comprehensive Approach

Caregiving involves attentiveness, vigilance, and readiness to address evolving needs. Effective problem-solving skills are crucial for caregivers to act decisively, implement solutions, and provide quality care, often under challenging circumstances. Research shows that problem-solving abilities can help reduce strain for dementia caregivers (Wilks & Croom, 2008). This section examines the significance of critical thinking and problem-solving for caregivers and strategies to cultivate these vital skills.

Problem-solving is a key competency for caregivers. It involves recognizing issues through observation, information gathering, and assessment, analyzing problems objectively, generating potential solutions, evaluating these solutions, and implementing and monitoring the chosen solutions. Developing effective problem-solving skills can help caregivers manage everyday challenges, emergency situations, and evolving care needs. It can also give caregivers a greater sense of control and self-efficacy (Beach et al., 2022).

Cultivating a problem-solving mindset, characterized by critical thinking, creativity, objectivity, and perseverance, is crucial for caregivers. This mindset can enable caregivers to approach problems in a more systematic, effective way, enhancing their ability to provide care (Wilks & Croom, 2008).

There are also several techniques and tools that caregivers can use to enhance their problem-solving skills. These include brainstorming, discussing scenarios and solutions with other caregivers, researching and analyzing best practices, and engaging in mentally stimulating activities. By employing these techniques, caregivers can bolster their critical thinking and problem-solving skills, improving their ability to navigate the challenges of caregiving (Beach et al., 2022).

Importance of Problem-Solving Skills for Caregivers

Recognizing Issues Through Observation, Information Gathering, and Assessment

Recognizing issues through observation, information gathering, and assessment is the first critical step in the problem-solving process. Caregivers often need to be detectives, using keen observation, thorough information gathering, and careful assessment to identify the problems that need to be addressed. The better caregivers become at recognizing issues, the more quickly they can begin working toward solutions (Wilks & Croom, 2008).

Observation is a fundamental skill for caregivers. They need to be constantly attuned to changes in the health, behavior, or mood of the person they are caring for. This could involve monitoring for physical symptoms, like changes in appetite or mobility, or psychological symptoms, such as mood swings or changes in sleep patterns. Observing these changes can help caregivers recognize when a problem is emerging and needs to be addressed (Beach et al., 2022).

Information gathering involves seeking out and interpreting relevant information about the problem. This could involve reading medical records, consulting with healthcare professionals, or conducting independent research. The aim is to gain a comprehensive understanding of the problem, which can inform the problem-solving process (Wilks & Croom, 2008).

Assessment involves integrating the information gathered to form a clear picture of the problem. This could involve identifying patterns, making connections between different pieces of information, or weighing up different factors to determine the most likely cause of the problem. A thorough assessment can help caregivers understand the nature and severity of the problem, which is crucial for determining the appropriate response (Beach et al., 2022).

Recognizing issues through observation, information gathering, and assessment is a crucial part of problem-solving for caregivers. By honing these skills, caregivers can quickly and accurately identify problems, enabling them to respond effectively and provide the best possible care (Wilks & Croom, 2008).

Analyzing Problems Objectively Despite Stress

Caregiving can be stressful, and stress can cloud judgment and impede effective problem-solving. However, it's crucial for caregivers to remain objective when analyzing problems. This involves setting aside personal biases and emotional reactions and approaching the problem with a clear, rational mind (Wilks & Croom, 2008).

It's important for caregivers to acknowledge their emotional reactions to problems. Emotions are natural and valid, but they can sometimes cloud judgment and impede objective analysis. By acknowledging these emotions, caregivers can prevent them from unduly influencing their problem-solving process (Beach et al., 2022).

Caregivers need to consciously adopt an objective mindset when analyzing problems. This could involve stepping back from the situation, taking a deep breath, and deliberately choosing to approach the problem from a logical, fact-based perspective. It can be helpful to ask objective, open-ended questions, such as "What are the facts of this situation?" or "What am I assuming about this problem?" (Wilks & Croom, 2008).

Caregivers can benefit from seeking out different perspectives to help ensure their analysis is objective. This could involve consulting with other caregivers, healthcare professionals, or trusted friends and family members. These different perspectives can provide new insights and challenge biases, enhancing the objectivity of the analysis (Beach et al., 2022).

Finally, caregivers can use specific problem-solving techniques, such as the scientific method or decision trees, to help ensure their analysis is objective. These techniques provide a structured approach to problem-solving, which can help prevent personal biases from skewing the analysis (Wilks & Croom, 2008).

By making a conscious effort to analyze problems objectively, caregivers can enhance their problem-solving abilities and improve the effectiveness of their solutions, even in the face of stress (Beach et al., 2022).

Generating Potential Solutions Creatively

Once a problem has been recognized and analyzed, the next step is to generate potential solutions. This requires creativity and flexibility. Creative problem-solving involves thinking creatively, generating multiple solutions, and considering unconventional approaches (Wilks & Croom, 2008).

One technique for creatively generating solutions is brainstorming. This involves writing down all viable solutions that come to mind without judging or dismissing any ideas at this stage. The aim is to generate a wide range of options, some of which may lead to innovative solutions (Beach et al., 2022).

Another technique is mind mapping. This involves creating a visual representation of the problem and potential solutions. The visual nature of mind mapping can stimulate creativity and help caregivers see connections between different ideas (Wilks & Croom, 2008).

A third technique is lateral thinking, which involves looking at the problem from different angles and considering unconventional solutions. This could involve challenging assumptions, combining unrelated ideas, or asking "What if?" questions (Beach et al., 2022).

Finally, caregivers can foster creativity by maintaining a positive, open-minded attitude. This involves believing in their ability to produce creative solutions, being willing to take risks, and being open to feedback and innovative ideas (Wilks & Croom, 2008).

Generating potential solutions creatively, caregivers can enhance their problem-solving abilities and produce innovative solutions to the challenges they face (Beach et al., 2022).

Evaluating Solutions Based on Feasibility and Likely Impact

After generating potential solutions, the next step is to evaluate these solutions based on their feasibility and impact. This involves considering the practicality of each solution, the resources required, and the potential outcomes (Wilks & Croom, 2008).

Caregivers need to consider the feasibility of each solution. This involves considering whether the solution is realistic given the current circumstances, resources, and constraints. This could involve considering factors such as time, cost, availability of resources, and the willingness and ability of the person being cared for to participate in the solution (Beach et al., 2022).

Caregivers need to consider the impact of each solution. This involves predicting the potential outcomes of each solution, based on the information available. This could involve considering the potential benefits and risks, the likelihood of success, and the potential impact on the person being cared for (Wilks & Croom, 2008).

Caregivers can use decision-making tools, such as pros and cons list or decision matrices, to help evaluate solutions. These tools can provide a structured approach to evaluation and help caregivers compare different solutions (Beach et al., 2022).

Caregivers should be prepared to revisit their evaluation as the latest information becomes available. The situation may change, added resources may become available, or the person being cared for may express new preferences. By being flexible and open-minded, caregivers can ensure their solution remains appropriate and effective (Wilks & Croom, 2008).

Evaluating solutions based on feasibility and impact, caregivers can choose the most effective solution to the problem at hand (Beach et al., 2022).

Implementing and Monitoring Chosen Solutions

The decisive step in the problem-solving process is implementing the chosen solution and monitoring its effectiveness. This requires adaptability, persistence, and a commitment to continuous learning (Wilks & Croom, 2008).

Implementation involves putting the chosen solution into action. This might involve scheduling activities, purchasing resources, coordinating with other caregivers, or communicating with the person being cared for. Caregivers need to be organized, proactive, and adaptable during this stage (Beach et al., 2022).

Monitoring involves tracking the outcomes of the solution and assessing its effectiveness. This could involve observing changes in the person's health, behavior, or mood, or collecting feedback from the person being cared for and other caregivers. If the solution is not as effective as hoped, caregivers may need to reassess the problem and consider alternative solutions (Wilks & Croom, 2008).

Caregivers should also be prepared to adjust the solution, as necessary. This might involve tweaking the approach, trying different techniques, or seeking additional resources. Caregivers should view this as a normal part of the problem-solving process, rather than a sign of failure (Beach et al., 2022).

Continuous learning is also important. By reflecting on what worked and what did not, caregivers can enhance their problem-solving skills and improve the quality of their care. They should aim to learn from each problem-solving experience and apply these lessons to future challenges (Wilks & Croom, 2008).

Implementing and monitoring chosen solutions, caregivers can effectively resolve problems and improve the quality of their care. This process of implementation and monitoring not only solves problems but also enhances caregivers' problem-solving skills, making them better equipped to handle future challenges (Beach et al., 2022).

Cultivating a Problem-Solving Mindset

Practicing Mindfulness Meditation

Mindfulness meditation, a technique that trains the mind to focus on the present moment, can enhance a caregiver's problem-solving abilities. It helps to lower stress, reduce cognitive bias, and manage emotions, all of which are crucial for effective problem-solving. Mindfulness helps create a peaceful mental state that allows for improved concentration, increased creativity, and a more balanced emotional state (Wong et al., 2018).

Regular mindfulness practice can help caregivers manage the daily stresses and challenges of their roles. Caregiving can be emotionally draining and mentally taxing. However, mindfulness can serve as a calming anchor, helping caregivers navigate their responsibilities with greater ease and resilience. By maintaining focus on the present moment, caregivers can avoid becoming overwhelmed by future worries or past regrets, enabling them to respond more effectively to the challenges at hand (Wong et al., 2018).

Moreover, mindfulness meditation fosters empathy and compassion, qualities that are invaluable in caregiving. When caregivers are fully present and attentive, they can better understand the needs and emotions of those they care for. This heightened awareness can lead to more effective communication and a more compassionate approach to problem-solving (Beach et al., 2022).

In practice, mindfulness meditation can be as simple as focusing on one's breath, paying attention to sensations in the body, or observing one's thoughts without judgment. It can be done anywhere and at any time, making it a flexible tool that can easily be incorporated into a caregiver's routine. There are numerous resources available, including guided meditation apps, online courses, and books, which can help caregivers get started with this practice (Wong et al., 2018).

Overall, mindfulness meditation is a powerful tool for cultivating a problem-solving mindset. It fosters mental clarity, emotional balance, and a deeper sense of compassion, all of which can enhance a caregiver's ability to effectively address the challenges they face (Beach et al., 2022).

Recognizing Negative Thought Patterns

Recognizing and challenging negative thought patterns is a crucial part of cultivating a problem-solving mindset. Negative thoughts can cloud judgment, limit creativity, and impede effective problem-solving. However, by using techniques from cognitive-behavioral therapy (CBT), caregivers can learn to identify and challenge these harmful thought patterns (Lloyd et al., 2016).

CBT is a form of psychological treatment that focuses on changing unhelpful or inaccurate thinking patterns, behaviors, and emotional responses. It involves recognizing distorted thought patterns, challenging their accuracy, and replacing them with more accurate and beneficial thoughts. This process can lead to a more balanced and effective approach to problem-solving (Lloyd et al., 2016).

Common cognitive distortions include "catastrophizing" (expecting the worst), "all-or-nothing thinking" (viewing situations in black-and-white terms), and "overgeneralization" (drawing broad conclusions based on a single event). These distortions can skew perceptions and lead to ineffective problem-solving. By learning to identify these distortions when they occur, caregivers can begin to challenge and change them (Lloyd et al., 2016).

Challenging cognitive distortions typically involves questioning the evidence behind these thoughts, considering alternative explanations, and testing out the reality of these thoughts in action. This can lead to a more balanced and realistic perspective, which in turn can enhance problem-solving abilities (Beach et al., 2022).

By recognizing and challenging negative thought patterns, caregivers can cultivate a more effective problem-solving mindset. This involves not only identifying cognitive distortions but also actively working to replace them with more accurate and helpful thoughts. This process, while challenging, can enhance a caregiver's ability to effectively address the challenges they face (Lloyd et al., 2016).

Developing Patience and Avoiding Rushing to Judgment

Patience is a virtue that can enhance problem-solving abilities. In the face of challenging situations, there can often be a sense of urgency to find a solution quickly. However, rushing to judgment can lead to ineffective solutions and even exacerbate the problem. Instead, caregivers need to take the time to fully understand the problem before attempting to solve it (Beach et al., 2022).

The first step in problem-solving is to clearly define the problem. This requires patience and careful observation. Caregivers need to gather all relevant information, which may involve observing symptoms, researching conditions, or consulting with healthcare professionals. They need to consider all aspects of the situation, including the physical, emotional, and environmental factors that might be contributing to the problem (Wilks & Croom, 2008).

Once the problem has been clearly defined, caregivers should take the time to brainstorm potential solutions. Again, this requires patience. Rather than jumping to the first solution that comes to mind, caregivers should explore a range of options, considering their pros and cons and how they might impact the person they are caring for (Beach et al., 2022).

After implementing a solution, caregivers need to patiently monitor the outcomes. It is important to give the solution time to work and to observe carefully to see if the situation improves. If the solution does not work as expected, caregivers may need to go back to the drawing board, using the information they have gathered to inform their next steps (Wilks & Croom, 2008).

Patience is a crucial component of effective problem-solving. By taking the time to fully understand the problem, explore potential solutions, and monitor outcomes, caregivers can enhance their problem-solving abilities and increase the likelihood of finding effective solutions (Beach et al., 2022).

Adopting a Curious, Open-Minded Attitude

An open mind and a sense of curiosity can enhance problem-solving abilities. These attitudes allow caregivers to view problems from different angles, explore a range of potential solutions, and learn from their experiences (Wilks & Croom, 2008).

An open-minded attitude means being willing to question assumptions, consider different perspectives, and be flexible in the face of changing circumstances. For caregivers, this might mean being open to new methods of care, considering alternative treatments, or adapting routines as the needs of the person they are caring for change. An open mind allows caregivers to be adaptable and responsive, enhancing their ability to solve problems effectively (Beach et al., 2022).

A curious attitude involves actively seeking to learn and understand. Instead of viewing problems as obstacles, caregivers can view them as opportunities for learning. Curiosity drives caregivers to ask questions, seek out information, and explore different solutions. This drive to learn and understand can lead to more innovative and effective problem-solving (Wilks & Croom, 2008).

In practice, cultivating curiosity and an open mind might involve activities such as reading widely on a range of topics, seeking out different viewpoints, asking questions, and experimenting with different strategies. It also involves being open to feedback and willing to learn from mistakes (Beach et al., 2022).

By adopting a curious and open-minded attitude, caregivers can enhance their problem-solving abilities. These attitudes foster flexibility, creativity, and a lifelong love of learning, all of which are invaluable in the caregiving journey (Wilks & Croom, 2008).

Believing in the Ability to Handle Challenges and Find Solutions

Believing in one's ability to handle challenges and find solutions, a concept known as self-efficacy, is crucial for effective problem-solving. This belief can motivate caregivers to tackle problems head-on, persist in the face of obstacles, and find effective solutions (Bandura, 1977).

Self-efficacy is based on past successes, vicarious experiences, verbal persuasion, and emotional states. By reflecting on past successes, caregivers can build confidence in their ability to handle new challenges. Observing others successfully managing similar situations can also enhance self-efficacy (Bandura, 1977).

Positive feedback and encouragement from others can also boost self-efficacy. Caregivers can seek out supportive communities, such as support groups or online forums, where they can share their experiences and receive validation and encouragement. These communities can also provide practical advice and insights, further enhancing caregivers' problem-solving abilities (Beach et al., 2022).

Managing emotional states is another crucial aspect of self-efficacy. Stress, anxiety, and negative emotions can undermine self-belief and impede problem-solving. However, by practicing stress management techniques, such as mindfulness, caregivers can maintain a positive emotional state and enhance their self-efficacy (Bandura, 1977).

By believing in their ability to handle challenges and find solutions, caregivers can cultivate a problem-solving mindset. This belief, or self-efficacy, motivates caregivers to tackle problems head-on, persist in the face of obstacles, and find effective solutions. Through reflection on past successes, seeking supportive communities, and managing emotional states, caregivers can enhance this belief and, in turn, their problem-solving abilities (Beach et al., 2022).

Tools for Enhancing Problem-Solving Skills

Brainstorming and Mapping Out Ideas Visually

Brainstorming is a dynamic problem-solving method that encourages the generation of a wide range of ideas. This technique is effective in the initial stages of problem-solving when caregivers are seeking to identify as many potential solutions as possible. By encouraging the free flow of ideas without judgment, brainstorming can lead to creative solutions that might not be discovered through more traditional problem-solving techniques (Mumford et al., 2012).

During brainstorming, it can be helpful to let thoughts flow freely, without attempting to evaluate or filter ideas. This unrestricted flow can lead to unexpected connections and novel solutions. Even ideas that may initially seem impractical or irrelevant may, upon reflection, lead to effective solutions (Wilks & Croom, 2008).

Mapping out ideas visually can further enhance the brainstorming process. This can involve creating diagrams, flowcharts, mind maps, or other visual aids to organize and explore ideas. Visual aids can make it easier to see the relationships between different concepts, identify patterns, and understand complex scenarios (Mumford et al., 2012).

Caregivers might also consider using digital tools, such as mind-mapping software or online whiteboards, to facilitate visual brainstorming. These tools can make it easier to organize and rearrange ideas, and they can be particularly useful for caregivers who are collaborating with others remotely (Wilks & Croom, 2008).

Overall, brainstorming, and visual mapping are powerful techniques for enhancing creativity in problem-solving. By encouraging open-mindedness and lateral thinking, these tools can help caregivers generate a diverse range of potential solutions to the challenges they face (Mumford et al., 2012).

Discussing Scenarios and Solutions with Other Caregivers

Discussing scenarios and potential solutions with other caregivers can provide valuable insights and new perspectives. Other caregivers, who have likely faced similar challenges, can offer practical advice, share their experiences, and provide emotional support. This collaborative approach can enhance problem-solving skills and reduce the feelings of isolation often experienced by caregivers (Beach et al., 2022).

For instance, caregiver support groups, either in-person or online, can be a valuable resource. These groups allow caregivers to connect with others who understand their experiences, exchange ideas, and learn from each other's successes and failures. This peer-to-peer learning can provide real-world insights that cannot be gained from books or formal training alone (Chen et al., 2015).

Furthermore, discussing scenarios and solutions with healthcare professionals can also be beneficial. Medical professionals can provide expert advice, share best practices, and help caregivers navigate the complexities of the healthcare system (Beach et al., 2022).

In addition to discussing scenarios and solutions in a structured setting like a support group or consultation, informal conversations with friends and family who have caregiving experience can also be immensely helpful. These conversations can provide a more relaxed environment for brainstorming solutions and can provide a wider range of perspectives (Chen et al., 2015).

Researching and Analyzing Best Practices

Researching and analyzing best practices in caregiving can provide caregivers with a wealth of information to aid in problem-solving. By learning from the experiences and expertise of others, caregivers can enhance their own skills and knowledge (Beach et al., 2022).

The process of researching and analyzing best practices can significantly enhance a caregiver's problem-solving skills. Through this method, caregivers can learn from the experiences and expertise of others, building upon their successes and avoiding potential pitfalls. They can gain a wealth of information, ranging from day-to-day caregiving tips to strategies for managing complex health conditions (Wilks & Croom, 2008).

Resources for research can include academic journals, books, authoritative websites, and educational videos. These can offer scientifically supported techniques and guidelines for care. For example, caregivers might research best practices for managing behavioral symptoms in dementia patients, or effective strategies for balancing caregiving with other responsibilities (Beach et al., 2022).

It is important for caregivers to critically evaluate the information they find, particularly when it comes to online resources. They should look for information from reliable sources, such as government health departments, reputable medical organizations, and universities. They should also be cautious of any advice that seems too good to be true or that contradicts established medical guidelines (Wilks & Croom, 2008).

In addition to formal research, caregivers can learn a lot from the experiences of other caregivers. Online forums, blogs, and social media groups can provide a wealth of practical tips and advice. These platforms can offer a sense of community and support, as caregivers share their own stories and solutions (Chen et al., 2015).

Caregivers should not only learn from best practices but also consider how to apply this knowledge to their specific situations. Every caregiving situation is unique, so it is important for caregivers to adapt best practices to their own needs and circumstances (Beach et al., 2022).

Engaging in Mentally Stimulating Hobbies

Engaging in mentally stimulating hobbies can enhance cognitive abilities, including problem-solving skills. Activities that challenge the brain can improve cognitive functions, promote mental agility, and keep the mind sharp. This can translate into enhanced problem-solving skills in the caregiving context (Hughes et al., 2010).

Puzzles such as crosswords, Sudoku, and jigsaw puzzles can be particularly beneficial. They require concentration, logical thinking, and pattern recognition – skills that are directly relevant to problem-solving. In addition, they can provide a relaxing diversion from caregiving responsibilities, offering much-needed stress relief (Beach et al., 2022).

Reading is another mentally stimulating hobby that can enhance problem-solving skills. It can expand knowledge, improve comprehension skills, and stimulate imagination. In the context of caregiving, reading can provide valuable information and insights, and it can also offer a welcome escape into different worlds (Hughes et al., 2010).

Learning new skills, such as a new language, playing a musical instrument, or taking up a craft, can also be beneficial. These activities challenge the brain in diverse ways, fostering mental flexibility and adaptability. They also promote lifelong learning, a mindset that is essential for effective problem-solving (Beach et al., 2022).

Engaging in mentally stimulating hobbies can not only enhance a caregiver's problem-solving skills but can also offer a range of other cognitive and emotional benefits. By integrating these activities into their daily routine, caregivers can nurture their mental health, enhance their abilities, and enrich their caregiving journey (Hughes et al., 2010).

Taking Courses in Problem-Solving Techniques

Taking courses in problem-solving techniques can provide caregivers with a structured and formal approach to problem-solving. These courses can offer valuable tools and strategies, enhance cognitive skills, and provide a comprehensive understanding of the problem-solving process (Beach et al., 2022).

Problem-solving courses often cover a range of topics, such as identifying problems, brainstorming solutions, evaluating options, implementing solutions, and assessing outcomes. By exploring these steps in depth, caregivers can develop a systematic approach to problem-solving that can be applied to a wide range of caregiving challenges (Wilks & Croom, 2008).

These courses may also introduce caregivers to different problem-solving methodologies, such as the Plan-Do-Study-Act (PDSA) cycle, Root Cause Analysis, or Decision Matrix Analysis. Understanding these methodologies can provide caregivers with a toolkit of strategies to tackle problems effectively (Beach et al., 2022).

Online platforms offer a range of problem-solving courses, many of which are free or relatively inexpensive. These can offer flexibility for caregivers, allowing them to learn at their own pace and in their own time. Some courses also offer certification upon completion, which can be an added bonus (Wilks & Croom, 2008).

Taking courses in problem-solving techniques can equip caregivers with the skills and knowledge they need to address the challenges they encounter in their roles. This formal education can complement their practical experience, enabling them to provide the best possible care to their loved ones (Beach et al., 2022).

2.5: Evidence-Based Communication Strategies for Caregivers

Effective and compassionate communication is a cornerstone of quality caregiving. Understanding patient needs, conveying critical information, and providing emotional support during vulnerable moments are all facilitated by effective communication skills. However, external factors such as heavy workloads, time constraints, and managing distressed patients can impede effective communication (Northouse & Northouse, 2021).

Despite these challenges, research suggests that strong communication and interpersonal skills can significantly improve patient health outcomes and overall satisfaction (Ha & Longnecker, 2010). This section will explore practical and research-backed communication strategies for caregivers.

Active listening is a fundamental communication technique that involves giving undivided attention to the patient, allowing them to speak without interruption, validating their emotions and experiences, and asking thoughtful questions to clarify understanding. Active listening fosters a therapeutic relationship that enables better assessment of patient needs and supports shared decision-making (Northouse & Northouse, 2021).

Clear communication is also crucial, especially when conveying complex medical information. Caregivers need to ensure that their explanations are understandable to the patient, considering their level of medical knowledge. Providing written summaries of key discussion points and encouraging questions can also improve patient understanding and compliance (Katz et al., 2005).

Sensitive communication is particularly important given the vulnerable position of patients. Caregivers need to adopt a warm, patient, and approachable demeanor, ensure privacy during sensitive conversations, and be mindful of verbal and non-verbal cues that communicate respect and sensitivity (Beach et al., 2022).

Engaging patients in medical decisions is an essential part of patient-centered care. Caregivers should explain disease progression, treatment options, risks, and benefits, and seek to understand patient preferences, values, and priorities. Adopting a collaborative approach can lead to better adherence and empower patients in their healthcare journey (Chewning et al., 2012).

In the following sections, we will delve deeper into these key aspects of caregiver communication, providing practical strategies and insights on active listening, clear communication, sensitive communication, and shared decision-making.

Active Listening

The Importance of Undivided Attention

Active listening is a fundamental component of effective communication in healthcare. The cornerstone of active listening begins with giving the patient your undivided attention. This demonstrates to the patient that their thoughts, concerns, and feelings are essential and valued (Ha & Longnecker, 2010).

To show undivided attention, caregivers should face the patient squarely, maintain a relaxed body posture, and maintain comfortable eye contact. This physical orientation communicates openness and interest in what the patient is sharing. This may mean arranging the physical environment to minimize distractions or positioning yourself at the patient's eye level to create a sense of equality and respect (Northouse & Northouse, 2021).

A caregiver's expression should also reflect attentiveness. This includes avoiding behaviors that might suggest distraction or disinterest, such as looking at a watch, fidgeting, or interrupting the patient. Even small facial expressions or gestures can convey a great deal about a caregiver's level of engagement and empathy (Beach et al., 2022).

Undivided attention also extends to the mental realm. It is important for caregivers to be fully present mentally and not let their thoughts drift to other matters. This may require conscious effort, especially during long or stressful days. Caregivers may find it useful to practice mindfulness techniques to help them stay focused and present in the conversation (Northouse & Northouse, 2021).

Ultimately, providing undivided attention sets the foundation for effective communication. It shows patients that their caregivers are genuinely interested in their well-being, which can enhance trust, improve the therapeutic relationship, and promote better health outcomes (Ha & Longnecker, 2010).

Allowing Patients to Speak Without Interruption

Another vital aspect of active listening involves allowing patients to speak without interruption. This fosters a sense of respect and patience, showing patients that their views and experiences are important and valued (Northouse & Northouse, 2021).

Resisting the urge to interrupt can be challenging, especially when caregivers are pressed for time or believe they already know what the patient is going to say. However, interruptions can make patients feel rushed or unheard of, which can hinder effective communication (Beach et al., 2022).

When caregivers let patients speak freely, they can gain a better understanding of the patients' perspectives. They can gather more information about the patient's symptoms, concerns, and health behaviors, which can inform a more accurate diagnosis and treatment plan (Northouse & Northouse, 2021).

In addition, allowing patients to speak without interruption can also facilitate emotional processing. Many patients appreciate having the time and space to express their thoughts and feelings about their health experiences. This opportunity for expression can be therapeutic and can help patients feel more understood and supported (Beach et al., 2022).

However, it is also crucial to balance this with the need to guide the conversation and keep it focused. Caregivers can do this by using subtle prompts or reflective statements to keep the discussion on track while still showing respect for the patient's narrative (Northouse & Northouse, 2021).

Validating Emotions and Experiences

Validating the patient's emotions and experiences is a critical aspect of active listening. Validation involves acknowledging the patient's feelings and expressing empathy, which can significantly enhance the patient-caregiver relationship and improve communication (Beach et al., 2022).

Acknowledging a patient's feelings shows that the caregiver is not only hearing the words the patient is saying but also understanding the emotions behind those words. Simple phrases like "That sounds really tough," or "I can understand why you would feel that way," can make a patient feel seen and understood (Northouse & Northouse, 2021).

Empathy is a powerful tool in healthcare, and it extends beyond acknowledging the patient's feelings. It involves truly trying to understand the patient's experiences from their perspective. Caregivers can express empathy through their words, tone of voice, and non-verbal cues, such as nodding or making sympathetic facial expressions (Beach et al., 2022).

Validation does not necessarily mean agreeing with the patient's perspective. It is possible to validate a patient's emotions and experiences even if the caregiver does not agree or share the same viewpoint. The goal of validation is to show the patient that their feelings are legitimate and that it is okay to feel the way they do (Northouse & Northouse, 2021).

Validation can have profound effects on the patient's experience. It can help build trust and rapport, make the patient feel safe and comfortable, and encourage further communication. Furthermore, feeling understood can have a therapeutic effect and can help patients better manage their health conditions (Beach et al., 2022).

Asking Thoughtful Questions for Clarification and Reflection

Active listening also involves asking thoughtful questions to clarify understanding and encourage patients to reflect on their experiences. These questions can play a crucial role in shaping the dialogue and uncovering valuable information about the patient's condition (Northouse & Northouse, 2021).

When asking clarifying questions, caregivers should use open-ended queries that allow patients to express their thoughts and feelings more freely. Such questions often begin with "how," "what," or "could you tell me more about..." This encourages a more detailed response than closed-ended questions, which can typically be answered with a simple "yes" or "no" (Beach et al., 2022).

Reflection is a key component of active listening and involves helping the patient explore their feelings and thoughts. Reflective questions might include, "How did that make you feel?" or "What does this mean for you?" By prompting the patient to reflect, caregivers can help them gain insight into their experiences and emotions (Northouse & Northouse, 2021).

It is crucial that these questions are posed in a non-judgmental and empathetic manner. Caregivers should avoid using leading questions, which might indicate a "right" or "wrong" answer, as they can make patients feel judged or pressured (Beach et al., 2022).

Overall, asking thoughtful, open-ended questions can enhance communication by fostering a deeper understanding of the patient's experiences, concerns, and expectations. This, in turn, can lead to more patient-centered and effective care (Northouse & Northouse, 2021).

Paraphrasing or Summarizing Points to Confirm Understanding

Finally, paraphrasing or summarizing what the patient has said is an effective tool to confirm understanding and demonstrate active listening. It ensures that both the caregiver and patient are on the same page, reducing the risk of misunderstandings that could impact care (Northouse & Northouse, 2021).

Paraphrasing involves restating the patient's words in the caregiver's own language. This shows the patient that the caregiver is trying to understand their perspective. It can also help clarify complex or ambiguous statements, ensuring that the caregiver has correctly grasified the patient's meaning (Beach et al., 2022).

Summarizing, on the other hand, involves giving a brief overview of the main points or themes of the conversation. Summaries are often used at the end of a discussion or before transitioning to a new topic. They help consolidate the information discussed and highlight the most crucial elements (Northouse & Northouse, 2021).

When paraphrasing or summarizing, it is important for caregivers to ask for the patient's input. They might ask, "Did I understand that correctly?" or "Is there anything else you would like to add?" This gives patients the opportunity to correct any misunderstandings and contribute to the summary of their conversation (Beach et al., 2022).

Paraphrasing and summarizing are powerful active listening techniques that caregivers can use to ensure clear and effective communication. They not only confirm understanding but also show patients that their experiences and perspectives are being valued and considered in their care (Northouse & Northouse, 2021).

Clear Communication

Assessing the Patient's Medical Vocabulary

One of the first steps towards clear communication with patients is assessing their medical vocabulary. This involves evaluating how well they understand common medical terms, procedures, and concepts. Caregivers can do this by asking simple, open-ended questions about their medical history or current health status. The way patients respond to these questions can provide caregivers with valuable insights into their level of medical knowledge and understanding (Katz et al., 2005).

Understanding a patient's medical vocabulary allows caregivers to tailor their explanations to suit the patient's needs. If a patient shows limited understanding of medical jargon, caregivers should adjust their communication style, replacing complex terms with simpler, more accessible language. This not only aids patient comprehension but also fosters a sense of partnership and inclusivity in the caregiver-patient relationship (Chewning et al., 2012).

Assessing a patient's medical vocabulary should be an ongoing process. Over time, a patient's comprehension and vocabulary can grow as they become more familiar with their condition and treatment. Regularly reassessing the patient's understanding can help caregivers adapt their explanations and provide the most effective communication possible (Katz et al., 2005).

In cases where a patient has a low level of health literacy or a limited medical vocabulary, it is especially important for caregivers to ensure that their explanations are understood. This might involve spending extra time explaining concepts, using simpler language, and checking in frequently to confirm understanding. It is not a caregiver's job to make a patient a medical expert, but rather to ensure they have a solid grasp of their health situation (Chewning et al., 2012).

It is crucial to consider cultural and linguistic differences when assessing a patient's medical vocabulary. Caregivers should be mindful of these differences and make necessary adjustments to ensure effective communication. This might involve the use of interpreters or culturally appropriate educational materials (Beach et al., 2022).

Breaking Down Information into Digestible Segments

Breaking down complex medical information into smaller, more manageable segments can enhance patient understanding. This approach allows patients to grasp one concept at a time, rather than being overwhelmed by a lot of information all at once. It is like constructing a building, you start with the foundation before adding more levels (Katz et al., 2005).

One effective way to break down information is by using the "chunk and check" method. This involves providing a piece ("chunk") of information, then checking for understanding before moving on to the next segment. This continuous feedback loop allows caregivers to assess patient understanding in real-time and to clarify or elaborate on points as needed (Chewning et al., 2012).

When breaking down information, it is important to prioritize the most critical details first. If a patient is dealing with a new diagnosis, for example, explaining what the diagnosis means and its immediate implications should come before detailed discussions about long-term management or potential complications (Katz et al., 2005).

In addition, caregivers should aim to use simple and straightforward language. Medical terminology can be overwhelming and confusing for patients, particularly when they are dealing with a new or complex health issue. By using plain language, caregivers can help ensure that the patient understands the information being presented (Chewning et al., 2012).

The process of breaking down information should be patient centered. This means that it should be guided by the patient's needs, concerns, and questions. Rather than providing a one-way flow of information, caregivers should engage in a dialogue with the patient, allowing them to take an active role in understanding and managing their health (Beach et al., 2022).

Use of Visual Aids, Demonstrations, and Patient-Friendly Print Material

Visual aids, demonstrations, and patient-friendly print materials can be invaluable tools in conveying complex medical information. These resources cater to different learning styles, supplementing verbal explanations, and providing a tangible reference that patients can return to later for review or clarification (Katz et al., 2005).

Visual aids can include diagrams, models, and charts. For example, a diagram of the human heart can help a patient understand their cardiovascular condition, while a model of a joint can aid in explaining a surgical procedure. These visuals can make abstract concepts more concrete and understandable, particularly for visual learners (Chewning et al., 2012).

Demonstrations can also be incredibly effective in conveying information. This can include demonstrating how to use a medical device, perform a physical therapy exercise, or administer medication. Not only does this give the patient a clear, step-by-step understanding of the process, but it also provides an opportunity for them to ask questions and practice under the guidance of the caregiver (Katz et al., 2005).

Patient-friendly print materials such as brochures, booklets, and fact sheets can provide additional support. These resources should use simple, plain language and include plenty of visuals to reinforce the information. They can be particularly useful for patients to reference after a medical appointment, serving as a reminder of the information discussed (Chewning et al., 2012).

It is important to remember, however, that these resources should supplement, not replace, verbal communication. While they can be especially useful tools, they cannot convey empathy, answer unique patient questions, or adapt to a patient's specific needs and circumstances in the way a human caregiver can (Beach et al., 2022).

Providing Written Summaries of Key Discussion Points

Providing written summaries of key discussion points can be a valuable practice to improve patient understanding and recall. After a medical appointment or a complex discussion, patients can easily forget or confuse details. A written summary can serve as a concrete reminder of the information shared and can be reviewed at the patient's own pace (Katz et al., 2005).

The summary should include key points from the discussion, including any diagnosis given, treatment options discussed, recommended next steps, and answers to any questions the patient had. By focusing on these key points, the summary can distill the conversation down to its most essential elements, making it easier for the patient to digest (Chewning et al., 2012).

In addition, these summaries can include action plans or instructions for the patient to follow. This might include medication schedules, exercise routines, dietary changes, or other care instructions. By having this information in writing, patients can refer to it as needed, ensuring they do not forget or misunderstand their care instructions (Katz et al., 2005).

Written summaries can also be shared with other healthcare providers, caregivers, or family members involved in the patient's care (with the patient's consent). This can ensure that everyone is on the same page and that care is coordinated effectively (Chewning et al., 2012).

However, it is crucial to ensure that these summaries are written in a way that the patient can understand. This means using plain language, avoiding complex medical jargon, and breaking down information into clear, concise points. Providing a written summary is only helpful if the patient can read and understand it (Beach et al., 2022).

Encouraging Patients to Ask Questions

Encouraging patients to ask questions is fundamental to clear communication in healthcare. Patients are not passive recipients of care - they are active participants in their healthcare journey. Encouraging questions empowers patients, reinforcing their agency and engagement in their own health management (Chewning et al., 2012).

Caregivers should create an open and welcoming environment where patients feel comfortable asking questions. This can be accomplished by using an approachable demeanor, reassuring patients that no question is too small or silly, and thanking them for their questions (Northouse & Northouse, 2021).

It is also important for caregivers to respond to questions with patience and respect. Even if a question seems simple or irrelevant, it is important to remember that it is significant to the patient. By answering questions thoroughly and respectfully, caregivers can validate the patient's concerns and facilitate their understanding (Beach et al., 2022).

Caregivers can also proactively solicit questions. Rather than waiting for the patient to speak up, caregivers can ask, "What questions do you have?" or "Is there anything you'd like me to explain further?" This can signal to patients that their questions are not only welcome but actively encouraged (Chewning et al., 2012).

Caregivers should ensure that the patient's questions are fully addressed. If the caregiver does not know the answer to a question, they should admit this to the patient and commit to finding the answer. If a question is beyond the caregiver's scope of practice, they should help the patient find the appropriate healthcare provider to ask (Northouse & Northouse, 2021).

Sensitive Communication

Adopting a Warm, Patient, and Approachable Demeanor

When communicating with patients, adopting a warm, patient, and approachable demeanor is of utmost importance. The caregiver's demeanor can significantly influence how comfortable patients feel discussing their health concerns and how well they understand and engage with their care (Beach et al., 2022).

A warm demeanor can reassure patients and help to establish trust. This can be conveyed through a friendly tone of voice, a genuine smile, or an empathetic comment. This kind of warmth can create a comfortable atmosphere, making patients feel more at ease and more willing to share their feelings and concerns (Northouse & Northouse, 2021).

Patience is another crucial aspect of effective communication. Health discussions can be confusing and emotional for patients. By taking the time to explain things clearly, listen attentively, and answer questions thoroughly, caregivers can show patients that they are valued and respected (Beach et al., 2022).

An approachable demeanor means being open and inviting to questions or concerns. This can involve using non-technical language, asking open-ended questions, or validating the patient's emotions and experiences. An approachable demeanor can help patients feel more engaged in their care and more comfortable expressing their thoughts and concerns (Northouse & Northouse, 2021).

Together, warmth, patience, and approachability can create a supportive environment in which patients feel valued and understood. This can significantly improve the quality of communication and contribute to better health outcomes (Beach et al., 2022).

Ensuring Privacy During Sensitive Conversations

Ensuring privacy during sensitive conversations is paramount in healthcare communication. Discussing health issues can be deeply personal and often involves sharing sensitive information. To ensure that patients feel safe and comfortable, caregivers must prioritize privacy (Beach et al., 2022).

This involves choosing an appropriate location for the conversation. Whenever possible, discussions should take place in a private, quiet environment where the conversation cannot be overheard. In a hospital setting, this could mean using a private consultation room or ensuring curtains or room dividers are in place (Northouse & Northouse, 2021).

Besides physical privacy, confidentiality is equally crucial. Patients must know that their information is secure and will not be shared without their consent. This reassurance can help build trust and encourage openness during discussions (Beach et al., 2022).

Caregivers should also be mindful of the patient's personal comfort and cultural considerations related to privacy. For some patients, having a family member present during discussions may provide comfort, while others may prefer to discuss their health concerns alone. Similarly, some cultures have specific customs or beliefs about privacy that should be respected (Northouse & Northouse, 2021).

Furthermore, electronic communications, such as emails or telehealth appointments, should also be conducted with privacy in mind. This means using secure, encrypted platforms and discussing sensitive information only when the patient has a private, secure environment on their end (Beach et al., 2022).

Being Mindful of Verbal and Non-Verbal Cues

Being mindful of both verbal and non-verbal cues is another important aspect of sensitive communication. These cues can communicate a lot about the caregiver's attitudes and feelings, and patients are often very attuned to them (Northouse & Northouse, 2021).

Verbal cues include the caregiver's tone of voice, pace of speech, and choice of words. A calm, steady tone can convey patience and understanding, while a rushed, loud tone may make the patient feel hurried or anxious. It is also crucial to consider the words used; simple, non-jargon language is often best to ensure clear communication (Beach et al., 2022).

Non-verbal cues encompass body language, facial expressions, and eye contact. Open body language, such as uncrossed arms and a relaxed posture, can signal approachability and attentiveness. Similarly, positive facial expressions and regular eye contact can demonstrate interest and empathy (Northouse & Northouse, 2021).

Active listening is an essential part of conveying empathy through verbal and non-verbal cues. This involves fully focusing on the patient, reflecting back what they have said to confirm understanding, and responding in a thoughtful, compassionate manner (Beach et al., 2022).

However, it is also essential to be aware of the patient's verbal and non-verbal cues. This can help the caregiver understand the patient's emotions and concerns better, even if they are not explicitly stated (Northouse & Northouse, 2021).

Asking Permission Before Physical Touch and Explaining Procedures

Maintaining respect and understanding in healthcare also involves asking permission before physical touch and explaining procedures thoroughly. This shows respect for the patient's autonomy and can help to reduce any anxiety or discomfort they may feel (Beach et al., 2022).

Before initiating any physical touch, such as an examination or procedure, caregivers should explain what they are going to do and why it is necessary. This explanation should be in a language that the patient understands, avoiding medical jargon wherever possible. Providing this context can help the patient understand the purpose and benefits of the procedure, which can reduce anxiety (Northouse & Northouse, 2021).

Once the patient understands the procedure, it is essential to ask for their permission before proceeding. This is known as obtaining informed consent. By asking for consent, caregivers are acknowledging the patient's autonomy and right to make decisions about their body and healthcare. It is essential to ensure that consent is freely given and that the patient does not feel pressured or rushed into making a decision (Beach et al., 2022).

During the procedure, caregivers should continue to communicate with the patient, explaining what they are doing and checking in on how the patient is feeling. This can make the procedure feel less intimidating and give the patient a sense of control. If the patient appears uncomfortable or asks to stop, the caregiver should respect their wishes (Northouse & Northouse, 2021).

After the procedure, the caregiver should debrief the patient, explaining what was done, any findings, and the next steps. This follow-up discussion can help to ensure that the patient understands what happened and what to expect moving forward (Beach et al., 2022).

Creating a Safe Environment for Disclosure

The last critical aspect of sensitive communication is creating a safe environment for disclosure. Patients should feel comfortable discussing their health concerns, fears, and uncertainties with their caregivers. Establishing this type of environment can lead to more open communication, better understanding of the patient's condition, and more effective care (Beach et al., 2022).

Creating a safe environment starts with showing empathy. Empathy involves understanding and sharing the feelings of another. In a healthcare setting, this means acknowledging the patient's emotions, validating their experiences, and expressing genuine concern for their well-being (Northouse & Northouse, 2021).

Withholding judgment is also crucial. Patients should feel that they can share their health behaviors and concerns without fear of being judged or criticized. This is particularly important when discussing sensitive topics such as sexual health, mental health, substance use, or health behaviors that can carry a stigma (Beach et al., 2022).

Additionally, providing reassurance can create a safe environment for disclosure. This might involve reassuring the patient about the confidentiality of their information, or that their concerns are valid and worth discussing. It could also involve providing reassurance about the patient's health concerns or fears (Northouse & Northouse, 2021).

Finally, a safe environment is one in which the patient feels heard. This means listening attentively to the patient, providing thoughtful responses, and ensuring that the patient's concerns guide the conversation. When patients feel heard, they are more likely to disclose valuable information, trust their caregiver, and engage in their care (Beach et al., 2022).

Sensitive communication in healthcare involves adopting a warm, patient, and approachable demeanor, ensuring privacy, being mindful of verbal and non-verbal cues, asking for permission and explaining procedures, and creating a safe environment for disclosure. These practices can help caregivers to communicate effectively with patients, fostering better understanding, trust, and patient engagement in their care (Northouse & Northouse, 2021).

Shared Decision-Making

Explaining Disease Progression, Treatment Options, and Risks/ Benefits

Shared decision-making can only occur when patients are fully informed. This begins with providing an accurate and understandable explanation of the patient's disease progression. This should be done in a compassionate and empathetic manner, ensuring that the patient is comfortable and prepared to absorb the information. Caregivers can use visuals, analogies, or simple language to explain complex medical terms. The emphasis should be on making the information digestible, without overwhelming the patient (Chewning et al., 2012).

Treatment options are the next area where patients need thorough information. Here, it is not merely about outlining the choices, but giving a clear picture of what each option entails. This includes detailing the process of the treatment, the duration, the potential side effects, and the expected results. Caregivers should encourage patients to ask questions and ensure they fully understand each option. This open dialogue can alleviate anxieties and allow patients to feel more in control (Elwyn et al., 2012).

Furthermore, caregivers need to carefully discuss the potential risks and benefits associated with each treatment option. This involves breaking down each risk and benefit in a way the patient can understand. It may include discussing possible short-term and long-term side effects, success rates of the treatment, and how the treatment can impact the patient's quality of life. The aim here is to paint a realistic picture of each option, so the patient can make an informed decision based on their personal circumstances (Chewning et al., 2012).

In addition, caregivers should also provide guidance to patients as they navigate through these decisions. The caregiver's role is not only to provide information but also to offer support, reassurance, and guidance during this process. This can help to foster a strong, trusting relationship between the caregiver and the patient (Elwyn et al., 2012).

Information should be provided in a continuous manner. As the disease progresses or new research emerges, caregivers must update the patient about any changes in their disease progression or potential new treatment options. This requires caregivers to stay abreast of the latest advancements in their field and to continually communicate this information to their patients in an accessible way (Chewning et al., 2012).

Understanding Patient Preferences, Values, and Priorities

Understanding a patient's preferences, values, and priorities is an essential step in shared decision-making. This requires an initial conversation where the caregiver asks the patient about their goals, priorities, and values related to their health and treatment. This may involve discussing their lifestyle, family situation, work commitments, and cultural or religious beliefs. This conversation should be open, respectful, and patient-focused to ensure the patient feels comfortable expressing their views (Elwyn et al., 2012).

As caregivers gather this information, they can begin to tailor their approach to the patient's unique needs. For instance, a patient who values quality of life over longevity might prefer a less aggressive treatment that has fewer side effects. Alternatively, a patient who wishes to see their child graduate may choose a more aggressive treatment to prolong their life. Caregivers should listen attentively to these preferences and incorporate them into the treatment discussion (Chewning et al., 2012).

Active listening is crucial in these conversations. Caregivers must show empathy and validate the patient's feelings, concerns, and wishes. This involves not just hearing but understanding and responding appropriately to the patient's words. Active listening can help to build trust and rapport, creating a safe space where patients feel heard and understood (Elwyn et al., 2012).

Consistent communication is also essential to understanding patient preferences. Patient values and priorities can change over time, particularly as their disease progresses. Regular check-ins allow caregivers to stay up to date with the patient's evolving needs and adjust the care plan accordingly. These continuous conversations can ensure that the patient's care remains person-centered and adaptable to their changing circumstances (Chewning et al., 2012).

Understanding patient preferences goes beyond just the patient. In many cases, caregivers may also need to engage with the patient's family or loved ones. Family members can provide additional insights into the patient's values and preferences, and their input can be valuable in reaching a decision that the patient is comfortable with (Elwyn et al., 2012).

Balancing Clinical Expertise and Patient Autonomy

Balancing clinical expertise and patient autonomy can be a challenging aspect of shared decision-making. On one hand, caregivers have the clinical knowledge and experience to make evidence-based recommendations. On the other hand, they must respect the patient's autonomy, their right to make their own decisions about their care (Elwyn et al., 2012).

The balance begins by ensuring the caregiver is up to date with the latest medical research and treatment guidelines. This allows them to provide the best possible advice to the patient. However, this expertise must be conveyed in a way that is understandable and accessible to the patient. The use of medical jargon should be minimized, and explanations should be straightforward and clear (Chewning et al., 2012).

Caregivers must also encourage patients to express their thoughts and opinions openly. This can be achieved by creating a safe and comfortable environment where patients feel they can voice their concerns or ask questions without fear of judgment. Caregivers should make it clear that while they can provide expert advice, the final decision rests with the patient (Elwyn et al., 2012).

In this respect, the role of the caregiver can be seen as a guide, helping the patient to navigate their way through the various treatment options. While caregivers can make recommendations based on their clinical expertise, they should also consider the patient's desires and feedback. This balance can lead to more effective care and increased patient satisfaction (Chewning et al., 2012).

The caregiver's role also includes respecting the decisions that the patient makes, even if they disagree. This can be difficult, especially if the caregiver believes the patient is making a decision that could negatively impact their health. However, if the patient is making an informed decision, their autonomy must be respected (Elwyn et al., 2012).

Reaching Mutually Agreed-Upon Treatment Plans

Reaching mutually agreed-upon treatment plans is the goal of shared decision-making. This requires open communication, understanding, and compromise from both the caregiver and the patient. By discussing diverse options, considering the patient's preferences and the caregiver's expertise, they can come to a consensus on the best course of action (Elwyn et al., 2012).

The first step towards this goal is to present all treatment options in a clear and understandable manner. This involves explaining the benefits, risks, process, and potential outcomes of each treatment. Patients should be encouraged to ask questions and share their thoughts about each option. This open dialogue can help the patient to fully understand their options and make an informed decision (Chewning et al., 2012).

Next, the caregiver and patient should discuss the patient's preferences and values. This may involve discussing the patient's lifestyle, family situation, work commitments, and any other factors that may influence their decision. This understanding can help to guide the treatment discussion, ensuring that the patient's needs and wishes are considered (Elwyn et al., 2012).

Then, a consensus must be reached. This might require further discussions, compromises, or even seeking a second opinion. The focus should be on finding a plan that the patient feels comfortable with, and that also aligns with their health goals and the caregiver's medical advice (Chewning et al., 2012).

Once an agreement has been reached, it is important for this decision to be recorded and communicated to all relevant parties. This can include other members of the healthcare team, the patient's family, or any other individuals involved in the patient's care. Clear communication can help to ensure everyone is on the same page and understands the agreed-upon plan (Elwyn et al., 2012).

Following Up on Treatment Actions

Following up on treatment actions is a critical part of shared decision-making. This involves regular check-ins to monitor the patient's response to treatment, discuss any concerns or side effects, and adjust the treatment plan, as necessary. This continuous monitoring can ensure that the care plan remains effective and that the patient's needs are being met (Chewning et al., 2012).

The first step is to establish a clear follow-up schedule. This might involve regular appointments, phone calls, or virtual check-ins. The frequency of these follow-ups will depend on the patient's condition, the treatment plan, and the patient's preferences. The key is to maintain consistent communication and ensure the patient feels supported throughout their treatment journey (Elwyn et al., 2012).

During these follow-ups, caregivers should assess the patient's response to the treatment. This can involve discussing the patient's symptoms, side effects, or any other changes they have noticed since starting the treatment. This information can provide valuable insights into how well the treatment is working and whether any adjustments are needed (Chewning et al., 2012).

In addition, these follow-ups are an opportunity to discuss any concerns or issues that the patient may have. This could include issues with medication adherence, difficulties managing side effects, or concerns about the treatment's impact on their lifestyle. By addressing these concerns, caregivers can help to improve the patient's adherence to the treatment and their overall satisfaction with their care (Elwyn et al., 2012).

Follow-up appointments are an opportunity for the caregiver to reaffirm the treatment goals and to reassess the patient's preferences and priorities. As the disease progresses or the patient's situation changes, their treatment goals or preferences may change. Regular follow-ups allow these changes to be addressed and the treatment plan to be adjusted accordingly (Chewning et al., 2012).

Chapter 3: Assessing Caregiver Needs

3.1: The Imperative of Comprehensive Caregiver Assessments: A Multifaceted Approach

The role of a caregiver is often overlooked in the healthcare system, yet it is of immense importance. Caregivers provide invaluable support to individuals who cannot care for themselves, such as the elderly, disabled, or those with chronic illnesses. However, the act of caregiving can also take a toll on the caregiver's physical, emotional, and mental well-being. Therefore, assessing the caregiver's needs and providing them with adequate support is essential (Beach et al., 2022).

Comprehensive caregiver assessments can effectively identify the needs of caregivers and ensure they receive the appropriate support. These assessments should be conducted by healthcare professionals with experience in assessing the needs of caregivers, such as psychologists, social workers, and nurses. The assessment should evaluate various aspects of the caregiver's life, including their physical health, emotional well-being, social support, and their ability to provide care (Reinhard et al., 2019).

Physical health is a crucial aspect of caregiver assessment. Caregivers often neglect their own health to care for their loved ones, which can lead to physical exhaustion and burnout. Emotional well-being is also critical, as caregiving can be emotionally draining and stressful, potentially leading to depression, anxiety, and other mental health issues. Social support is essential for caregivers, as caregiving can be isolating, leading to loneliness and social isolation. Lastly, assessing the caregiver's ability to provide care is key. This involves evaluating their caregiving responsibilities, workload, financial resources, and training to determine if additional support is needed (Beach et al., 2022).

In the sections that follow, we will delve deeper into each of these key components of caregiver assessment, providing a comprehensive understanding of the importance of these assessments and the strategies that can be used to conduct them effectively.

Physical Health

Impact of Caregiving on Physical Health

The toll of caregiving on a person's physical health is multifaceted, often going unnoticed amid the daily caregiving tasks. For starters, many caregivers are actively involved in the physical care of their loved ones, assisting them with day-to-day tasks such as bathing, dressing, and mobility. This can be a physically demanding task, depending on the level of care required by the care recipient (Beach et al., 2022).

Moreover, the physical demands of caregiving often do not end with daylight hours. Many caregivers provide round-the-clock care, frequently waking up throughout the night to assist their loved ones. This can disrupt their sleep patterns, causing fatigue and exhaustion, and over time may lead to more serious health problems like sleep disorders, which can impair cognitive function and emotional health, further impacting their ability to provide care (Reinhard et al., 2019).

The potential for illness and infection is another critical issue. Caregivers are often exposed to a range of health conditions, from common colds and flu to more serious diseases depending on the care recipient's health status. Their constant exposure, combined with stress-induced weakening of the immune system, makes them more susceptible to falling ill. This vulnerability increases further if the caregiver has pre-existing health conditions that compromise their immune system (Beach et al., 2022).

The physical risks are further exacerbated by the fact that caregivers often put the health needs of their care recipient ahead of their own. Routine health check-ups are frequently skipped, and early signs of illness may be ignored or downplayed. This neglect can delay the detection and treatment of potential health issues, putting the caregiver at risk of developing serious health conditions (Reinhard et al., 2019).

The caregiver's dietary habits often take a backseat as they prioritize the nutritional needs of their loved ones. Lack of time or energy can lead to skipped meals or reliance on convenience foods, which are typically high in fats and sugars and low in essential nutrients. This poor nutrition, coupled with the physical exertion and lack of rest, can lead to drastic changes in weight, either loss or gain, which may in turn contribute to the development of other health complications such as cardiovascular disease, diabetes, or malnutrition (Beach et al., 2022).

Assessing Overall Health, Nutrition, Exercise, and Sleep Patterns

When assessing a caregiver's overall health, it is vital to adopt an integrated approach that covers the key pillars of health, namely nutrition, physical activity, and sleep. Nutrition is often the first aspect to be neglected by caregivers. With their focus primarily on the care recipient's dietary needs, their own food choices may lack the necessary balance of proteins, carbohydrates, fats, vitamins, and minerals required for optimal health. Moreover, caregivers may find themselves skipping meals or opting for fast food or other convenient, but not necessarily healthy, options due to lack of time (Reinhard et al., 2019).

An assessment of a caregiver's dietary habits should delve into the frequency and timing of their meals, their usual food choices, any food allergies or intolerances, and the availability and accessibility of healthy food options. This information can be used to develop a personalized dietary plan that ensures the caregiver receives the necessary nutrients to maintain their health and energy levels. Education about the importance of nutrition and practical tips on meal planning and preparation can also be beneficial (Beach et al., 2022).

Physical activity, while crucial for overall health and stress management, is another area often compromised in caregivers' lives. Caregiving duties may leave little time for structured exercise, and caregivers may also feel guilty about taking time for themselves. However, regular physical activity can significantly improve their physical health and well-being. The assessment should therefore explore whether and how the caregiver incorporates physical activity into their routine (Reinhard et al., 2019).

The type of physical activities preferred, the duration and frequency of these activities, and any barriers to exercise should be discussed. The assessment can then provide tailored suggestions for incorporating more physical activity into the caregiver's routine. This could include brief bouts of exercise throughout the day, chair exercises that can be done while supervising the care recipient, or even engaging in physical activities with the care recipient, such as walking, if possible (Beach et al., 2022).

Sleep patterns are another key aspect of physical health that needs to be assessed by caregivers. Chronic sleep deprivation can lead to a host of health problems, from increased susceptibility to infections to increased risk of chronic diseases such as heart disease and diabetes. The assessment should inquire about the caregiver's sleep duration and quality, any sleep disturbances they experience, and any daytime symptoms such as fatigue or lack of focus. If sleep problems are identified, appropriate interventions, such as sleep hygiene education or referral to a sleep specialist, may be recommended (Reinhard et al., 2019).

Medical Tests and Preventative Care

Medical tests form an integral part of a comprehensive caregiver physical health assessment. Regular medical tests can help identify potential health issues that may be developing unnoticed. This is especially important for caregivers, who often ignore their own health in favor of their caregiving duties. Such tests could include blood pressure checks, blood glucose tests, lipid profile tests, and other necessary screenings based on the caregiver's age, sex, and medical history (Beach et al., 2022).

These tests can help detect early signs of diseases like hypertension, diabetes, and heart disease, allowing for early intervention and management. Chronic pain conditions, which are common among caregivers due to the physical demands of their role, can also be detected and managed. Regular medical tests thus serve as a preventative measure, catching health issues before they become serious and more difficult to treat (Reinhard et al., 2019).

Regular check-ups and screenings also form a crucial part of preventative care. Screenings such as mammograms, colonoscopies, and bone density tests can help detect early signs of diseases like cancer and osteoporosis. Regular check-ups also provide an opportunity for caregivers to discuss any health concerns or symptoms they may have noticed (Beach et al., 2022).

In addition to detecting potential health issues, regular check-ups also provide an opportunity for healthcare professionals to educate caregivers about maintaining their physical health. This could include advice on nutrition, exercise, stress management, and ensuring adequate rest. Healthcare providers can also reinforce the importance of the caregiver prioritizing their own health and well-being alongside their caregiving responsibilities (Reinhard et al., 2019).

While these tests and check-ups are essential, it is also important to consider barriers to accessing healthcare. Many caregivers may lack health insurance or be worried about the cost of medical care. In these cases, referrals to low-cost or free community health resources can be helpful. Additionally, facilitating access to telemedicine services or home health services can help caregivers who find it difficult to leave their care recipient to attend medical appointments (Beach et al., 2022).

Health Education and Referrals

Education forms a significant part of the support system for caregivers' physical health. Caregivers should be provided with comprehensive health education that covers a range of topics, from the importance of proper nutrition and regular exercise to adequate rest and stress management. Education about the physical effects of stress and the link between physical and mental health can also help caregivers understand the importance of taking care of their own health (Reinhard et al., 2019).

This education can take many forms, from one-on-one consultations with healthcare providers to group workshops and online resources. Topics should be tailored to the caregiver's needs and circumstances and delivered in a way that is accessible and easy to understand. For example, a caregiver looking after someone with dementia may benefit from education about the physical demands of caregiving, while a caregiver for a cancer patient may benefit from information about infection control and immune health (Beach et al., 2022).

When health issues are identified through assessments, medical tests, or discussions, healthcare professionals can refer caregivers to the appropriate services. This could involve connecting them with a primary care physician, a dietician for nutritional advice, or a physical therapist for guidance on physical activity and managing any physical strain related to caregiving. Other specialists such as psychologists or sleep therapists may also be needed, depending on the caregiver's health status (Reinhard et al., 2019).

Referrals should consider the caregiver's circumstances, including their accessibility to these services. For example, a caregiver living in a remote location may benefit from telehealth services. Alternatively, caregivers with limited financial resources may need referrals to community health resources or programs that provide free or subsidized care (Beach et al., 2022).

Supporting the Caregiver's Physical Health

Supporting a caregiver's physical health requires a comprehensive approach that not only addresses health issues but also provides them with the resources and tools they need to maintain their health. This involves teaching caregivers about proper body mechanics to avoid injury when assisting care recipients. For example, they may need guidance on how to safely lift and move their loved one, or how to adapt tasks to reduce physical strain (Reinhard et al., 2019).

Incorporating physical activity into their routine is another key aspect of supporting a caregiver's physical health. While it may be challenging to find time for exercise, there are ways to incorporate it into daily tasks. Caregivers can be guided on how to include simple exercises in their routine, like doing leg lifts while washing dishes or doing seated exercises while watching

TV. Group exercise classes for caregivers can also be a beneficial resource, offering the bonus of social interaction (Beach et al., 2022).

Nutrition is another crucial factor. Caregivers can be provided with resources and tools for healthy meal planning and preparation, such as easy and quick recipes, information about healthy food choices, and practical tips for meal prep. They could also relate to services like meal delivery or community meal programs, which can help ensure they have access to nutritious food without adding to their workload (Reinhard et al., 2019).

Lastly, providing caregivers with access to respite care is vital to ensure they get the rest and recovery they need. Respite care services can give caregivers a much-needed break to rest, attend to their own health needs, or simply have some time for themselves. These services can range from volunteer companionship programs and adult day care services to short-term residential care facilities. Encouraging caregivers to utilize these services, and facilitating access to them, can go a long way in supporting caregivers' physical health (Beach et al., 2022).

Emotional Well-Being

Emotional Impact of Caregiving

Caring for a loved one often means navigating through an intricate maze of emotions. It can stir profound feelings of love and empathy, but it also brings to the surface emotions such as frustration, sorrow, and guilt. These complex emotional responses are in large part due to the challenges and realities caregivers face, such as the declining health of their loved one, dealing with difficult behaviors, and making challenging decisions regarding care. These experiences can lead to significant emotional distress that, if not managed properly, can adversely affect their overall health and well-being (Beach et al., 2022).

Furthermore, caregivers often find themselves managing several roles and responsibilities. Trying to balance caregiving with work, parenting, and other personal responsibilities can cause feelings of being overwhelmed, leading to emotional exhaustion and burnout. The incessant demand for care often leaves caregivers with little to no time to tend to their emotional needs, leading to emotional distress, which if left unchecked, can spiral into chronic stress or even depression (Reinhard et al., 2019).

The social isolation caregivers further compound the emotional strain of caregiving often experience. As more time is devoted to caregiving, caregivers' social networks often shrink, leading to feelings of loneliness and isolation. This lack of social interaction and support can exacerbate feelings of stress, potentially leading to mental health issues like depression and anxiety (Beach et al., 2022).

The type of illness or condition that the care recipient has can also influence the emotional impact of caregiving. For instance, caring for someone with a cognitive impairment like dementia can be particularly demanding due to changes in behavior and communication difficulties that come with the disease. These challenges can be emotionally draining, leading to frustration and even despair (Reinhard et al., 2019).

Assessing the emotional well-being of caregivers thus becomes an indispensable part of the caregiving process. This assessment helps to understand the emotional struggles caregivers are facing, and it forms the basis for tailored interventions aimed at alleviating emotional distress and enhancing the caregivers' overall well-being (Beach et al., 2022).

Assessing Mood, Stress Levels, and Coping Abilities

The emotional state of a caregiver can be ascertained by evaluating their mood, stress levels, and coping mechanisms. This can be achieved through a variety of tools such as questionnaires, interviews, and psychological tests. These methods can provide valuable insights into the caregiver's emotional well-being, helping identify the right approach and resources to support them (Beach et al., 2022).

A caregiver's mood can be an indicator of their emotional state. Persistent feelings of sadness, hopelessness, irritability, or a lack of interest in activities once enjoyed may point towards depression, a common issue among caregivers. In contrast, constant worry, restlessness, and feelings of being on edge could be signs of anxiety (Reinhard et al., 2019).

Stress levels of caregivers can be determined by examining the various stressors in their lives, which can range from caregiving duties and work-related stress to financial strain and interpersonal conflicts. Chronic elevated levels of stress can not only adversely affect the caregiver's emotional health but also impact their physical health, thus emphasizing the need for stress management (Beach et al., 2022).

A caregiver's ability to cope with stress provides insight into how they are handling the emotional challenges of caregiving. Some caregivers may adopt healthy coping strategies such as seeking social support, practicing relaxation techniques, or indulging in self-care activities. In contrast, others may resort to maladaptive coping mechanisms, such as substance abuse or self-isolation, which can escalate their emotional distress (Reinhard et al., 2019).

Providing Counseling and Support Groups

After a comprehensive assessment of the caregiver's emotional needs, healthcare professionals can start to connect them with the appropriate resources. Counseling services can be particularly helpful for caregivers. Therapists or counselors can provide a safe, non-judgmental space for caregivers to express their feelings, discuss their struggles, and learn coping strategies that can help manage their emotional load (Beach et al., 2022).

Counseling can take many forms, depending on the needs of the caregiver. Individual therapy can help caregivers understand and manage their feelings, while family therapy can help all family members understand the impact of caregiving on the family dynamics and learn to support each other more effectively. Cognitive-behavioral therapy can also be beneficial in helping caregivers to challenge and change thought patterns that lead to stress and anxiety (Lloyd et al., 2016).

Support groups, on the other hand, offer an opportunity for caregivers to connect with others who are going through similar experiences. They can offer emotional support, practical advice, and a sense of community, which can alleviate feelings of loneliness and isolation. The shared experiences and understanding within support groups can also help caregivers to realize that they are not alone in their struggles and that their feelings are normal and validated (Chen et al., 2015).

Support groups can be accessed through a variety of platforms. They can be found in the local community through healthcare providers, churches, or social services. They are also available online, which can be particularly beneficial for caregivers who have difficulty leaving their loved ones for an extended period or who live in remote locations (Beach et al., 2022).

In both counseling and support groups, it is important for the caregivers to feel comfortable and safe in expressing their feelings. The professionals leading these groups should be compassionate and understanding, fostering an environment where caregivers feel valued and heard (Chen et al., 2015).

Promoting Stress Management Techniques

In addition to counseling and support groups, promoting stress management techniques can significantly aid a caregiver's emotional well-being. Techniques such as mindfulness, meditation, deep breathing, and progressive muscle relaxation can help caregivers manage their stress levels, enhance their emotional resilience, and improve their overall quality of life (Wong et al., 2018).

Mindfulness encourages an individual to stay present in the moment, focusing their attention on their current experiences without judgment. It is a self-awareness skill that can help caregivers to pause, reflect, and effectively manage their emotions amidst the demanding nature of caregiving. Caregivers can cultivate mindfulness through activities such as mindful eating, mindful walking, or even washing dishes mindfully, transforming everyday activities into opportunities for stress reduction (Wong et al., 2018).

Meditation, particularly mindfulness meditation, has been shown to reduce stress and improve mental clarity. By teaching caregivers to concentrate on their breath or a particular phrase (known as a mantra), meditation promotes relaxation and helps to alleviate stress. Guided meditations, available through various apps or online platforms, can make the practice more accessible for caregivers, offering a convenient way for them to calm their minds even on a busy schedule (Wong et al., 2018).

Deep breathing is a stress management technique that can be easily incorporated into a caregiver's routine. By simply taking a few moments to focus on their breath, caregivers can trigger a relaxation response, slowing the heart rate and lowering blood pressure. This can be particularly helpful during stressful situations, providing immediate stress relief (Reinhard et al., 2019).

Progressive muscle relaxation involves sequentially tensing and relaxing different muscle groups in the body, promoting physical relaxation and reducing muscle tension. This technique can be particularly helpful for caregivers who experience physical symptoms of stress, such as headaches or back pain (Wong et al., 2018).

Exercise, as a stress management technique, has wide-ranging benefits. Regular physical activity can not only alleviate symptoms of stress but also enhance the caregiver's energy levels, improve sleep, and boost overall mood. Even brief bouts of physical activity, such as a quick walk around the block or a short yoga session, can provide significant stress-relief benefits (Beach et al., 2022).

Supporting the Caregiver's Emotional Well-being

The ultimate goal of these measures is to support the emotional well-being of caregivers. Caregiving can be a deeply rewarding experience, but it can also be emotionally draining. Providing caregivers with the emotional support they need can enhance their resilience, improve their quality of life, and help them continue providing care for their loved ones in a sustainable way (Reinhard et al., 2019).

By implementing regular assessments of the caregiver's emotional health, healthcare professionals can identify any areas of concern early on and provide the necessary support. This could be in the form of counseling, support groups, or teaching stress management techniques (Beach et al., 2022).

Moreover, fostering connections between caregivers and supportive networks can play a significant role in supporting their emotional health. By encouraging caregivers to seek help when they need it and to maintain connections with others, healthcare professionals can help reduce the feelings of isolation that often accompany caregiving (Chen et al., 2015).

Caregivers also need to recognize their own emotional needs and understand that it is okay to ask for help. They need to remember that caring for their own emotional well-being is not a luxury, but a necessity. By taking care of their emotional health, they will be better equipped to take care of their loved ones (Reinhard et al., 2019).

Supporting a caregiver's emotional well-being is a continuous process that adapts to the evolving challenges of caregiving. It is important that caregivers receive regular check-ins and reassessments to ensure that the support provided remains relevant and effective. With proper emotional support, caregivers can continue to provide care for their loved ones without compromising their own well-being (Beach et al., 2022).

Social Support

The Importance of Social Support

Social support plays a significant role in a caregiver's well-being. It provides a crucial buffer against the stress and challenges associated with caregiving. The support that caregivers receive from their social networks can take several forms, including emotional support (such as empathy, trust, and caring), informational support (advice, suggestions, and information), and tangible support (financial assistance or help with tasks) (Chen et al., 2015).

Caregiving, especially for chronic or severe illnesses, can be a time-consuming and emotionally draining task. This can leave caregivers feeling isolated or disconnected from their previous social activities and relationships. Without adequate social support, caregivers may face higher levels of stress, anxiety, and depression. Furthermore, lack of social support can reduce the caregivers' resilience and ability to cope with the demands of their role (Beach et al., 2022).

By understanding the importance of social support, healthcare professionals can better tailor their interventions to meet caregivers' needs. This may involve strategies to help caregivers maintain their existing social connections, develop new ones, or access various forms of social support when needed. Strengthening social support for caregivers can lead to improved mental and physical health, enhanced well-being, and a more sustainable caregiving experience (Chen et al., 2015).

Assessing Social Connections and Activities

An important aspect of social support is the caregiver's engagement in social connections and activities. This involves assessing the caregiver's relationships with friends, family, and community members, as well as their participation in social activities outside of their caregiving responsibilities. Engagement in social activities can provide caregivers with a sense of belonging, improve their mood, and offer a break from caregiving tasks (Chen et al., 2015).

The assessment should consider the quality and quantity of the caregiver's social interactions. A caregiver may have many social connections but lack deep, meaningful relationships that provide emotional support. Alternatively, a caregiver may be isolated in terms of quantity but have a few close relationships that offer significant emotional support. Healthcare professionals need to understand these nuances to provide appropriate interventions (Beach et al., 2022).

Additionally, the assessment should also take into account the caregiver's own perceptions of their social support. Even if a caregiver has many social connections, they may not feel supported if their needs are not being met.

Therefore, understanding the caregiver's perceived social support is also critical in designing effective interventions (Chen et al., 2015).

Connecting Caregivers to Community Resources

One effective way to enhance caregivers' social support is to connect them with community resources. These resources can offer a range of services that can reduce caregivers' isolation and provide them with practical support. For instance, caregiver support groups can provide a forum for caregivers to share their experiences, challenges, and strategies with others in similar situations. These groups can offer emotional support, reduce feelings of isolation, and provide valuable information and resources (Chen et al., 2015).

Community centers, recreational activities, and volunteering opportunities can also enhance caregivers' social support. Participation in these activities can provide caregivers with a break from their responsibilities, improve their mood, and enhance their sense of community. Furthermore, these activities can help caregivers maintain their identities outside of their caregiving roles, contributing to their overall well-being (Beach et al., 2022).

Connecting caregivers to these resources may involve providing information about local services, making referrals, or helping caregivers navigate the system. By facilitating caregivers' access to community resources, healthcare professionals can contribute to their social well-being and improve their caregiving experience (Chen et al., 2015).

Providing Respite Care Services

Respite care services are another critical support for caregivers. Respite care provides temporary relief for caregivers, allowing them to take a break from their caregiving duties. This break can provide caregivers with time for self-care, relaxation, or participation in social activities. By allowing caregivers to rest and recharge, respite care can reduce their stress levels, prevent burnout, and improve their overall well-being (Beach et al., 2022).

Respite care can take various forms, including in-home services, adult day care centers, or short-term residential care. The type and frequency of respite care needed may depend on the caregiver's situation, the care recipient's health condition, and the availability of services. Healthcare professionals can play a key role in informing caregivers about respite services and helping them access these services (Chen et al., 2015).

Supporting the Caregiver's Social Support Networks

Supporting the caregiver's social support networks is essential for their overall well-being. This can involve encouraging caregivers to maintain their relationships with friends and family, helping them communicate their needs to their social networks, or advocating for the caregivers within these networks (Chen et al., 2015).

Healthcare professionals can also help strengthen caregivers' social support networks by providing education and training. For instance, they can offer training sessions for family members or friends on caregiving tasks, stress management, or communication skills. These sessions can increase the network's understanding of the caregiver's role and enhance their ability to provide support (Beach et al., 2022).

Overall, by supporting the caregiver's social support networks, healthcare professionals can contribute to the caregiver's resilience, improve their mental health, and enhance their capacity to provide care (Chen et al., 2015).

Understanding Caregiving Responsibilities and Workload

Understanding the caregiver's responsibilities and workload is a key aspect of the caregiver assessment. The caregiver's tasks may vary widely depending on the care recipient's health condition, the caregiver's other responsibilities, and the availability of other support. Tasks may include personal care (such as bathing, dressing, and feeding), medical care (such as administering medication or monitoring health conditions), household tasks, fiscal management, and coordinating healthcare services (Beach et al., 2022).

The caregiver's workload involves not only the number of tasks but also the time spent on caregiving and the emotional and physical strain associated with these tasks. Caregiving can be a full-time job, often added to other responsibilities such as paid work, household chores, or childcare. The demands of caregiving can lead to physical exhaustion, emotional stress, and lack of time for self-care or relaxation (Reinhard et al., 2019).

By understanding the caregiver's responsibilities and workload, healthcare professionals can identify areas where the caregiver may be overburdened and need additional support. This understanding can guide the design of interventions to reduce the caregiver's workload, provide practical support, or enhance the caregiver's coping and stress management skills (Beach et al., 2022).

Assessing Financial Resources and Training

Caring for a loved one can place substantial financial strain on caregivers, including costs for medical care, supplies, home modifications, and lost income (Rainville et al., 2022). This financial burden negatively impacts caregivers' well-being and caregiving abilities (Beach et al., 2021). Therefore, healthcare providers should thoroughly assess caregivers' financial situations and connect them with appropriate assistance programs and resources to help manage expenses (Rainville et al., 2022).

Providers also need to evaluate any training needs caregivers have related to medical or caregiving tasks. Targeted education and skills training enhances caregivers' competence and confidence in providing care (Sheehan-Smith, 2020). Ongoing assessment and training can empower caregivers over the course of their caregiving journey (Vandepitte et al., 2016).

Identifying Needs for Additional Support

A comprehensive caregiver assessment identifies needs for supplementary support across multiple domains, including physical health, mental health, social connectivity, and direct caregiving abilities (Gibson et al., 2020). Caregivers frequently require extra assistance to manage their own health conditions, cope with emotional demands, maintain social relationships, and perform complex caregiving responsibilities (Dam et al., 2020).

Healthcare professionals should collaborate with caregivers to pinpoint their unique support needs and preferences. This ensures interventions like counseling, support groups, or respite services are optimally matched to each caregiver (Miller et al., 2021). A participatory process enables caregivers to engage in developing appropriate solutions for their situation (Rainville et al., 2022).

Connecting Caregivers to Educational Resources and Training

Equipping caregivers with education and training tailored to their needs and learning preferences is crucial for building caregiving competence (Kent et al., 2016). A variety of modalities, like classes, workshops, online modules, or individual training, can cover relevant topics such as medical conditions, care skills, stress management, patient advocacy, and navigating healthcare systems (Vandepitte et al., 2016).

These resources empower caregivers with valuable knowledge and practical skills to provide quality care with greater confidence and reduced stress (Sheehan-Smith, 2020). Education further enables caregivers to effectively advocate for themselves and care recipients within the healthcare system (Mosquera et al., 2021).

Providing Practical Support

Along with other interventions, many caregivers require practical assistance to manage intensive caregiving responsibilities (Beach et al., 2021). Support services like in-home healthcare, meal deliveries, or transportation directly help with complex care tasks and reduce caregiver burden (Miller et al., 2021).

Healthcare professionals play a vital role in assessing caregivers' practical support needs and connecting them with appropriate services (Gibson et al., 2020). Tailoring practical support to each caregiver's unique situation enhances their capacity to provide quality care while maintaining their own health and well-being (Dam et al., 2020).

Overall, comprehensive assessment and tailored support across multiple domains are essential to bolster caregivers' abilities and sustain them in their vital role (Rainville et al., 2022). By evaluating and addressing caregivers' multifaceted needs, healthcare providers can significantly impact caregiver and care recipient outcomes (Kent et al., 2016).

3.2: Evaluating the Physical and Emotional Health of Caregivers

While caregiving can provide profound personal fulfillment, it also imposes significant emotional and physical demands (*Rainville et al., 2022*). The intensive effort required to care for loved ones relying on support often leads to high levels of caregiver stress and strain (*Vandepitte et al., 2016*).

If overlooked, the continual strains of caregiving can contribute to caregivers' own health issues, including sleep disturbances, chronic pain, lowered immunity, anxiety, and depression (*Kent et al., 2016*). Caregiving responsibilities disrupt normal routines and tap finite emotional reserves (*Dam et al., 2020*). Over time, the cumulative stresses take a toll across all aspects of caregivers' lives and well-being (*Sheehan-Smith, 2020*).

Therefore, proactively addressing caregivers' physical and mental health needs is imperative (*Miller et al., 2021*). Providing assessment and support sustains caregivers' capacity to deliver care while safeguarding their overall health (*Beach et al., 2021*). Intervening is both an ethical obligation and a practical necessity for facilitating effective long-term caregiving (*Gibson et al., 2020*).

Support enables caregivers to withstand demands and maintain their own wellness amid intense challenges (*Rainville et al., 2022*). Robust assessment, education, skills training, and ongoing backup empower caregivers to stay healthy while handling this vital yet taxing role (*Sheehan-Smith, 2020*). Overall, caring for caregivers protects their functioning and enhances outcomes for all involved (*Miller et al., 2021*).

Psychoeducational Interventions

Understanding the Stress Threshold

Understanding the stress threshold is a crucial part of psychoeducational interventions. The stress threshold varies between individuals and is influenced by a range of factors such as genetics, upbringing, and past experiences (Payne, 2016). In everyday life, we face numerous challenges and stressors, but our ability to cope with them depends on our stress threshold (Zarit et al., 2014). When we stay within our stress threshold, we can generally manage stress without any significant harm (Vitaliano et al., 2011). However, when our stress levels rise above our stress threshold, we may experience overwhelming emotional distress and physical symptoms such as fatigue, headaches, and insomnia (Glaser & Kiecolt-Glaser, 2005).

In the context of caregiving, stress levels can often rise due to the demands and responsibilities of the caregiving role (Park et al., 2015). Caregivers may face emotional stressors such as worry about a loved one's health and physical stressors such as lack of sleep or constant physical exertion (Haley et al., 2004). Over time, these stressors can exceed the caregiver's stress threshold, leading to physical and mental health issues such as burnout, anxiety, and depression (Fonareva & Oken, 2014).

Implementing Psychoeducational Interventions

Psychoeducational interventions are carefully designed programs aimed at equipping caregivers with the necessary knowledge and skills to manage their stress levels effectively (Dam et al., 2021). The implementation of these interventions involves several steps, starting with a thorough assessment of the caregiver's needs, stressors, and coping mechanisms (Vázquez et al., 2014). This assessment helps in creating a personalized intervention plan that addresses the specific challenges and needs of each caregiver (Brown & Schinka, 2019).

In the intervention phase, caregivers are taught about stress and its impacts on physical and mental health (Losada-Baltar et al., 2021). They are also introduced to various stress management techniques such as relaxation exercises, cognitive strategies, and problem-solving skills (Laode et al., 2019). These techniques provide caregivers with a toolkit of strategies they can use to manage stress in their daily lives (Siachos et al., 2018).

The effectiveness of psychoeducational interventions also depends on regular follow-up and feedback (Gaugler et al., 2005). Healthcare professionals monitor the progress of caregivers and provide guidance and support as needed (Corry et al., 2019). They may also adjust the intervention strategies based on the caregiver's feedback and progress (Wilz et al., 2019). The goal of these interventions is to enable caregivers to manage their stress effectively and maintain their well-being, leading to a more balanced and fulfilling caregiving experience (Kitko et al., 2013).

The Role of Psychologists

Psychologists play a leading role in delivering psychoeducational interventions to caregivers (Kwok et al., 2013). With their specialized knowledge of human behavior and the mechanisms of stress, psychologists are uniquely positioned to guide caregivers through the process of understanding and managing their stress (Gallagher-Thompson et al., 2012). They provide the theoretical knowledge about stress and stress management, ensuring that caregivers understand why they are feeling the way they do and how their stress responses can be managed effectively (Lynch et al., 2013).

Psychologists also help caregivers identify their individual stressors – these could be emotional, such as worrying about a loved one's health, or practical, such as managing time and tasks (Losada et al., 2010). They help caregivers explore their emotional responses to these stressors and develop healthier coping mechanisms (Acton, 2002). Through techniques such as cognitive behavioral therapy, psychologists can help caregivers reframe negative thoughts, manage their emotions, and develop a more positive outlook (Gallagher-Thompson & Coon, 2007).

Furthermore, psychologists provide ongoing support to caregivers throughout their journey (Sörensen et al., 2002). They offer a safe and supportive environment where caregivers can express their feelings, concerns, and challenges (Steffen, 2000). They also monitor the caregiver's progress and provide feedback, encouragement, and further guidance as needed (Sorensen et al., 2002). Through their expertise and empathetic approach, psychologists can significantly contribute to the success of psychoeducational interventions and the well-being of caregivers (Gonyea et al., 2005).

The Benefits of Psychoeducational Interventions

Psychoeducational interventions provide several benefits to caregivers. One of the most significant benefits is the improved understanding of stress and its impacts (Losada et al., 2015). As caregivers learn more about their stress responses and how to manage them, they can better navigate the emotional and physical challenges of caregiving (Beinvenu & Dunn, 2001). This deeper understanding can lead to improved mental health, reduced risk of burnout, and improved quality of care provided to their loved ones (Sörensen et al., 2002).

Another important benefit of psychoeducational interventions is the development of effective stress management skills (Gallagher-Thompson et al., 2000). These skills, including relaxation techniques, cognitive strategies, and problem-solving skills, provide caregivers with practical tools they can use in their daily lives (Losada et al., 2006). These skills can help caregivers reduce their stress levels, improve their emotional regulation, and enhance their resilience against future stressors (Chien et al., 2011).

Additionally, psychoeducational interventions can promote a sense of self-efficacy among caregivers (Gitlin et al., 2003). This sense of self-efficacy, or belief in one's ability to handle challenging situations, can be a powerful motivator and source of resilience (Bandura, 1977). When caregivers feel confident in their ability to manage their stress and navigate the challenges of caregiving, they are more likely to persist in their role, maintain their well-being, and provide high-quality care (Gallagher et al., 2011).

Coping Strategies

Coping strategies are a crucial part of psychoeducational interventions for caregivers. These strategies provide caregivers with practical tools they can use to manage their stress levels and navigate the challenges of their role (Haley et al., 1987). One important coping strategy is relaxation techniques, such as deep breathing, progressive muscle relaxation, and guided visualization (Losada et al., 2015). These techniques can be easily learned and practiced at home, providing immediate relief from stress, and promoting physical and mental well-being (Williams et al., 2014).

Cognitive strategies are another important set of coping strategies. These strategies involve changing the way caregivers think about their stressors and their responses to stress (Losada et al., 2006). Techniques such as positive self-talk, cognitive reframing, and assertive communication can help caregivers manage their emotional reactions to stress, reduce negative thinking, and maintain a positive outlook (Gitlin et al., 2008). These cognitive strategies can be particularly helpful in managing the emotional stressors of caregiving, such as worry, guilt, and frustration (Gallagher-Thompson & Coon, 2007).

Problem-solving and planning skills are also critical for caregivers (Gitlin et al., 2008). Caregiving often involves complex tasks and decision-making, and effective problem-solving and planning can help caregivers manage these tasks more efficiently (Tremont et al., 2017). These skills can also help caregivers anticipate and prepare for future challenges, reducing stress and improving their capacity to provide care (Williams et al., 2014).

Long-Term Benefits of Coping Strategies

The benefits of learning coping strategies extend beyond immediate stress relief. Over the long term, these strategies can enhance caregivers' resilience and ability to manage stress *(Sörensen et al., 2002)*. As caregivers regularly practice these strategies, they become better equipped to handle future stressors, reducing the risk of burnout and improving their overall well-being *(Gallagher-Thompson et al., 2003)*.

Another long-term benefit is the improvement in caregivers' mental health *(Cooper et al., 2007)*. By learning to manage their stress effectively, caregivers can reduce their risk of mental health issues such as anxiety and depression *(Mahoney et al., 2005)*. This can lead to improved mood, better sleep, and increased energy levels, improving the caregiver's quality of life *(McCurry et al., 2007)*.

The coping strategies learned in psychoeducational interventions can also benefit the care recipients *(Gitlin et al., 2003)*. When caregivers are less stressed and more resilient, they can provide better care to their loved ones *(Gaugler et al., 2009)*. This can lead to improved health and well-being for the care recipients, as well as a more positive and fulfilling caregiving relationship *(Beinvenu & Dunn, 2001)*.

Psychoeducational interventions aimed at improving caregivers' coping and stress management skills have been shown to provide long-term mental health benefits *(Losada et al., 2015)*. In a study of dementia caregivers, those who received an intervention focused on improving coping skills and resilience showed reduced anxiety and depression that persisted over a two-year follow-up period *(Losada et al., 2015)*. This suggests that the coping skills learned can lead to sustained improvements in caregiver mental health.

Coping strategies like cognitive restructuring and problem solving have been associated with lower perceived stress and burnout among caregivers of patients with dementia *(Papastavrou et al., 2007)*. As these caregivers practiced adaptive coping strategies over six months, they reported improvements in their ability to manage caregiving demands and maintain their well-being *(Papastavrou et al., 2007)*.

For cancer caregivers as well, coping strategies have been linked to positive long-term outcomes such as lower distress and better physical health *(Northouse et al., 2010)*. Cancer caregivers often face prolonged strain, but learning techniques to regulate emotions and reframe thoughts can build resilience and prevent deterioration of mental and physical health *(Northouse et al., 2010)*.

Enhancing caregivers' ability to cope effectively does not just benefit the caregivers themselves. It also has positive effects on care recipients' health outcomes. Cancer patients whose caregivers received coping skills training showed better physical functioning at later follow-ups, demonstrating benefits extending to care recipients *(Northouse et al., 2010)*.

By equipping caregivers with lifelong coping abilities, psychoeducational interventions can thus lead to sustained improvements in resilience, mental health, and quality of care for both caregivers and care recipients *(McMillan et al., 2006)*. The long-term gains highlight the value of teaching caregivers how to manage stress and challenges beyond the intervention period.

Assessment Tools

The Need for Assessment Tools

The importance of assessment tools in the context of caregiver support cannot be overstated. The role of a caregiver is multifaceted, encompassing physical, psychological, and emotional aspects (Bastawrous, 2013). Given the broad range of duties and responsibilities, it is imperative to gauge the caregiver's capacity and well-being to ensure they can deliver the best care possible (Family Caregiver Alliance, 2012). However, assessing caregiver needs accurately is a complex process that requires a structured approach (Cheung et al., 2021).

Assessment tools provide this structured approach, enabling a comprehensive evaluation of the caregiver's situation (Gwyther, 2014). These tools are meticulously designed to capture information about various aspects of the caregiver's life, including their physical health, mental health, social circumstances, and the type and level of care they provide (Cheung et al., 2020). This inclusive assessment facilitates a deep understanding of the caregiver's needs, challenges, and potential areas of strain (Dunn et al., 2019).

Without such assessment tools, the support provided may not fully address the caregiver's needs, leading to increased strain and, potentially, decreased quality of care (Kent et al., 2016). Caregivers may find themselves overwhelmed and unsupported, which can lead to caregiver burnout—a state of physical, emotional, and mental exhaustion (Srisuphan et al., 2021).

The use of assessment tools allows for early detection of potential problems (Adelman et al., 2014). Caregiver strain can manifest in many ways, from physical ailments to mental health issues like anxiety and depression (Joling et al., 2018). Early detection through assessment tools can pave the way for timely intervention and prevent further deterioration of the caregiver's well-being (Hirschman et al., 2015).

Assessment tools can also help to illustrate the effectiveness of support measures (Lynn et al., 2014). By providing a quantitative or qualitative measure of the caregiver's situation, these tools can demonstrate whether interventions are working as intended or if adjustments are needed (Hirdes et al., 2010).

Understanding the Caregiver Strain Index

The Caregiver Strain Index (CSI) is a prominent example of an assessment tool that is widely used in caregiver support (Sullivan, 2002). CSI is a concise yet powerful tool, consisting of thirteen items that measure the caregiver's perceived level of strain (Bastawrous, 2013). It was designed to quickly identify caregivers who may be experiencing elevated levels of strain, enabling timely intervention (Robinson, 1983).

At its core, the CSI evaluates caregiver strain across multiple domains, including time constraints, emotional adjustment, role strain, personal strain, and financial strain (Cheung et al., 2020). Each item in the index probes a different aspect of the caregiver's life, providing a comprehensive picture of their situation (Kim & Chang, 2020).

For example, one item on the CSI examines whether the caregiver has had to make adjustments in their work due to their caregiving responsibilities (Thornton & Travis, 2003). Another item assesses whether caregiving has caused the individual to lose personal time or time for other family members (Bastawrous, 2013). By covering a wide variety of domains, the CSI ensures that no aspect of the caregiver's life is ignored (Sullivan, 2002).

The CSI is scored by adding up the number of items for which the caregiver responds affirmatively, which provides a measure of the overall level of strain (Bastawrous, 2013). The higher the score, the greater the strain the caregiver is experiencing. This score can then be used to guide interventions and support (Cheung et al., 2020).

One of the main strengths of the CSI is its versatility (Robinson, 1983). It can be used with a wide variety of caregivers, regardless of the care recipient's age, disease, or disability. This makes it a valuable tool for healthcare professionals across different settings (Sullivan, 2002).

The Role of Healthcare Providers in Assessment

Healthcare providers play a crucial role in conducting caregiver assessments (Cheung et al., 2020). They are often the first point of contact for individuals seeking help for their caregiving responsibilities (Kent et al., 2016). As such, healthcare providers are in a unique position to identify caregivers who may be at risk of caregiver strain and initiate early interventions (Joling et al., 2018).

When healthcare providers administer assessment tools like the CSI, they gain a holistic view of the caregiver's situation (Bastawrous, 2013). This view extends beyond the caregiver's immediate physical health, covering aspects of their mental health, social circumstances, and caregiving duties (Sullivan, 2002). This comprehensive understanding allows healthcare providers to identify areas where the caregiver may require additional support (Cheung et al., 2021).

In addition to identifying caregiver strain, healthcare providers also play a crucial role in interpreting the results of the assessment (Gwyther, 2014). They can explain the results to the caregiver, providing valuable insights into their caregiving experiences, their stressors, and potential areas of support (Hirschman et al., 2015). This feedback can empower caregivers, making them aware of their strengths and areas for improvement (Lynn et al., 2014).

Furthermore, healthcare providers can use the results of the caregiver assessment to guide their recommendations for support and interventions (Dunn et al., 2019). For example, if the assessment reveals that a caregiver is experiencing elevated levels of emotional strain, the healthcare provider might recommend psychological support such as counseling or therapy (Adelman et al., 2014).

Healthcare providers also play a critical role in maintaining a relationship with the caregivers (Kent et al., 2016). This ongoing relationship allows for regular assessments and follow-ups, ensuring that the caregiver continues to receive the support they need over time (Srisuphan et al., 2021).

Impact of Assessment on Caregiver Support

Implementing assessment tools is a critical first step in providing effective support to caregivers. Carefully selected, evidence-based assessment tools can identify caregivers at risk for strain and facilitate early interventions (Cheung et al., 2020). The implementation process requires thoughtful planning and sensitively engaging caregivers (Kent et al., 2016).

The first step involves selecting an appropriate, validated assessment tool that aligns with the caregiver population and addresses multiple domains of strain (Bastawrous, 2013). Factors in selecting a tool include demonstrated reliability and validity, cultural sensitivity, and feasibility for administration (Family Caregiver Alliance, 2012). Input from caregivers themselves can help determine the most suitable tool (Cheung et al., 2021).

Once a tool is selected, caregivers must be introduced to the assessment process through education about its purpose and benefits (Gwyther, 2014). They should understand that the goal is identifying their needs to provide personalized support (Adelman et al., 2014). Addressing any concerns about privacy or discomfort with assessment can build trust in the process (Kent et al., 2016).

Administration should be facilitated by a trained professional who can ensure proper implementation (Cheung et al., 2020). Self-report questionnaires are common, but interviews or observational tools may also be appropriate (Bastawrous, 2013). Accommodations in administration, such as assistive technology or translated materials, may help include diverse caregivers (Family Caregiver Alliance, 2012).

Scoring and analysis of results should follow standardized procedures for the selected tool (Sullivan, 2002). Additional qualitative insights can complement scored data (Cheung et al., 2021). Results should then be clearly communicated to the caregiver in a supportive, collaborative way (Gwyther, 2014). This discussion is the foundation for developing an appropriate support plan.

Interpreting the Results of the Assessment

Interpreting assessment results requires an experienced professional who can synthesize scored data with the caregiver's unique circumstances (Cheung et al., 2020). Input from the caregiver is also essential for accurate interpretation (Family Caregiver Alliance, 2012). Results should be explained clearly using non-technical language (Kent et al., 2016).

The interpretation should highlight the caregiver's specific stressors, strengths, and areas of need revealed through assessment (Bastawrous, 2013). For example, the caregiver may require training in medical tasks, help with financial planning, or self-care strategies (Adelman et al., 2014). Identifying gaps in knowledge, skills, or resources allows the creation of a tailored support plan (Sullivan, 2002).

Caregivers should have the opportunity to provide feedback on the interpretation of results (Cheung et al., 2021). Their perspectives can clarify or expand on the needs identified through assessment (Gwyther, 2014). Supportive communication helps ensure caregivers feel understood as the team collaborates to determine appropriate next steps (Hirschman et al., 2015).

Documenting results in the caregiver's records informs coordinated support (Kent et al., 2016). It provides a baseline for evaluating interventions and guides other providers involved in the caregiver's care

(Srisuphan et al., 2021). Ongoing assessment and updating of records allow support to evolve with the caregiver's changing needs (Cheung et al., 2020).

Formulating an Action Plan

After assessment and interpretation, the team collaborates with the caregiver to develop an action plan for support (Family Caregiver Alliance, 2012). This comprehensive plan addresses needs identified through assessment and the caregiver's priorities (Adelman et al., 2014). Interventions may include education, skills training, counseling, connection to resources, or other services (Kent et al., 2016).

The action plan outlines specific interventions, resources, referrals, and goals associated with each aspect of support (Bastawrous, 2013). It includes timelines for implementing support and follow-up assessments (Sullivan, 2002). Plans should remain flexible to accommodate the caregiver's changing needs over time (Srisuphan et al., 2021).

Caregivers should receive a documented action plan summarizing recommended support (Gwyther, 2014). Their active involvement in developing and updating the plan contributes to engagement and personalized care (Cheung et al., 2021). Clear communication about the purpose and process facilitates successful implementation of supportive interventions (Hirschman et al., 2015).

Follow-Up and Monitoring

Follow-up and monitoring are essential components of caregiver support. After the action plan has been implemented, it is important to monitor the caregiver's situation and adjust the plan as necessary (Kent et al., 2016). This can be achieved through regular follow-up appointments with the caregiver (Bastawrous, 2013).

During these appointments, the effectiveness of the interventions can be assessed (Sörensen et al., 2002). This involves discussing with the caregiver their experiences with the interventions, any challenges they have encountered, and any perceived changes in their stress levels or well-being

(Gallagher-Thompson et al., 2003). This feedback can provide valuable insights into the effectiveness of the interventions and identify any areas that need adjustment (Gaugler et al., 2009).

Monitoring also involves reassessing the caregiver's needs and risks (Cheung et al., 2020). This can be done using the same assessment tool that was initially used, allowing for a direct comparison of results over time (Family Caregiver Alliance, 2012). If the caregiver's situation has changed, or if new areas of strain have emerged, these can be identified and addressed (Adelman et al., 2014).

Additionally, ongoing monitoring can help to prevent caregiver burnout (Kent et al., 2016). By regularly checking in on the caregiver's well-being and adjusting the support plan as necessary, the risk of the caregiver becoming overwhelmed or burned out can be reduced (Joling et al., 2018). This can enhance the quality of care provided to the care recipient (Sörensen et al., 2002).

Moreover, regular follow-up provides an opportunity for the caregiver to voice any concerns or difficulties they are experiencing (Gallagher-Thompson et al., 2003). It is a chance for the caregiver to feel heard and validated, which can be incredibly beneficial for their mental and emotional health (Gaugler et al., 2009). It also reinforces the notion that they are not alone in their caregiving journey, providing a sense of ongoing support and community (Kent et al., 2016).

The Role of Assessment in Long-Term Caregiver Support

Assessment tools play a vital role in long-term caregiver support (Bastawrous, 2013). By providing a structured way to identify and address the needs of caregivers, these tools can ensure that caregivers receive targeted, effective support (Sullivan, 2002). Regular assessments can also help to prevent caregiver burnout, promote the caregiver's well-being, and enhance the quality of care provided to the care recipient (Sörensen et al., 2002).

The use of assessment tools can facilitate early interventions for caregivers at risk of strain (Kent et al., 2016). Early identification of stressors or difficulties can allow for timely support and interventions, potentially preventing the onset of serious physical and emotional health problems (Adelman et al., 2014). This proactive approach can significantly improve the caregiver's quality of life and their ability to provide care (Joling et al., 2018).

Furthermore, regular assessments can guide the ongoing development of personalized support plans (Gallagher-Thompson et al., 2003). As the caregiving situation changes over time, the caregiver's needs and stressors may also change. Regular assessments can ensure that these changes are identified and that the support provided continues to align with the caregiver's needs (Gaugler et al., 2009).

In addition, assessment tools can provide valuable data for research and policy development (Cheung et al., 2020). By collecting systematic data on caregiver's experiences and needs, these tools can contribute to our understanding of caregiving and inform the development of effective support services and policies (Family Caregiver Alliance, 2012).

Finally, the use of assessment tools can empower caregivers by involving them in the process of identifying their needs and planning their support (Sörensen et al., 2002). This can enhance the caregiver's sense of control and agency, promoting their resilience and capacity to cope with the challenges of caregiving (Kent et al., 2016).

The Role of Psychoeducational Interventions in Caregiver Support

Psychoeducational interventions play a significant role in providing ongoing support to caregivers (Losada et al., 2015). These interventions aim to equip caregivers with the knowledge, skills, and coping strategies they need to effectively fulfill their caregiving responsibilities while maintaining their own well-being (Beinvenu & Dunn, 2001).

Psychoeducational interventions typically cover a range of topics relevant to caregiving (Gallagher-Thompson et al., 2003). These can include information about the care recipient's condition, training in caregiving skills, advice on managing caregiving-related stress, and strategies for balancing caregiving with other life responsibilities (McMillan et al., 2006). By providing caregivers with this knowledge, psychoeducational interventions can help them feel more prepared and confident in their caregiving role (Sörensen et al., 2002).

Another key aspect of psychoeducational interventions is skill-building (Gitlin et al., 2008). Caregiving often requires specific practical skills, such as how to safely transfer a person from a bed to a chair, how to manage medication, or how to perform basic physical therapy exercises (Gaugler et al., 2009). Providing caregivers with training in these skills can help them provide better care and reduce the risk of injury or other complications (Coon et al., 2003).

Psychoeducational interventions also focus on building caregivers' emotional resilience (Sörensen et al., 2002). Caregiving can be emotionally challenging, leading to feelings of stress, anxiety, and depression (Gallagher-Thompson et al., 2003). By teaching coping strategies, such as stress management techniques, mindfulness exercises, and cognitive-behavioral strategies, these interventions can help caregivers maintain their emotional health (Beinvenu & Dunn, 2001).

Finally, psychoeducational interventions can also provide social support (Cheung et al., 2020). Many interventions involve group sessions where caregivers can interact with others in similar situations (Gitlin et al., 2008). These sessions provide a safe space for caregivers to share their experiences, learn from each other, and form supportive relationships (Sörensen et al., 2002). This social aspect can help reduce feelings of isolation often associated with caregiving (Gaugler et al., 2009).

Ongoing Support

The Importance of Ongoing Support

Ongoing support for caregivers is not just beneficial but essential (Kent et al., 2016). Caregiving is an ever-evolving role that often comes with escalating demands (Bastawrous, 2013). The health of the individual being cared for can fluctuate, their needs can change, and the emotional toll on the caregiver can mount over time (Sörensen et al., 2002). Without ongoing support, caregivers may find themselves unable to cope with these increasingly challenging demands (Gallagher-Thompson et al., 2003).

The importance of ongoing support lies in its capacity to provide caregivers with resources and interventions on a continual basis (Gaugler et al., 2009). This support helps to ensure that caregivers are not left to fend for themselves when new challenges arise (Cheung et al., 2020). Rather, they have a network of resources to lean on that can provide guidance, assistance, and relief (Family Caregiver Alliance, 2012).

Ongoing support also provides an outlet for caregivers to express their feelings and struggles (Adelman et al., 2014). The emotional toll of caregiving should not be underestimated. Caregivers often juggle their responsibilities with other personal and professional commitments, leading to stress, anxiety, and burnout (Joling et al., 2018). By providing ongoing support, caregivers are reassured that they are not alone in their journey, and they can share their experiences and feelings in a safe and understanding environment (Kent et al., 2016).

Beyond emotional support, ongoing assistance can provide concrete resources and interventions to improve the caregiving experience (Sörensen et al., 2002). This can range from training in specific care techniques to providing respite care to allow caregivers some much-needed time off (Gallagher-Thompson et al., 2003). It also involves providing caregivers with the latest resources and information, ensuring they are up-to-date and well-equipped to provide the best possible care (Gaugler et al., 2009).

Ongoing support plays a pivotal role in the caregiver's self-care (Cheung et al., 2020). Caregivers often overlook their own health and well-being due to their caregiving responsibilities (Family Caregiver Alliance, 2012). By providing ongoing support, focus can also be placed on the caregiver's health, ensuring they have the physical and emotional strength to continue their caregiving duties (Adelman et al., 2014).

Personalizing Support to the Caregiver

Personalization is the cornerstone of effective caregiver support (Gitlin et al., 2008). Each caregiver's journey is unique, shaped by the needs and health condition of the care recipient, the caregiver's personal circumstances, and numerous other factors (Sörensen et al., 2002). Thus, it is imperative that support plans are tailored to each caregiver's individual situation (Gallagher-Thompson et al., 2003).

The first step in personalizing support is understanding the caregiver's unique stressors (Gaugler et al., 2009). These can range from the physical demands of caregiving to emotional stress, financial burdens, and time constraints (Cheung et al., 2020). By understanding these stressors, support can be designed to specifically address these areas, providing targeted relief and assistance (Family Caregiver Alliance, 2012).

Next, it is important to consider the caregiver's coping mechanisms (Adelman et al., 2014). Everyone has diverse ways of managing stress and adversity (Joling et al., 2018). Some people might find solace in physical activities like exercise, while others might prefer meditation or talking to a friend (Sörensen et al., 2002). By understanding the caregiver's preferred coping mechanisms, support plans can recommend strategies that align with the caregiver's natural tendencies (Gallagher-Thompson et al., 2003).

Resources available to the caregiver also play a significant role in personalizing support (Gaugler et al., 2009). Some caregivers might have a large network of family and friends who can help, while others might be mostly on their own (Gitlin et al., 2008). Some might have financial resources to hire professional help, while others might be financially strained (Sörensen et al., 2002). By understanding the caregiver's resources, support plans can be designed to maximize these resources and provide additional help where needed (Gallagher-Thompson et al., 2003).

Personalizing support to the caregiver does not just make the support more effective – it also makes it more enjoyable and less stressful for the caregiver (Gaugler et al., 2009). By aligning with the caregiver's needs and preferences, personalized support plans are more likely to be welcomed and implemented by the caregiver, leading to better outcomes for both the caregiver and the care recipient (Cheung et al., 2020).

The Role of Care Teams in Providing Support

Care teams are multidisciplinary groups of professionals who work collaboratively to provide comprehensive support to caregivers (Kent et al., 2016). These teams typically include healthcare providers such as doctors and nurses, psychologists or therapists, social workers, and other professionals who can provide a range of services and support (Bastawrous, 2013).

These professionals bring their unique expertise to the table to create a holistic support plan for the caregiver (Sullivan, 2002). Healthcare providers can provide medical advice and training to help the caregivers provide proper care (Sörensen et al., 2002). Psychologists or therapists can provide mental health support, helping the caregiver manage stress and emotional challenges (Gallagher-Thompson et al., 2003). Social workers can assist with navigating social services and resources, and other professionals, like dietitians or physiotherapists, can provide specialized advice based on the care recipient's needs (Gaugler et al., 2009).

Care teams are not just about providing the caregiver with resources and advice (Cheung et al., 2020). They also play a critical role in assessing the caregiver's needs (Family Caregiver Alliance, 2012). Through regular contact and communication, they can monitor the caregiver's stress levels, health, and overall well-being (Adelman et al., 2014). They can also observe the effectiveness of the support being provided and adjust the support plan as needed (Joling et al., 2018).

Another key role of care teams is to provide a sense of community for the caregiver (Kent et al., 2016). By regularly interacting with the care team, caregivers can feel less isolated and more supported (Sörensen et al., 2002). The care team can provide a listening ear, a shoulder to lean on, and a source of advice and guidance (Gallagher-Thompson et al., 2003).

Sustaining Caregiver Support Over Time

Sustaining caregiver support over time is a dynamic process that requires active engagement from both the caregiver and the care team (Kent et al., 2016). The goal is to ensure that the caregiver feels continuously supported and their needs are met as their situation changes (Bastawrous, 2013). This requires regular communication, consistent reassessment of needs, and the flexibility to adapt the support plan as necessary (Sullivan, 2002).

Consistent communication is key to understanding the changing needs of the caregivers (Sörensen et al., 2002). This can include regular meetings or check-ins with the care team, as well as providing the caregiver with an open line of communication for any immediate concerns or questions they may have (Gallagher-Thompson et al., 2003). Through these regular touchpoints, the care team can stay informed about the caregiver's situation and provide timely assistance (Gaugler et al., 2009).

Reassessment of needs is another crucial component of sustaining support (Cheung et al., 2020). As the caregiving journey progresses, the caregiver's needs are likely to change (Family Caregiver Alliance, 2012). For example, as the care recipient's health condition evolves, the caregiver may need to learn new caregiving skills (Adelman et al., 2014). Regular reassessment ensures that the support provided remains relevant and effective (Joling et al., 2018).

Flexibility is also paramount in sustaining support (Kent et al., 2016). Caregiving is unpredictable, and caregivers can encounter unexpected challenges at any time (Sörensen et al., 2002). The care team needs to be adaptable and prepared to modify the support plan in response to these changes (Gallagher-Thompson et al., 2003). This could mean bringing in additional resources, providing several types of support, or adjusting the frequency or intensity of interventions (Gaugler et al., 2009).

Maintaining caregiver support over time also involves keeping the caregiver engaged in the process (Cheung et al., 2020). Caregivers are more likely to utilize support services if they feel they have a say in their support plan (Family Caregiver Alliance, 2012). Regularly seeking the caregiver's feedback and incorporating their preferences into the support plan can help ensure their continued engagement and satisfaction (Adelman et al., 2014).

The Impact of Ongoing Support

The impact of ongoing support on caregivers can be profound. With regular and personalized support, caregivers can better manage their stress levels, maintain their physical and emotional health, and prevent caregiver burnout (Joling et al., 2018). This, in turn, allows them to provide better care for their loved ones (Sörensen et al., 2002).

Regularly receiving support can significantly reduce caregivers' stress levels (Gallagher-Thompson et al., 2003). By providing resources, coping strategies, and a listening ear, ongoing support can help caregivers feel less overwhelmed and more capable of handling their caregiving duties (Gaugler et al., 2009). This can lead to a more positive caregiving experience and improved mental health for the caregiver (Kent et al., 2016).

Ongoing support also plays a crucial role in maintaining the caregiver's physical health (Cheung et al., 2020). Caregiving can be physically demanding, and without proper support, caregivers can neglect their own health (Family Caregiver Alliance, 2012). Ongoing support can promote self-care behaviors among caregivers, such as regular exercise, proper nutrition, and adequate rest, ensuring they have the physical strength to continue their caregiving duties (Adelman et al., 2014).

Furthermore, ongoing support can prevent caregiver burnout (Joling et al., 2018). Caregiver burnout is a state of physical, emotional, and mental exhaustion that can occur when caregivers do not get the help they need (Sörensen et al., 2002). By providing consistent support, caregivers can have some of the burden lifted off their shoulders, preventing them from reaching this state of burnout (Gallagher-Thompson et al., 2003).

Ongoing support can enhance caregivers' resilience, equipping them to better handle the inevitable challenges of caregiving (Gaugler et al., 2009). This resilience can lead to improved care for their loved ones and a more rewarding caregiving experience (Kent et al., 2016). Thus, the impact of ongoing support extends beyond the caregiver to also affect the individuals positively they care for (Cheung et al., 2020).

3.3: Identifying and Leveraging Social Support Networks for Caregivers

Identifying and Leveraging Social Support Networks for Caregivers

The role of a caregiver is a complex and demanding one, often requiring a significant commitment of time, emotional energy, and physical effort (Bastawrous, 2013). The weight of these responsibilities can, over time, lead to physical exhaustion, emotional distress, and in some cases, even health complications (Sörensen et al., 2002). While the act of caregiving can be fulfilling and rewarding, it can also be a source of considerable stress, making the need for robust support systems crucial (Gallagher-Thompson et al., 2003).

Social support networks are essential for mitigating the strains associated with caregiving (Gaugler et al., 2009). They offer emotional comfort, practical assistance, and a sense of community, helping caregivers navigate the challenges they face more effectively (Cheung et al., 2020). These networks can include family members, friends, and broader community resources, each offering unique forms of support (Family Caregiver Alliance, 2012).

The importance of these social support networks cannot be overstated (Adelman et al., 2014). They not only provide immediate relief and comfort to caregivers but also serve as a protective factor, buffering against the physical and psychological impacts of caregiver stress (Joling et al., 2018). By recognizing and making effective use of these support systems, caregivers can protect their well-being, bolster their resilience, and enhance their effectiveness in their caregiving role (Kent et al., 2016).

Here we will aim to provide an in-depth look at the diverse types of social support networks available to caregivers (Sullivan, 2002). It will delve into the unique roles played by family, friends, and community resources in providing support, offering practical recommendations for how caregivers can tap into these networks (Sörensen et al., 2002). The goal is to empower caregivers with the knowledge and tools they need to cultivate robust support systems, fostering their well-being and resilience as they navigate the rewarding yet challenging journey of caregiving (Gallagher-Thompson et al., 2003).

The Role of Family Support

For many caregivers, family members form the foundation of their support system (Kent et al., 2016). Spouses, adult children, siblings, and extended family can provide invaluable emotional, instrumental, and financial assistance (Bastawrous, 2013). However, effectively leveraging family support requires open communication about caregiving needs (Sullivan, 2002).

Caregivers should clearly express their needs and delegate specific tasks to family members suited to their abilities (Sörensen et al., 2002). For example, local siblings can assist with medical appointments or household chores, while distant relatives can provide emotional support through regular phone calls (Gallagher-Thompson et al., 2003). Setting clear expectations preserves family harmony (Gaugler et al., 2009).

It is also important for caregivers to prioritize self-care and set boundaries (Cheung et al., 2020). Taking regular respite allows caregivers to sustainably manage responsibilities (Family Caregiver Alliance, 2012). Caregivers should not feel guilty about taking breaks or asking for help when needed (Adelman et al., 2014). Preserving caregiver well-being enables them to optimally care for their loved one (Joling et al., 2018).

Leveraging Friend Networks

Beyond family, friends can provide a vital source of psychosocial support for caregivers (Kent et al., 2016). Caregivers should maintain social connections and share feelings openly with close friends (Sullivan, 2002). This provides an emotional outlet and sense of normalcy beyond the caregiving role (Sörensen et al., 2002).

Friends can also take on caregiving tasks temporarily through respite care (Gallagher-Thompson et al., 2003). This may involve preparing meals, running errands, or spending time with the care recipient to allow the caregiver time off (Gaugler et al., 2009). Friends with relevant professional expertise can additionally offer guidance to the caregiver (Cheung et al., 2020).

However, caregivers must also be mindful not to overburden friends (Family Caregiver Alliance, 2012). Checking in about friends' capacity and comfort with providing support preserves these relationships (Adelman et al., 2014). Caregivers should express gratitude for any support friends provide (Joling et al., 2018).

Community and Peer Support

Connecting to community resources and peer support groups is invaluable (Kent et al., 2016). These provide access to respite services, practical training, financial assistance, and supportive communities who deeply understand the caregiving experience (Sullivan, 2002). Geriatric care managers, support groups, and nonprofits catering to specific care needs are especially helpful (Sörensen et al., 2002).

Seeking this wider support enables the caregiver to share the caregiving journey with others who empathize (Gallagher-Thompson et al., 2003). By integrating diverse social supports, caregivers enhance their own resilience and ability to provide quality care over the long term (Gaugler et al., 2009).

Family Support

The Role of Family in Caregiving

Family members play an integral role in the caregiving process, often providing the backbone of a caregiver's support network (Bastawrous, 2013). The shared experiences, history, and emotional bonds that develop within families create a unique support system that can be instrumental in helping caregivers cope with the challenges they face (Sörensen et al., 2002).

It is not uncommon for caregivers to feel overwhelmed, stressed, or uncertain. This is where the emotional support offered by family members can be of immense value (Gallagher-Thompson et al., 2003). They can provide empathy, understanding, encouragement, and validation that help bolster the caregiver's spirits, improving their resilience and capacity to manage stress (Gaugler et al., 2009).

Family support is not just about being there in times of crisis or difficulty; it's also about celebrating achievements, acknowledging progress, and reassuring the caregiver of their capabilities (Cheung et al., 2020). A family member's vote of confidence can go a long way in boosting a caregiver's morale and fostering a sense of self-efficacy (Family Caregiver Alliance, 2012).

Instrumental Support from Family

The support rendered by family members is not limited to emotional backing. It also extends to instrumental support, which can take on various forms such as financial assistance, help with caregiving tasks, or providing respite care (Adelman et al., 2014).

Financial support from family members can be a lifeline for caregivers, helping to offset the high medical expenses or the cost of essential caregiving equipment and supplies (Joling et al., 2018). This kind of support can significantly alleviate the financial burdens that caregivers often face, allowing them to focus more on the physical and emotional aspects of caregiving (Kent et al., 2016).

Assistance with caregiving tasks can lighten the caregiver's load, making it more manageable (Sullivan, 2002). This might involve helping with tasks such as medication management, personal care, or household chores (Sörensen et al., 2002). Respite care, on the other hand, offers the caregiver a much-needed break to rest, recharge, and attend to their personal needs (Gallagher-Thompson et al., 2003).

Navigating Family Dynamics

Caregiving can bring the complexities of family dynamics to the surface (Gaugler et al., 2009). It is crucial for caregivers to carefully navigate these dynamics, ensuring that their needs are met without causing undue conflict or tension within the family (Cheung et al., 2020).

This might involve having open and honest discussions about the caregiving responsibilities, expectations, and the distribution of tasks (Family Caregiver Alliance, 2012). It is important for family members to understand the scope of the caregiver's duties and the challenges they face (Adelman et al., 2014). This understanding can help foster empathy and encourage participation in caregiving tasks (Joling et al., 2018).

It is also beneficial to establish clear boundaries and roles within the family (Kent et al., 2016). This clarity can prevent misunderstandings and promote a harmonious caregiving environment (Sullivan, 2002). In instances where disagreements or conflicts arise, seeking external assistance such as family therapy or mediation can be a helpful tool to manage and resolve these issues (Sörensen et al., 2002).

The Long-Term Impact of Family Support

The support of family members can have a profound long-term impact on a caregiver's well-being (Gallagher-Thompson et al., 2003). It offers immediate relief and support, but it also fosters a sense of shared responsibility and unity within the family (Gaugler et al., 2009). This sense of togetherness can prevent caregiver isolation and burnout, enhancing the caregiver's resilience and capacity to provide quality care over time (Cheung et al., 2020).

The benefits of family support extend beyond the immediate caregiving situation (Family Caregiver Alliance, 2012). It can strengthen family bonds, improve communication within the family, and enhance the family's ability to cope with future challenges (Adelman et al., 2014). Moreover, the shared experiences of caregiving can deepen mutual understanding among family members, creating a more robust support network for the caregiver overall (Joling et al., 2018).

Friend Support

The Emotional Support of Friends

Family members play an integral role in the caregiving process, often providing the backbone of a caregiver's support network (Bastawrous, 2013). The shared experiences, history, and emotional bonds that develop within families create a unique support system that can be instrumental in helping caregivers cope with the challenges they face (Sörensen et al., 2002).

It is not uncommon for caregivers to feel overwhelmed, stressed, or uncertain. This is where the emotional support offered by family members can be of immense value (Gallagher-Thompson et al., 2003). They can provide empathy, understanding, encouragement, and validation that help bolster the caregiver's spirits, improving their resilience and capacity to manage stress (Gaugler et al., 2009).

Family support is not just about being there in times of crisis or difficulty; it's also about celebrating achievements, acknowledging progress, and reassuring the caregiver of their capabilities (Cheung et al., 2020). A family member's vote of confidence can go a long way in boosting a caregiver's morale and fostering a sense of self-efficacy (Family Caregiver Alliance, 2012).

Instrumental Support from Family

The support rendered by family members is not limited to emotional backing. It also extends to instrumental support, which can take on various forms such as financial assistance, help with caregiving tasks, or providing respite care (Adelman et al., 2014).

Financial support from family members can be a lifeline for caregivers, helping to offset the high medical expenses or the cost of essential caregiving equipment and supplies (Joling et al., 2018). This kind of support can significantly alleviate the financial burdens that caregivers often face, allowing them to focus more on the physical and emotional aspects of caregiving (Kent et al., 2016).

Assistance with caregiving tasks can lighten the caregiver's load, making it more manageable (Sullivan, 2002). This might involve helping with tasks such as medication management, personal care, or household chores (Sörensen et al., 2002). Respite care, on the other hand, offers the caregiver a much-needed break to rest, recharge, and attend to their personal needs (Gallagher-Thompson et al., 2003).

Navigating Family Dynamics

Caregiving can bring the complexities of family dynamics to the surface (Gaugler et al., 2009). It is crucial for caregivers to carefully navigate these dynamics, ensuring that their needs are met without causing undue conflict or tension within the family (Cheung et al., 2020).

This might involve having open and honest discussions about the caregiving responsibilities, expectations, and the distribution of tasks (Family Caregiver Alliance, 2012). It is important for family members to understand the scope of the caregiver's duties and the challenges they face (Adelman et al., 2014). This understanding can help foster empathy and encourage participation in caregiving tasks (Joling et al., 2018).

It is also beneficial to establish clear boundaries and roles within the family (Kent et al., 2016). This clarity can prevent misunderstandings and promote a harmonious caregiving environment (Sullivan, 2002). In instances where disagreements or conflicts arise, seeking external assistance such as family therapy or mediation can be a helpful tool to manage and resolve these issues (Sörensen et al., 2002).

The Long-Term Impact of Family Support

The support of family members can have a profound long-term impact on a caregiver's well-being (Gallagher-Thompson et al., 2003). It offers immediate relief and support, but it also fosters a sense of shared responsibility and unity within the family (Gaugler et al., 2009). This sense of togetherness can prevent caregiver isolation and burnout, enhancing the caregiver's resilience and capacity to provide quality care over time (Cheung et al., 2020).

The benefits of family support extend beyond the immediate caregiving situation (Family Caregiver Alliance, 2012). It can strengthen family bonds, improve communication within the family, and enhance the family's ability to cope with future challenges (Adelman et al., 2014). Moreover, the shared experiences of caregiving can deepen mutual understanding among family members, creating a more robust support network for the caregiver overall (Joling et al., 2018).

Community Support

The Role of Community in Supporting Caregivers

Communities can provide critical assistance for caregivers, offering resources that give practical help, emotional backing, and chances to connect socially (Brown & Ruggiano, 2022). These aids can help caregivers feel less secluded and overwhelmed, providing necessary rest and reinforcement in their caregiving path.

The community's part in supporting caregivers can be diverse. Fundamentally, the community can give a sense of belonging and comprehension, reassuring caregivers they are not alone on their journey. This feeling of belonging can be emotionally comforting, decreasing isolation and helplessness (Kumar et al., 2022).

Support groups are a pivotal community resource for caregivers. These groups can be a safe space to share experiences and trials, learn from other similar situations, and gain emotional assistance (Llanque et al., 2016). Hospitals, mental health programs, places of worship, and caregiver organizations often host support groups, providing an accessible and supportive setting.

In addition to emotional gains, these support groups can also provide practical advice and tactics for managing caregiving duties. Participants can share tips on navigating healthcare, managing care routines, and balancing caregiving with life (Rainville et al., 2022). This practical input can be invaluable in improving efficiency and success in roles.

Practical Support from the Community

Communities can also give tangible, practical support to caregivers in many forms, depending on available resources (Malhotra et al., 2022). Some communities may have adult day programs for daytime care, providing respite. Home care services could assist with caregiving tasks professionally.

Volunteer respite care providers can offer temporary relief, allowing caregivers to rest, recharge, and focus on themselves (Junger et al., 2021). This could involve volunteers providing care for hours or days.

Programs like Meals on Wheels can deliver nutritious meals, easing meal preparation burdens (Thomas et al., 2022). This can be especially helpful for caregivers struggling to balance duties.

Many governments and non-profit organizations provide online search tools to locate local resources, significantly easing practical demands and freeing up time and energy for self-care and responsibilities.

Navigating Community Resources

While community resources can be beneficial, navigating them can be complex. The vast options, uncertainty about fit, and confusion about criteria and costs can be daunting (Cumming et al., 2022).

However, caregivers do not have to go alone. Many communities offer professionals like social workers, psychologists, or community health workers to assist in the process. These experts can identify needs, guide resource selection, and facilitate access (Eifert et al., 2015).

For example, a social worker can navigate insurance or government aid intricacies, provide eligibility data, assist with paperwork, and advocate in disputes.

Similarly, mental health experts like psychologists or counselors can provide emotional assistance (Au et al., 2018). They can aid coping, self-care strategies, and direct caregivers to local mental health resources like groups or counseling.

Online platforms can also be a useful navigation tool, aggregating local resource data, descriptions, and reviews. Online groups allow caregivers to share recommendations and experiences.

Despite challenges, investing time to understand and use community resources can significantly ease caregiving demands, providing relief and support.

The Long-Term Impact of Community Support

Long-term community support impacts on caregivers can be profound. By providing practical help, emotional backing, and social links, community resources can reduce stress, improve mental health, and build resilience (Lee et al., 2022).

Over time, consistent resource use can improve overall well-being and help maintain balance, reducing burnout risk and improving care capacity.

Furthermore, the connection and belonging from community involvement can have lasting effects, fostering understanding and empathy, and creating a more supportive setting.

Community support can transform caregivers by enhancing health, improving quality of life, and increasing care capacity. Therefore, caregivers should be encouraged to utilize their community and seek support when required.

3.4: Appraisal of Caregiver Educational Needs and Development of Tailored Interventions

Caregiving is a complex role often assumed by family members or friends providing crucial support to loved ones (Bom et al., 2019). This unpaid position requires substantial emotional, physical, and financial commitments, potentially resulting in caregiver burden (Chiao et al., 2015). Caregiver burden encompasses objective components, like financial strain, and subjective aspects, including emotional distress (Chwalisz & Kisler, 1995).

If unresolved, caregiving challenges can lead to heightened stress, fatigue, and burnout, significantly impacting caregiver well-being and care quality (Tartaglini et al., 2022). Therefore, appraising caregiver educational needs and developing tailored interventions is critical for effective caregiving.

Comprehensively evaluating caregiver needs provides the foundation for relevant education and training (Gérain & Zech, 2019). Caregivers require knowledge and skills to deliver quality care, necessitating ongoing guidance and support (Goins et al., 2013). Identifying specific educational needs enables personalized interventions catering to each caregiver's unique circumstances (McMillan et al., 2006). Further, this approach emphasizes continuous learning and adaptability as responsibilities evolve (Judge et al., 2010).

Given caregiving's long-term nature, consistent support is vital, including regular needs assessments, skill-building, and emotional support to prevent burnout (Kent et al., 2016). Adequately prepared caregivers can better manage responsibilities, ensuring optimal care for loved ones (Ornstein et al., 2017).

Unveiling Educational Needs

The first step in addressing caregiver burden is identifying the educational needs of caregivers. These needs may vary based on the caregiver's experience, the patient's condition, and the caregiver's personal circumstances and capacity. Identification of these needs is crucial as it sets the stage for the development of tailored interventions (Petriwskyj et al., 2022).

Caregivers often need to understand the medical condition of their loved ones to provide adequate care. This includes knowledge about medication, symptoms, progression of the disease, and complications (Gérain & Zech, 2019). Furthermore, caregivers may need to learn specific skills such as administering medication, assisting with physical therapy exercises, or managing medical equipment (Spelten et al., 2020).

In addition to medical knowledge and skills, caregivers also need to develop emotional coping strategies. Caregiving can be an emotionally taxing process, leading to feelings of stress, anxiety, and sadness (Li et al., 2022). Emotional coping strategies can help caregivers manage these feelings and prevent burnout (Wilde & Sonley, 2021).

Moreover, caregivers often need to navigate complex healthcare systems and advocate for their loved ones. This involves understanding insurance policies, communicating effectively with healthcare providers, and making informed decisions about care (Hawranik et al., 2022). Hence, caregivers may require education in these areas to effectively navigate the healthcare system (Reinhard et al., 2020).

Caregivers may also have unique needs based on their personal circumstances such as balancing caregiving with work or caring for other family members (Stewart et al., 2021). These needs should also be considered when identifying the educational needs of caregivers.

Strategies for Assessment

Assessing the educational needs of caregivers involves multiple strategies. These strategies should be comprehensive, considering the multifaceted nature of the caregiving role. The assessment should explore the caregiver's knowledge about the patient's condition, their caregiving skills, their emotional coping strategies, and their navigation of the healthcare system (Gérain & Zech, 2019).

One effective way to assess caregivers' educational needs is through validated assessment tools. These tools are designed to comprehensively capture the various aspects of caregiving and can provide valuable insights into the caregiver's needs (Roth et al., 2015). They usually involve questionnaires or surveys that caregivers can complete, providing a structured format for assessment.

In-person assessments are another effective strategy. Healthcare professionals can conduct interviews or discussions with caregivers to understand their needs (Spelten et al., 2020). In-person assessments allow for a more personalized approach and can capture nuances that may be missed in structured assessment tools.

Home visits can also be a useful strategy for assessment. By observing caregivers in their home environment, healthcare professionals can gain insights into the practical challenges caregivers face and the skills they may need to improve (Reinhard et al., 2020).

Support groups can also be valuable in assessing caregivers' educational needs. These groups can provide a platform for caregivers to share their experiences and challenges, providing insights into common issues that may need to be addressed (Hawranik et al., 2022).

Continuous monitoring and reassessment are crucial as caregivers' needs may change over time. This involves regular check-ins and updates to ensure that the educational interventions remain relevant and effective (Petriwskyj et al., 2022).

From Assessment to Intervention

After assessing caregivers' educational needs, interventions can be developed to address these needs. These interventions should be tailored to the individual caregiver's needs and circumstances, ensuring that they are relevant and effective (Gérain & Zech, 2019).

Psychoeducational interventions can be a helpful tool for caregivers. These interventions focus on providing caregivers with information about the patient's condition and teaching them skills to manage caregiving tasks (Li et al., 2022). These interventions can be delivered through various modalities such as workshops, online courses, or one-on-one sessions.

Emotional support is another important intervention that can help caregivers manage the emotional stress associated with caregiving. This can include counseling services, stress management techniques, or mindfulness practices (Wilde & Sonley, 2021). These interventions can help caregivers develop coping strategies and prevent burnout.

Support groups can also be an effective intervention. These groups provide a platform for caregivers to share their experiences, learn from others, and receive emotional support (Hawranik et al., 2022). They can be particularly helpful in addressing feelings of isolation that caregivers may experience.

Respite care is another crucial intervention for caregivers. This involves providing temporary relief to caregivers, allowing them to rest and recharge (Reinhard et al., 2020). Respite care can be provided by other family members, friends, or professional caregiving services. It can be particularly helpful in preventing caregiver burnout and ensuring the sustainability of the caregiving role.

Continuous education and training are important interventions for caregivers. As the patient's condition changes, caregivers may need to learn new skills or gain more knowledge (Petriwskyj et al., 2022). Continuous education ensures that caregivers are equipped to handle these changes and provide effective care.

Beyond Immediate Educational Needs

Caregiving is a long-term responsibility, and caregivers' needs may evolve over time. Therefore, it is essential to go beyond immediate educational needs and develop a long-term plan for caregiver education and support (Spelten et al., 2020).

Ongoing assessment of caregivers' needs is crucial. Regular check-ins and reassessments can ensure that the educational interventions remain relevant and effective (Petriwskyj et al., 2022). They can also help identify new needs that may arise over time.

Continuous education and training should be provided to caregivers. This can involve workshops, online courses, or one-on-one sessions (Li et al., 2022). Continuous education ensures that caregivers are equipped with the latest knowledge and skills to provide effective care.

Emotional support should be provided on an ongoing basis. Caregiving can be emotionally challenging, and caregivers may need continuous support to manage these challenges (Wilde & Sonley, 2021). This can involve counseling services, support groups, or stress management techniques.

Respite care should be a part of the long-term plan. Providing caregivers with regular breaks can prevent burnout and ensure the sustainability of the caregiving role (Reinhard et al., 2020). Respite care can be provided by other family members, friends, or professional caregiving services.

Advocacy and support in navigating the healthcare system should be provided (Hawranik et al., 2022). Caregivers often need to advocate for their loved ones and make important decisions about their care. Providing caregivers with the necessary knowledge and support in this area can help them effectively navigate the healthcare system.

Addressing Caregiver Burnout

Caregiver burnout is a significant problem that can lead to physical, psychological, and social issues (Kent et al., 2020). It is therefore essential to address caregiver burnout in the development of caregiver educational interventions.

The first step in addressing caregiver burnout is awareness. Caregivers often ignore their own needs and focus solely on the needs of their loved ones

(Hartke et al., 2021). Raising awareness of caregiver burnout and its signs can help caregivers recognize when they need help.

Emotional support can help manage caregiver burnout. Counseling services, support groups, and stress management techniques can provide caregivers with the emotional support they need to cope with the challenges of caregiving (McClellan et al., 2020).

Respite care is a crucial part of preventing caregiver burnout. By providing temporary relief to caregivers, respite care allows them to rest and recharge, preventing burnout (Tretteteig et al., 2021).

Self-care strategies should be taught to caregivers. This can involve teaching them techniques for managing stress, maintaining a healthy diet, getting regular exercise, and ensuring adequate sleep (Hartke et al., 2021). These strategies can boost caregivers' physical and mental health and help prevent burnout.

It is important to create a supportive environment for caregivers. This can involve providing them with the necessary resources, creating a supportive community of other caregivers, and advocating for their rights and needs (McClellan et al., 2020). This supportive environment can help caregivers feel valued and supported, reducing the risk of burnout.

Addressing guilt and grief is key. Caregivers often experience guilt over feeling burnt out and grief over role changes (Tretteteig et al., 2021). Validating these feelings can help caregivers cope.

Ongoing support is essential. Regular check-ins, counseling, and support groups help caregivers manage stress and prevent burnout over the long term (Kent et al., 2020).

Caregiver education and support are crucial in managing caregiver burden and preventing caregiver burnout (Hartke et al., 2021). By identifying caregivers' needs, developing interventions, and providing ongoing support, caregivers can be better equipped to provide effective care while protecting their own well-being.

3.5: Leveraging Assessment Instruments for Comprehensive Caregiver Needs Analysis

In the context of an aging global population and the increasing prevalence of chronic illnesses, the role of caregivers has become increasingly crucial (Bom et al., 2019). These caregivers, often family members, or close friends, provide a lifeline of support to those needing care. However, the task of caregiving often extends beyond simply meeting the physical needs of the care recipient. It involves a complex interplay of emotional, psychological, and social components, all of which can exert significant pressure on the caregiver (Chen et al., 2020).

The potential strain on a caregiver's physical and emotional health, coupled with the possible impact on their social and financial circumstances, underscores the need for robust, comprehensive support systems (Bom et al., 2019). These systems, however, can only be as effective as the understanding of the caregiver's unique needs and challenges that underlies them. Therefore, the use of thorough, targeted assessment tools is of paramount importance in the quest to support caregivers effectively (Dam et al., 2016).

Assessment tools designed with caregivers in mind can offer in-depth insights into their unique challenges, stresses, and needs (Chen et al., 2020). These insights can then inform the design and implementation of comprehensive caregiver support programs, ensuring that these programs are tailored to address the needs of each individual caregiver. By leveraging these tools effectively, we can enhance our ability to support caregivers in their essential roles while protecting their own health and well-being (Dam et al., 2016).

Here, we will aim to explore how these tools can be effectively utilized. It delves into the role of comprehensive caregiver support programs, the function and use of assessment tools, and the unique perspective of caregivers themselves (Bom et al., 2019). The goal is to equip caregivers, psychologists, and healthcare providers with the knowledge and skills required to ensure that caregiver needs are accurately understood and effectively addressed.

Comprehensive Caregiver Support Programs

Understanding the Role of Support Programs

Increasingly, comprehensive caregiver support programs have emerged as a response to the escalating demand for caregiving. These programs are designed to empower caregivers by providing them with the necessary tools, resources, and support that they need to fulfill their caregiving responsibilities effectively (Dam et al., 2017). The role of these programs is crucial in alleviating the potential stress and strain associated with caregiving (Kent et al., 2020).

Caregiving, by its nature, is an intricate task that often requires the management of medical, emotional, and logistical challenges. As a result, caregivers often face significant physical, emotional, and financial stressors (Reinhard et al., 2020). Comprehensive caregiver support programs are designed to address these challenges, offering a wide array of services that include education and training, respite care, mental health services, and assistance with navigating complex healthcare and social service systems (Dam et al., 2017).

The educational component of these programs often focuses on equipping caregivers with the practical knowledge and skills they need to provide care. This could include training in medical procedures, medication management, mobility assistance, and other care-related tasks (Li et al., 2022). The goal of this training is to increase caregiver competence and confidence, thereby reducing the stress associated with caregiving tasks (Kent et al., 2020).

Respite care services, another key component of caregiver support programs, provide temporary relief for caregivers, allowing them to take a break from their caregiving responsibilities (Tretteteig et al., 2021). This break can be essential for caregiver well-being, preventing burnout and promoting overall mental health. Respite care can take various forms, including in-home care, adult day care, or even short-term residential care (Reinhard et al., 2020).

Comprehensive caregiver support programs also provide mental health services and assistance in navigating healthcare and social service systems (Dam et al., 2017). Given the emotional toll that caregiving can take, access to counseling and other mental health services is vital. Similarly, guidance in navigating the often-complex healthcare and social service systems can reduce caregiver stress and ensure that care recipients receive the services they need (Kent et al., 2020).

The effectiveness of caregiver support programs hinges on their ability to meet the unique needs of each caregiver (Li et al., 2022). This necessitates a thorough understanding of the unique challenges each caregiver faces, which can be facilitated using specific assessment tools designed to evaluate caregiver needs.

Assessment tools allow for a structured approach to collecting relevant data, enabling a comprehensive understanding of the caregiver's situation (Tretteteig et al., 2021). These tools can assess various aspects of the caregiver's life, including their physical health, mental health, social support, financial situation, and the specific caregiving tasks they are responsible for.

By identifying areas where caregivers experience the most stress or strain, these tools provide valuable insights into where support is most needed (Reinhard et al., 2020). For instance, a caregiver who is physically exhausted may benefit most from respite care or physical health interventions. In contrast, a caregiver struggling with feelings of isolation may need more social support or mental health services.

Moreover, it is important to note that caregiver needs can evolve over time (Dam et al., 2017). A caregiver's situation can change due to factors such as changes in the health status of the care recipient, changes in the caregiver's personal life, or the development of caregiver burnout. Therefore, ongoing assessment is crucial to continually tailor the support provided to match the caregiver's current needs (Kent et al., 2020).

The Role of Assessment Tools in Support Programs

Assessment tools are integral to the design and implementation of comprehensive caregiver support programs (Li et al., 2022). By offering a clear understanding of the caregiver's needs and challenges, these tools enable the creation of targeted, individualized support strategies.

These strategies are then incorporated into the caregiver support program, ensuring that the services and resources provided align closely with the caregiver's unique needs (Tretteteig et al., 2021). This alignment not only enhances the effectiveness of the support program but also ensures efficient use of resources.

The use of assessment tools also allows for tracking progress and evaluating the effectiveness of the support program (Reinhard et al., 2020). By comparing assessment data collected at different points in time, it is possible to see whether the caregiver's stress levels, overall health, and well-being are improving. This ongoing evaluation can inform necessary adjustments to the program, further enhancing its effectiveness and ensuring it continues to meet the caregiver's evolving needs (Dam et al., 2017).

The Long-Term Impact of Comprehensive Support Programs

The effectiveness of comprehensive caregiver support programs can have a profound long-term impact on both caregivers and care recipients (Kent et al., 2020). For caregivers, these programs not only help to reduce stress and prevent burnout but also can significantly improve their overall well-being.

By providing caregivers with the necessary knowledge, skills, and resources, these programs enable them to deliver high-quality care consistently and sustainably (Li et al., 2022). This greater consistency and sustainability can lead to improved health outcomes for care recipients, offering tangible benefits such as better management of chronic conditions, fewer hospitalizations, and an overall higher quality of life (Tretteteig et al., 2021).

Furthermore, by reducing caregiver stress and preventing burnout, these programs can also contribute to a better quality of life for caregivers themselves (Reinhard et al., 2020). The role of a caregiver can often be isolating and emotionally draining, leading to mental health challenges such as anxiety and depression. Through providing mental health support, along with practical tools and resources, these programs can promote better emotional health and overall well-being for caregivers.

In addition to improving mental health, comprehensive caregiver support programs can also promote better physical health for caregivers (Dam et al., 2017). The physical demands of caregiving, along with the stress associated with the role, can lead to a range of health issues, from chronic pain to heart disease. By providing respite care, physical health resources, and stress management techniques, caregiver support programs can help to mitigate these risks.

Beyond the immediate health benefits, there are also long-term financial benefits associated with comprehensive caregiver support programs (Kent et al., 2020). By empowering caregivers with the skills and knowledge to provide high-quality care, these programs can reduce the need for professional care services or institutional care, leading to significant cost savings. Moreover, by reducing caregiver stress and improving their health, these programs can also reduce healthcare costs associated with caregiver illness.

The long-term impact of comprehensive caregiver support programs extends beyond the individual caregiver and care recipient to benefit society (Li et al., 2022). By supporting caregivers in their role, these programs can enhance the overall quality of care provided in the community, reduce healthcare costs, and promote better health and well-being for all.

The effectiveness of a caregiver support program, however, is not a static measure (Tretteteig et al., 2021). It requires continual evaluation and adjustment to ensure it remains aligned with the evolving needs of caregivers. This commitment to ongoing improvement is what enables these programs to continue delivering significant long-term benefits for caregivers, care recipients, and the broader community (Reinhard et al., 2020).

Caregiver Perspectives

Valuable Insights from Caregivers

Caregivers, by virtue of their role, are often the closest observers of their care recipients' health, behavior, and needs. Their daily involvement in caregiving positions them uniquely to provide essential insights into the challenges and rewards of their role (Kent et al., 2020). These insights, often overlooked in formal healthcare settings, can serve as a rich source of information for designing better support interventions and policies for caregivers.

By closely observing caregivers, we can develop a deeper understanding of their needs, motivations, and coping strategies (Chen et al., 2020). Some caregivers may struggle with the emotional burden of caregiving, while others may find it difficult to navigate the complexities of the healthcare system. Understanding these nuanced experiences can help in the design of support interventions that are more in line with the realities faced by caregivers (Reinhard et al., 2020).

Moreover, caregivers' perspectives can also help identify strengths and successful strategies that they employ in their roles (Li et al., 2022). These can be leveraged to inform other caregivers and healthcare professionals about effective techniques and approaches to caregiving. For example, caregivers often develop unique strategies to manage care recipients' behaviors or to communicate effectively with healthcare providers. Sharing these strategies can improve caregiving practices across the board.

Furthermore, caregivers often provide insights into the resources they find most useful (Tretteteig et al., 2021). Whether it is community support groups, online resources, or respite care services, understanding what works for caregivers can help refine these offerings and make them more accessible. This can significantly enhance the quality of support provided to caregivers, helping them manage their roles more effectively.

Caregivers can provide an in-depth understanding of the specific challenges faced by different types of caregivers (Dam et al., 2016). For instance, the needs and experiences of a young caregiver looking after a parent may be vastly different from an older spouse caring for their partner. Recognizing these differences can help develop more tailored and effective support services for diverse caregiver groups.

Influence on Healthcare Advances

Caregivers' experiences and insights can have far-reaching implications for healthcare advances. Their firsthand accounts can shed light on the gaps in current healthcare services and highlight areas that require improvement or innovation (Kent et al., 2020). Notably, their perspectives can serve as a catalyst for change in healthcare practices, policies, and services.

For instance, caregivers often witness the impact of various treatment regimens on their loved ones' quality of life. They are privy to side effects, the effectiveness of treatments, and the psychological and physical toll of chronic illnesses (Chen et al., 2020). This information can be invaluable in refining treatment protocols, improving patient outcomes, and enhancing quality of life for both patients and caregivers.

Caregivers interact with various facets of the healthcare system, from hospitals and clinics to pharmacies and home health agencies. Their experiences can highlight inefficiencies, bureaucratic hurdles, and areas lacking in patient-centric care (Reinhard et al., 2020). These insights can guide healthcare organizations towards more streamlined and empathetic service delivery.

Additionally, caregivers also identify unmet needs in healthcare delivery. This could be in the form of services that are not available, resources that are difficult to access, or aspects of care that are overlooked (Li et al., 2022). By sharing these perspectives, caregivers can significantly contribute to the development of new services and policies tailored to these needs.

Furthermore, caregivers' perspectives can also influence technological advancements in healthcare. For instance, caregivers may express a need for better care coordination tools, remote monitoring devices, or mobile applications that provide health information (Tretteteig et al., 2021). Such insights can guide the development of health technologies that make caregiving more manageable and efficient.

Caregivers also play a crucial role in advocating for policy changes. Their experiences highlight the need for better support at the policy level, whether it is improved access to healthcare, financial support, or legal protections (Dam et al., 2016). By voicing these needs, caregivers can influence policy decisions that have a direct impact on the quality of care and support available to them and their loved ones.

Ongoing Process

The role of a caregiver is not static but evolves over time. As the health and needs of the care recipient change, so too does the caregiver's role and needs (Kent et al., 2020). This dynamic nature of caregiving necessitates an ongoing process for caregiver needs analysis, ensuring that support interventions remain relevant and responsive.

Continuous assessment allows for the timely identification of emerging issues or challenges (Chen et al., 2020). For example, a caregiver may initially find their role manageable but may struggle as the care recipient's health deteriorates. Regular reassessment can identify such changes early, enabling timely intervention and support to help the caregiver adapt.

Moreover, the ongoing assessment process can also capture changes in the caregiver's personal life that may impact their ability to provide care (Reinhard et al., 2020). For instance, changes in employment, family situation, or physical health can significantly affect a caregiver's capacity. By regularly monitoring these aspects, support interventions can be adjusted to align with the caregiver's changing circumstances.

This ongoing process also plays a crucial role in maintaining the health and well-being of caregivers. The stress and demands of caregiving can often take a toll on caregivers' mental and physical health (Li et al., 2022). Regular monitoring of stress levels, mental health, and physical well-being can help identify potential health issues early.

The proactive management of caregivers' health is vital, as minor health issues can quickly escalate if left unaddressed (Tretteteig et al., 2021). By identifying and addressing these issues early, caregivers can maintain their health, even amidst the demands of caregiving. This proactive approach ensures that caregivers can continue to provide care without compromising their own well-being.

An ongoing assessment process allows for the continuous refinement of support interventions (Dam et al., 2016). As we gather more information about caregivers' needs and experiences, we can continue to improve and tailor the support available. This iterative process ensures that interventions remain effective and relevant, providing caregivers with the best possible support.

Leveraging Assessment Instruments for Comprehensive Caregiver Needs Analysis

Comprehensive caregiver needs analysis is a critical process in supporting caregivers. Various assessment tools can provide a nuanced understanding of the unique challenges each caregiver faces (Kent et al., 2020). These tools, when used effectively, can guide the development of tailored support interventions that address individual needs.

Assessment tools can range from questionnaires and surveys that capture caregivers' subjective experiences, to more objective measures such as stress indices or health status indicators (Chen et al., 2020). The choice of tools should be guided by the specific objectives of the needs analysis, as well as the resources available for assessment.

For instance, in-depth interviews or focus groups can provide a rich understanding of caregivers' experiences and needs (Reinhard et al., 2020). They allow for exploratory discussions that can uncover nuanced insights into the challenges and rewards of caregiving. However, these methods can be time-consuming and resource intensive.

On the other hand, standardized questionnaires or surveys can be more efficient for gathering data from a large number of caregivers (Li et al., 2022). They can provide quantifiable data on various aspects of caregiving, such as the level of burden, coping strategies, or caregiver health. However, they may not capture the depth and richness of caregivers' experiences as effectively as qualitative methods.

Moreover, it is important to consider the diversity of caregivers when selecting assessment tools (Tretteteig et al., 2021). Diverse types of caregivers may face unique challenges, and these should be reflected in the assessment. For example, the needs of a spouse caregiver may be different from those of a child caregiver or a professional caregiver.

A combination of different assessment methods may be most effective in capturing a comprehensive understanding of caregiver needs (Dam et al., 2016). This mixed-methods approach allows for the capture of both breadth and depth of information, providing a holistic view of caregivers' experiences and needs.

By leveraging these assessment tools, we can gain a deeper understanding of the realities of caregiving. This understanding, combined with the valuable insights provided by caregivers themselves, can guide the development of effective support interventions. By adopting an ongoing approach to needs analysis, we can ensure that caregivers receive the support they need, when they need it, enhancing their ability to provide care and maintain their own well-being.

Maintaining Health Despite Challenges

Continuous assessment also plays a crucial role in maintaining the health and well-being of caregivers (Kent et al., 2020). By regularly monitoring their stress levels, mental health, and physical well-being, potential health issues can be identified and addressed early. This proactive approach to health management can prevent minor issues from escalating into serious health problems, ensuring caregivers can maintain their health even amidst the demands of caregiving.

Leveraging assessment instruments for comprehensive caregiver needs analysis is a vital process in supporting caregivers (Chen et al., 2020). Assessment tools, when used effectively, can provide a nuanced understanding of the unique challenges each caregiver faces, guiding the development of tailored support interventions.

Caregiver perspectives further enrich this understanding, providing valuable insights into the realities of caregiving (Reinhard et al., 2020). By adopting an ongoing approach to needs analysis, caregivers can receive the support they need, when they need it, ensuring they can continue to provide care without compromising their own well-being (Li et al., 2022).

However, it is important to recognize that the caregiving journey often spans many years and caregivers' needs may change over time (Kent et al., 2020). Regular reassessment is key to ensure support interventions adapt accordingly.

For instance, caregivers may take on more complex medical tasks as a care recipient's health declines, requiring additional training and support (Chen et al., 2020). Or their own physical capacity may diminish due to aging, necessitating ergonomic aids, respite care, and other assistance (Tretteteig et al., 2021).

Major life events can also impact caregivers' ability to continue providing care. Retirement, having a baby, or family relocations may require adjustments in support services (Dam et al., 2016). It is vital to continuously evaluate how these changes affect caregivers.

Grief support is also an evolving need as bereavement approaches or after a care recipient passes away. Feelings of loss, stress from adjustments in routine, and financial concerns require validation and assistance (Reinhard et al., 2020).

Caregivers give so much of themselves in their roles. It is imperative that our systems of support give back through understanding their experiences and perspectives, assess their needs comprehensively over time, and adapt interventions accordingly (Li et al., 2022). This empowers caregivers to provide the best care while maintaining their own health and well-being.

The caregiving journey is a dynamic one, and our approaches to needs analysis must be similarly responsive (Kent et al., 2020). By making caregivers' needs and voices central to this process, we uphold them as partners and ensure caregiving is a sustainable and rewarding experience (Chen et al., 2020). This benefits caregivers, care recipients, and our communities (Tretteteig et al., 2021).

Strategies for Assessment

The Necessity of Assessment Tools

Assessment tools in the context of caregiving serve as invaluable instruments to gauge the educational needs and stressors of caregivers. These mechanisms are essential in the healthcare landscape as they offer a structured and systematic way to identify the challenges caregivers encounter, their coping mechanisms, and their support needs (Bom et al., 2019). By leveraging these tools, healthcare providers can obtain a nuanced understanding of caregivers' experiences that goes beyond the surface level (Kent et al., 2020).

Moreover, assessment tools can help map the caregiving journey, thereby shedding light on the specific stressors that caregivers may face at various stages (Chen et al., 2020). This can include the initial stages of caregiving, where the role might be new and unfamiliar, through to the later stages, where burnout can become a significant issue. Hence, assessment tools can inform healthcare providers about the most pressing needs of caregivers at every stage of their journey (Reinhard et al., 2020).

These tools also provide a quantitative measure that can be used to track changes over time (Li et al., 2022). This can help identify whether a caregiver's situation is improving, remaining consistent, or deteriorating. This type of longitudinal data can be immensely helpful in identifying long-term trends and predicting future needs or challenges (Tretteteig et al., 2021).

Furthermore, the use of these tools promotes active involvement of the caregivers in their own health and well-being (Dam et al., 2016). By participating in assessments, caregivers can engage in self-reflection about their situation, potentially leading to greater self-awareness and empowerment.

Assessment tools offer a structured way for healthcare providers to collect information, ensuring that key areas of caregiver well-being are not overlooked (Bom et al., 2019). This thorough, systematic approach can help ensure that caregivers receive the comprehensive support they need.

Psychometrically Valid Tools

Psychometrically valid tools such as the Philadelphia Geriatric Center Caregiving Appraisal Scale are extremely effective for assessing various facets of the caregiving experience (Kent et al., 2020). This tool, in particular, is designed to measure the subjective experience of caregiving, encompassing positive and negative aspects.

The use of psychometrically validated tools ensures the reliability and validity of the data collected, which is crucial for developing evidence-based interventions (Chen et al., 2020). These tools have been tested for their ability to accurately and consistently measure what they are intended to, providing confidence in the results they produce.

The Philadelphia Geriatric Center Caregiving Appraisal Scale, for instance, considers several dimensions of caregiving including stressors, self-esteem, satisfaction, and the impact of caregiving on the caregiver's personal life (Reinhard et al., 2020). By using this comprehensive approach, healthcare providers can gain a well-rounded understanding of the caregiver's needs.

Moreover, these tools offer a standardized way to evaluate and compare caregiver experiences (Li et al., 2022). This can be particularly useful when looking at caregiver experiences across different settings, populations, or time periods. It also enables healthcare providers to identify common trends or patterns, which can inform the development of general interventions (Tretteteig et al., 2021).

In addition, these tools can help identify high-risk caregivers who may be experiencing significant stress or burnout (Dam et al., 2016). Early identification of these individuals can allow for timely interventions, potentially preventing the development of physical and/or mental health problems.

Role of Family Nurse Practitioners

Family nurse practitioners (FNPs) occupy a pivotal position in the healthcare system when it comes to supporting caregivers. Their all-encompassing understanding of family dynamics, health issues, and medical care equips them with the tools to provide comprehensive support to caregivers (Bom et al., 2019).

FNPs, with their wide-ranging skill set, are well-placed to assess the needs of caregivers (Kent et al., 2020). They can identify potential stressors, gaps in knowledge, and areas where caregivers may need additional support or education. This can include practical aspects of caregiving, such as managing medications or performing physical care tasks, as well as emotional aspects, like coping with stress and managing difficult emotions (Chen et al., 2020).

In addition to performing assessments, FNPs can also play a key role in delivering interventions (Reinhard et al., 2020). Their close relationship with the caregivers and their unique understanding of each family's circumstances can help ensure that interventions are tailored to the caregivers' specific needs and circumstances.

FNPs are often a trusted source of information and support for caregivers (Li et al., 2022). They can provide accurate, up-to-date information about the patient's health condition and care needs, as well as advice on how to manage common caregiving challenges. This can help reduce caregiver stress and increase their confidence in their caregiving role (Tretteteig et al., 2021).

FNPs can serve as a bridge between caregivers and the wider healthcare system (Dam et al., 2016). They can advocate for the caregivers' needs to other healthcare providers and help coordinate care, ensuring that caregivers receive the support they need.

Survey and Feedback

Surveys and feedback forms serve as an accessible and straightforward method for assessing caregivers' needs (Bom et al., 2019). By asking caregivers about their experiences, healthcare providers can gain a comprehensive understanding of the caregiver's educational needs, their challenges, and the kind of support they desire (Kent et al., 2020).

Surveys can provide a snapshot of the caregiver's current situation, including their perceived strengths, weaknesses, and areas of need (Chen et al., 2020). Moreover, by asking open-ended questions, surveys can capture the caregiver's voice and personal experience, providing valuable qualitative data that can inform intervention development (Reinhard et al., 2020).

Surveys also offer an opportunity for caregivers to express their views and concerns in a structured, anonymous manner (Li et al., 2022). This can be particularly helpful for caregivers who may feel uncomfortable discussing certain issues in a face-to-face context. Anonymity can encourage honesty and openness, leading to more accurate assessment results (Tretteteig et al., 2021).

Feedback forms, on the other hand, can be used to gather caregivers' opinions about the support they have received so far (Dam et al., 2016). This feedback can provide insights into what is working well and what could be improved. By continually seeking and responding to feedback, healthcare providers can ensure that their support services are meeting caregivers' needs and expectations.

Moreover, surveys and feedback forms can be administered repeatedly over time, allowing healthcare providers to monitor changes in caregivers' needs and experiences (Bom et al., 2019). This can help identify emerging issues or trends, as well as assess the effectiveness of interventions.

Early Identification and Intervention

Early identification of caregiver burden is crucial for the prevention of negative health outcomes (Kent et al., 2020). Caregiver stress, if left unchecked, can lead to a range of physical and mental health problems, including depression, anxiety, and burnout. It can also impact the quality of care provided to the patient, potentially leading to adverse outcomes for both the caregiver and the patient (Chen et al., 2020).

Assessment strategies can play a vital role in the early identification of caregiver burden (Reinhard et al., 2020). Regular assessments can help detect signs of stress or burnout early on, providing an opportunity for timely intervention. This early intervention can potentially mitigate the severity of caregiver burden and prevent the development of more serious health problems (Li et al., 2022).

Early identification can also help healthcare providers to better understand the trajectory of caregiver burden (Tretteteig et al., 2021). It can provide insights into how caregiver stress develops and changes over time, which can inform the timing and type of interventions provided.

Early identification and intervention can enhance the caregiver's self-awareness and coping skills (Dam et al., 2016). By recognizing the signs of stress and burnout early on, caregivers can be better equipped to seek help and implement self-care strategies.

From Assessment to Intervention

Once the assessment process has identified areas where the caregiver needs additional support, tailored interventions can be developed (Bom et al., 2019). These interventions should be based on the caregiver's specific needs and could encompass a range of strategies, from providing information and education to offering practical training in caregiving skills (Kent et al., 2020).

The development of tailored interventions is a dynamic process that requires careful consideration of the caregiver's unique circumstances and needs (Chen et al., 2020). It involves taking the information gathered during the assessment and using it to devise a plan of action that addresses the caregiver's identified needs in a targeted and personalized way (Reinhard et al., 2020).

One key aspect of tailored interventions is providing relevant and accessible information (Li et al., 2022). Caregivers often have a range of questions about the patient's condition, treatment options, and care needs. By providing accurate, up-to-date information in a format that the caregiver can easily understand, healthcare providers can help reduce uncertainty and stress (Tretteteig et al., 2021).

Practical training in caregiving skills is another key component of tailored interventions (Dam et al., 2016). Many caregivers have little or no prior experience in caregiving when they take on the role (Bom et al., 2019). Therefore, providing training in essential caregiving skills, such as how to safely move and handle the patient, administer medications, and manage symptoms, can increase caregivers' confidence and competence (Kent et al., 2020).

Delivery Modes

The mode of delivery for caregiver interventions is another important consideration. Different caregivers may have different preferences and needs when it comes to how they receive support (Chen et al., 2020).

Therefore, it is important to offer a range of delivery modes to cater to these diverse needs (Reinhard et al., 2020).

Group sessions can be an effective delivery mode for some caregivers (Li et al., 2022). They provide an opportunity for caregivers to learn from and share experiences with others who are in a comparable situation. This can help reduce feelings of isolation and provide valuable peer support (Tretteteig et al., 2021).

Individual counseling sessions, on the other hand, can be beneficial for caregivers who prefer a more undisclosed setting or who have complex needs that require individual attention (Dam et al., 2016). These sessions can provide a safe space for caregivers to discuss their concerns, explore their feelings, and develop coping strategies.

Online platforms can provide a convenient and flexible option for caregivers who may find it difficult to attend in-person sessions due to time constraints or geographical distance (Bom et al., 2019). They can offer a range of resources, including informational materials, online training modules, and peer support forums (Kent et al., 2020).

Telephone counseling and support lines are another alternative for caregivers who cannot easily access in-person services (Chen et al., 2020). These allow caregivers to get advice and support over the phone from the comfort of their own home. Phone support can be particularly helpful for rural caregivers or those caring for bedbound patients (Reinhard et al., 2020).

Home visits by healthcare providers represent a useful delivery mode for frail or isolated caregivers (Li et al., 2022). Home visits allow providers to observe the caregiving environment, while also saving the caregiver the effort of traveling. This can help ensure that homebound caregivers still receive adequate support and training (Tretteteig et al., 2021).

A multi-modal approach that incorporates different delivery formats can help provide holistic support to diverse caregivers with varying needs and constraints (Dam et al., 2016). The key is offering flexibility and choice in delivery modes to maximize accessibility and effectiveness of interventions.

Support Groups, Respite Care, and Peer Mentoring

Support Groups

Support groups are an invaluable resource for caregivers, providing an outlet for sharing experiences, venting frustrations, and seeking advice (Kent et al., 2020). These groups typically consist of individuals who are in similar situations, providing care for a loved one or friend. They can be found in many communities and online, catering to a variety of caregiving situations, including specific diseases or general caregiving (Chen et al., 2020).

In these support groups, caregivers can find solace in the shared experience (Reinhard et al., 2020). It is a setting where everyone understands the challenges and rewards of caregiving, and where one can express feelings without judgment. Importantly, it can help caregivers realize they are not alone in their journey, which can be comforting and reduce feelings of isolation (Li et al., 2022).

Moreover, support groups are valuable sources of practical tips and strategies (Tretteteig et al., 2021). Caregivers can learn from others who have encountered similar situations or challenges and may have discovered effective ways of dealing with them. This can save caregivers time and energy, and potentially lessen some of the stress that comes with caregiving.

In addition, support groups can also provide emotional support (Dam et al., 2016). Caring for a loved one can be emotionally draining, and having a safe space to express emotions, fears, and frustrations can be therapeutic. Group members often provide empathy, encouragement, and reassurance to one another, which can be very uplifting.

Many support groups also provide educational resources about the specific conditions their members are dealing with (Bom et al., 2019). This can help caregivers better understand the condition, which in turn can help them provide better care and cope with the situation more effectively.

Respite Care

Respite care is a service that provides temporary relief to those who care for family members, particularly those with special needs, serious illnesses, or disabilities (Kent et al., 2020). It can be a lifeline for caregivers, providing a much-needed break from their responsibilities, reducing stress, and preventing burnout.

Respite care can take many forms, and its flexibility is one of its key strengths (Chen et al., 2020). It can be provided in the caregiver's home, allowing the caregiver to leave the house for a few hours or even a few days knowing their loved one is in safe hands. Alternatively, it can take place in a community setting, such as a day care center or a residential care facility (Reinhard et al., 2020).

The duration of respite care can also vary, from a few hours to several weeks (Li et al., 2022). This allows caregivers to take breaks that suit their needs, whether it is to run errands, attend to personal matters, or even go on vacation. Flexibility can also accommodate unexpected emergencies that require the caregiver's attention.

Respite care can also provide additional benefits to the person receiving care (Tretteteig et al., 2021). It can offer them the opportunity to interact with other people, engage in different activities, and experience a change of scenery, all of which can be stimulating and enjoyable.

Importantly, respite care can improve the overall quality of care (Dam et al., 2016). Caregivers who are well-rested and less stressed are likely to be more patient, attentive, and effective in their caregiving role. It can also improve the caregiver's health and well-being, which is important as caregivers often neglect their own needs.

Peer Mentoring Programs

Peer mentoring programs can provide caregivers with one-on-one support from someone who has walked a similar path (Bom et al., 2019). These programs pair a caregiver with a mentor who has had similar experiences and can offer guidance, advice, and emotional support.

One of the main benefits of peer mentoring is the shared experience (Kent et al., 2020). A peer mentor understands firsthand the challenges and emotions that come with caregiving. This deep understanding can provide a unique form of comfort and reassurance that cannot be found elsewhere.

Peer mentors can also offer practical advice based on their own experiences (Chen et al., 2020). Whether it is navigating the healthcare system, managing daily care tasks, or coping with difficult emotions, a peer mentor can offer insights and strategies that have been tested in the real world.

Furthermore, the relationship between the caregiver and the peer mentor can offer a sense of companionship and understanding (Reinhard et al., 2020). It is a partnership rooted in empathy and mutual respect. The caregiver can feel heard and understood, reducing feelings of isolation and loneliness.

Another key advantage of peer mentoring programs is their flexibility (Li et al., 2022). They can be conducted in person, over the phone, or online, making them accessible to caregivers regardless of their location or schedule. The mentoring relationship can also be tailored to the caregiver's needs, whether they need emotional support, practical advice, or both (Tretteteig et al., 2021).

Evaluating the Effectiveness of Interventions

Once interventions have been put in place, it is essential to assess their effectiveness (Dam et al., 2016). This evaluation process should involve several aspects, including follow-up assessments, feedback from the caregiver, and tracking the caregiver's stress levels and overall well-being (Bom et al., 2019).

Follow-up assessments are important to measure the impact of the intervention on the caregiver's situation (Kent et al., 2020). This can involve structured interviews, surveys, or questionnaires that gauge the caregiver's stress levels, coping skills, and overall satisfaction with the intervention (Chen et al., 2020).

Feedback from the caregiver is another crucial component of the evaluation process (Reinhard et al., 2020). The caregiver's perspectives and experiences can provide valuable insights into the intervention's effectiveness, as well as any areas for improvement. This feedback can be gathered through informal conversations, structured feedback sessions, or anonymous surveys (Li et al., 2022).

Monitoring the caregiver's stress levels and overall well-being is also essential (Tretteteig et al., 2021). This involves observing any changes in the caregiver's health, mood, or behavior that might suggest increased stress or burnout. Tools such as stress scales or well-being questionnaires can be helpful in tracking these changes over time (Dam et al., 2016).

Additionally, it can be beneficial to monitor any changes in the caregiving situation itself (Bom et al., 2019). This could include changes in the care recipient's health status, adjustments in the caregiver's other responsibilities, or shifts in the caregiver's support network. These changes can all impact the effectiveness of the intervention and may necessitate modifications (Kent et al., 2020).

It is important to consider the caregiver's sustained engagement with the intervention (Chen et al., 2020). If a caregiver stops attending a support group, using respite care services, or communicating with their peer mentor, it may suggest that the intervention is not meeting their needs or expectations (Reinhard et al., 2020).

Long-Term Support and Intervention Adaptation

Providing long-term support for caregivers is crucial, as their needs and challenges can evolve over time (Li et al., 2022). The caregiving journey is often a marathon, not a sprint, and caregivers may require distinct types of support at various stages (Tretteteig et al., 2021).

For instance, a caregiver may initially need practical training and resources to learn how to provide care (Dam et al., 2016). But as they become more comfortable with their caregiving duties, they may need more emotional support to cope with the ongoing stresses and challenges (Bom et al., 2019). Alternatively, a caregiver may need more respite care as their loved one's condition progresses and caregiving becomes more demanding (Kent et al., 2020).

This emphasizes the need for interventions to be adaptable. As the caregiver's situation changes, the interventions should be adjusted to continue to provide the most effective support (Chen et al., 2020). This might involve changing the frequency or format of support group meetings, adjusting the hours or type of respite care provided, or focusing on different topics in peer mentoring sessions (Reinhard et al., 2020).

Adapting interventions over time requires ongoing communication with the caregiver and regular re-evaluation of their needs and challenges (Li et al., 2022). It is essential to have a system in place for regular check-ins and assessments, and to maintain an open dialogue with the caregiver about their experiences and needs (Tretteteig et al., 2021).

At the same time, it is important to be flexible and responsive. Caregiving situations can change rapidly, and the ability to quickly adjust interventions can make a substantial difference in their effectiveness (Dam et al., 2016). This may require collaboration among different service providers, as well as a willingness to try innovative approaches when necessary (Bom et al., 2019).

Long-term support and adaptive interventions are key to providing effective support for caregivers (Kent et al., 2020). By understanding and responding to caregivers' evolving needs, we can help them navigate their caregiving journey with greater confidence and resilience (Chen et al., 2020).

Beyond Immediate Educational Needs

The Need for Ongoing Education

Caregivers' needs are not static; they evolve along with the progression of their loved ones' health conditions and their own personal growth and adaptation to their roles (Reinhard et al., 2020). The initial educational needs a caregiver may have at the outset of their caregiving journey may not remain the same as time progresses. Consequently, it is vital to develop a long-term plan aimed at meeting these evolving educational needs, which requires a dynamic and adaptive approach (Kent et al., 2020).

To achieve this, regular reassessments of the caregiver's needs should be conducted (Chen et al., 2020). These assessments can help identify new areas where the caregiver may need additional training or support and can serve as an opportunity to reevaluate the effectiveness of the current support plan. This ongoing evaluation process enables healthcare providers to ensure that the caregiver is equipped with the most relevant and up-to-date knowledge and skills (Li et al., 2022).

The provision of ongoing education and training should be an integral part of this long-term plan (Tretteteig et al., 2021). This education can come in various forms, ranging from formal training programs to informal learning opportunities. It could involve teaching caregivers' new skills, updating them on the latest research and best practices, or providing them with resources to learn more about specific aspects of caregiving.

Furthermore, it is important to consider the caregiver's personal circumstances and learning preferences when developing an ongoing education plan (Dam et al., 2016). Some caregivers may prefer learning in a group setting, while others may prefer one-on-one instruction. Some may prefer in-person learning, while others may find online or self-paced learning more convenient. By tailoring the education plan to the caregiver's preferences, we can increase engagement and effectiveness.

Ongoing education can also serve as a means of empowerment for caregivers (Bom et al., 2019). By continually learning and growing in their roles, caregivers can gain a sense of control and confidence. This can lead to an improved quality of care for their loved ones, as well as increased satisfaction and reduced stress for the caregivers themselves.

Care Support Teams

Care support teams are an essential part of providing ongoing education and support to caregivers (Kent et al., 2020). These teams typically comprise various healthcare professionals, such as nurses, doctors, social workers, and occupational therapists. By working collaboratively, they can provide a comprehensive and integrated approach to caregiver support.

Each member of a care support team brings a unique perspective and set of skills to the table (Chen et al., 2020). For instance, nurses can provide practical advice on managing a loved one's daily needs, doctors can offer insights into the disease process, social workers can connect caregivers with resources, and occupational therapists can provide strategies for managing physical challenges.

Care support teams can regularly monitor the caregiver's situation and provide necessary education based on their observations and assessments (Reinhard et al., 2020). They can identify areas where the caregiver may be struggling and offer targeted education and support to address these challenges.

The care support team can also adapt the support plan as needed (Li et al., 2022). As the caregiver's needs change, the team can adjust the plan, accordingly, ensuring it remains relevant and effective. This might involve changing the focus of the education, bringing in new team members with specific expertise, or connecting the caregiver with different resources.

In addition, care support teams can provide emotional support to caregivers (Tretteteig et al., 2021). Caring for a loved one can be emotionally challenging and having a team of professionals who understand and validate these emotions can be incredibly beneficial. This emotional support can help prevent feelings of isolation and burnout and can promote resilience in the face of caregiving challenges.

Role of Community Resources

Community resources can be invaluable in providing ongoing education and support to caregivers (Dam et al., 2016). These resources can help to supplement the support provided by care teams and can provide additional opportunities for learning and connection.

Local support groups, for instance, can provide caregivers with a sense of community and understanding (Bom et al., 2019). They offer a space for caregivers to share their experiences, learn from others in similar situations, and gain emotional support. These groups can also provide practical advice and tips, as members often share strategies that have worked for them.

Educational workshops, another community resource, can provide caregivers with in-depth knowledge on specific topics (Kent et al., 2020). They may be run by healthcare professionals or experienced caregivers and can cover a wide range of topics, from managing specific symptoms to navigating healthcare systems. These workshops can be a valuable source of practical, actionable information.

Access to respite care services is another community resource that can support caregivers (Chen et al., 2020). Respite care allows caregivers to take a temporary break from their caregiving responsibilities, providing them with time to rest, recharge, or attend to other aspects of their lives. This can help to prevent burnout and improve the overall quality of care.

By connecting caregivers with these community resources, care support teams can ensure that caregivers continue to receive the comprehensive support they need over the long term (Reinhard et al., 2020). These resources can also help caregivers feel more connected to their communities, which can enhance their well-being and resilience.

The Importance of Flexibility

Flexibility is key in providing effective long-term caregiver support (Li et al., 2022). The nature of caregiving is such that needs and circumstances can change rapidly, often without warning. A support plan that was effective one month may no longer be relevant the next. Therefore, the ability to adapt and pivot as needed is a crucial aspect of caregiver support.

Regular check-ins and updates on the support plan are essential to maintaining its relevance and effectiveness (Tretteteig et al., 2021). These check-ins provide an opportunity to assess how well the support plan is meeting the caregiver's needs and to adjust, as necessary. They also allow for the early identification of new needs or challenges, so that they can be addressed promptly.

Flexibility also means being able to provide support in a variety of ways (Dam et al., 2016). This could involve offering support in different formats (such as in-person, online, or over the phone), at various times (to accommodate the caregiver's schedule), or on different topics (based on the caregiver's changing needs). It could also involve bringing in different members of the care support team, depending on the caregiver's needs at any given time.

Moreover, flexibility is important in addressing the uniqueness of each caregiver's situation (Bom et al., 2019). Each caregiver has their own set of skills, experiences, and preferences, and their loved one's health condition is unique as well. Therefore, the support plan should be personalized to fit these unique circumstances, rather than being a one-size-fits-all solution.

Flexibility involves being able to respond to unexpected changes or crises (Kent et al., 2020). In the course of caregiving, emergencies or unforeseen challenges can arise. In these situations, the caregiver support plan should be able to adapt quickly to provide the necessary support and resources.

The Impact of Ongoing Education

The impact of ongoing education for caregivers can be profound (Chen et al., 2020). By continually improving their knowledge and skills, caregivers can enhance their ability to provide care, leading to better outcomes for their loved ones. But the benefits of ongoing education extend beyond improved caregiving skills.

Ongoing education can help caregivers manage stress more effectively (Reinhard et al., 2020). By understanding more about their loved one's health condition, caregivers can feel more in control and less anxious about the future. They can also learn strategies for managing their own stress and maintaining their own well-being, which can reduce the risk of burnout.

Ongoing education can also empower caregivers (Li et al., 2022). With increased knowledge comes increased confidence in their caregiving abilities. This can lead to greater satisfaction in their role and a stronger sense of purpose. It can also help caregivers advocate more effectively for their loved ones in healthcare settings.

In addition, ongoing education can provide caregivers with a sense of community (Tretteteig et al., 2021). Through educational workshops or support groups, caregivers can connect with others who are facing similar challenges. This can help alleviate feelings of isolation and provide much-needed emotional support.

Ongoing education can have a positive impact on the care recipient as well (Li et al., 2022). When caregivers are well-informed and skilled, they can provide higher quality care. This can lead to improved health outcomes for the care recipient and a higher quality of life (Tretteteig et al., 2021).

The Role of Care Support Teams

Care support teams play a significant role in preventing caregiver burnout (Dam et al., 2016). These teams, often multidisciplinary, can include medical professionals, social workers, counselors, and community resources. They work together to provide comprehensive support for caregivers, addressing their physical, emotional, and logistical needs (Bom et al., 2019).

Education is a key component of care support teams' work (Kent et al., 2020). They provide caregivers with information about their loved one's condition, treatment options, and what to expect in the future. This education can help caregivers feel more prepared and confident in their caregiving role (Chen et al., 2020).

Support teams also provide practical resources to help manage caregiving responsibilities (Reinhard et al., 2020). This can include assistance with coordinating medical appointments, providing home health equipment, or connecting caregivers with respite care services. They can also help caregivers navigate complex healthcare and social service systems, reducing the logistical stress associated with caregiving (Li et al., 2022).

Emotional support and counseling are another crucial aspect of care support teams' work (Tretteteig et al., 2021). They can provide therapy or counseling services, facilitate support groups, or simply offer a compassionate ear to listen to caregivers' experiences and concerns. This emotional support can help caregivers manage the psychological stress of caregiving and reduce feelings of isolation and overwhelm (Dam et al., 2016).

Providing ongoing support and education is another key role of care support teams (Bom et al., 2019). Caregiving is a dynamic process, with caregivers' needs changing over time as their loved one's condition progresses. Care support teams need to continually reassess caregivers' needs and adjust their support strategies accordingly (Kent et al., 2020). This could mean providing additional education, adjusting the level of practical support, or offering more intensive emotional support (Chen et al., 2020).

Appraising Caregiver Educational Needs and Tailored Interventions

Understanding the unique educational needs of caregivers is crucial in providing effective support and preventing caregiver burnout (Reinhard et al., 2020). This process involves identifying caregivers' knowledge gaps, using assessment tools to guide this process, and developing interventions based on these needs (Li et al., 2022).

The first step in this process is identifying what caregivers need to learn (Tretteteig et al., 2021). This could involve understanding their loved one's condition, learning specific care skills, managing medications, or navigating healthcare systems. Conversations with caregivers, along with observations of their caregiving practices, can help identify these educational needs (Dam et al., 2016).

Assessment tools can be used to further guide this process (Bom et al., 2019). These tools, such as questionnaires or surveys, can help identify areas where caregivers lack confidence or feel overwhelmed. They can also provide insight into caregivers' learning preferences, which can inform the development of educational interventions (Kent et al., 2020).

Once caregivers' educational needs have been identified, tailored interventions can be developed (Chen et al., 2020). These interventions should be designed to address caregivers' specific needs and learning preferences. For example, if a caregiver is struggling with managing their loved one's medications, an intervention could involve a one-on-one education session with a pharmacist. If a caregiver is feeling overwhelmed by their loved one's behavioral changes, an intervention could involve counseling or a support group for caregivers of individuals with similar conditions (Reinhard et al., 2020).

Providing ongoing support and education is crucial to meet the long-term needs of caregivers (Li et al., 2022). This can involve regular check-ins to reassess caregivers' educational needs, adjusting educational interventions as needed, and providing resources for continued learning (Tretteteig et al., 2021). By providing tailored education and ongoing support, we can help caregivers feel more confident and capable in their caregiving roles, reducing their risk of burnout and ensuring they can provide the best care for their loved ones (Dam et al., 2016).

Chapter 4: Implementing and Managing Caregiver Support Programs

Caregiver support programs are critical interventions that offer services and resources designed to assist caregivers in managing their responsibilities more effectively (Bom et al., 2019). These programs aim to enhance the duration and quality of care provision, alleviate symptoms of caregiver depression, anxiety, and stress, and prevent or delay the need for expensive institutional care (Kent et al., 2020). The development and organization of these programs are crucial to ensure their efficacy and sustainability.

The role of caregivers, often unpaid and informal, is a vital component in the healthcare system, especially in the care of older adults and individuals with chronic conditions (Chen et al., 2020). As the population ages, the demand for caregiver support is projected to grow significantly (Reinhard et al., 2020). However, the task of caregiving can take a toll on the physical, emotional, and financial well-being of caregivers, necessitating the need for structured support (Li et al., 2022).

The importance of caregiver support programs extends beyond the immediate relief they provide to caregivers. By empowering caregivers with the necessary skills, resources, and respite, these programs indirectly contribute to improved patient outcomes and reduced healthcare costs (Tretteteig et al., 2021). They also foster a sense of community among caregivers, providing them with a platform to share experiences and learn from each other (Dam et al., 2016).

In this chapter, we will delve into the intricate process of developing and implementing caregiver support programs. We will explore the various stages involved, from program planning to execution, and the challenges that may arise along the way. We will also discuss strategies for maintaining and expanding these programs, emphasizing their long-term sustainability and scalability.

We will highlight some successful examples of caregiver support programs and draw lessons from their experiences (Bom et al., 2019). These case studies will provide a practical perspective on how theoretical concepts translate into real-world applications and the impact they have on caregivers' lives (Kent et al., 2020).

4.1: Program Development and Planning

Developing and planning a caregiver support program is a critical initial step that lays the foundation for the program's subsequent implementation and management. This process involves a thorough understanding of the needs of caregivers, identifying the resources required to meet these needs, and defining the program's goals and objectives (Bom et al., 2019).

The first stage in program development is conducting a needs assessment. This assessment aims to gather detailed information about the needs, experiences, and characteristics of the target population of caregivers (Kent et al., 2020). Using methods such as surveys, focus groups, and interviews, the needs assessment provides a comprehensive picture of what caregivers require most urgently (Chen et al., 2020).

The needs assessment should involve a range of stakeholders, including caregivers themselves, healthcare providers, social workers, and community organizations (Reinhard et al., 2020). These stakeholders offer diverse perspectives that enrich the understanding of caregivers' needs. Their involvement also fosters a sense of ownership and collaboration, which can be beneficial for the program's implementation and sustainability (Li et al., 2022).

Once the needs assessment has been conducted, the next step is the formulation of a program plan. This plan outlines the goals and objectives of the program, the activities that will be undertaken to achieve these goals, and the resources required (Tretteteig et al., 2021). Care should be taken to ensure that the program plan aligns with the needs identified in the assessment.

The program plan should also define the target population for the program, including eligibility criteria and referral processes (Dam et al., 2016). This clarity ensures that the program reaches those who need it most and prevents the misallocation of resources. The plan should be based on evidence-based practices and best practices in caregiver support, ensuring its effectiveness and efficiency.

It is essential for the program to be sustainable and scalable (Bom et al., 2019). Sustainability refers to the program's ability to continue operating over time, while scalability refers to the program's capacity to expand to serve more caregivers. Achieving these requires strategic partnerships with community organizations, healthcare providers, and government agencies, as well as diversified funding sources (Kent et al., 2020).

Needs Assessment

The needs assessment is a critical part of developing a caregiver support program. It informs the program's design by identifying the needs and characteristics of caregivers in a specific population (Chen et al., 2020). This section delves deeper into the process of conducting a needs assessment, its importance, and how its outcomes can guide the program's development.

The first step in conducting a needs assessment is defining the scope of the assessment (Reinhard et al., 2020). This involves identifying the caregiver population to be assessed, the geographic area to be covered, and the specific needs to be investigated. The scope should be broad enough to capture a representative sample of caregivers but specific enough to provide actionable insights (Li et al., 2022).

The next step is data collection. Various methods can be used for this, including surveys, focus groups, and interviews. Surveys are useful for reaching a large number of caregivers and collecting quantifiable data, while focus groups and interviews provide qualitative insights into caregivers' experiences and needs (Tretteteig et al., 2021).

Data analysis follows data collection. This involves processing the collected data to identify trends and patterns and draw conclusions about the caregivers' needs (Dam et al., 2016). The analysis should be objective and systematic to ensure that the results accurately reflect the caregivers' needs and experiences.

The findings from the needs assessment should be presented in a clear and understandable format. This could include a written report, a presentation, or a visual representation such as a chart or graph. The presentation should highlight the key findings and their implications for the caregiver support program (Bom et al., 2019).

The needs assessment should be used to inform the development of the caregiver support program. The identified needs should guide the program's goals and objectives, the services and resources provided, and the target population (Kent et al., 2020). Furthermore, the needs assessment should be revisited periodically to ensure that the program continues to meet the changing needs of caregivers (Chen et al., 2020).

Program Plan Development

Once the needs assessment is completed, a program plan can be developed. This plan outlines the program's goals, objectives, and strategies, and identifies the resources required (Reinhard et al., 2020). It serves as a roadmap for the implementation of the caregiver support program.

The first step in developing a program plan is setting the program goals (Li et al., 2022). These should be broad, long-term outcomes that the program aims to achieve. For instance, a goal could be to reduce caregiver burnout or improve the quality of care provided by caregivers (Li et al., 2022).

Next, the program objectives should be defined (Tretteteig et al., 2021). These are specific, measurable steps towards achieving the program goals. They should be SMART - specific, measurable, achievable, relevant, and time-bound. For example, an objective could be to provide training to one hundred caregivers in stress management techniques within the first year of the program (Dam et al., 2016).

The activities to be undertaken to achieve these objectives should then be outlined (Bom et al., 2019). These could include workshops, counseling sessions, respite care services, and so on. The activities should be chosen based on their effectiveness in meeting the program objectives and their feasibility given the available resources (Kent et al., 2020).

The program plan should also identify the resources required for the program (Chen et al., 2020). These include financial resources, human resources, and material resources. The plan should detail how these resources will be obtained, whether through government grants, private donations, partnerships, or other means (Reinhard et al., 2020).

The program plan should set out the target population for the program and the process for identifying and referring eligible caregivers (Li et al., 2022). This ensures that the program is accessible to those who need it most and prevents the misallocation of resources (Tretteteig et al., 2021).

Sustainability and Scalability

A successful caregiver support program should not only be effective but also sustainable and scalable. Sustainability ensures that the program can continue to provide support to caregivers over time, while scalability allows the program to expand to reach more caregivers. Both are crucial for the long-term impact of the program (Dam et al., 2016).

Sustainability starts with securing stable funding. This can be achieved through a combination of government grants, private donations, and fundraising events (Bom et al., 2019). Diversifying funding sources can help ensure that the program can continue to operate even if one source of funding is lost (Kent et al., 2020).

Partnerships with community organizations, healthcare providers, and government agencies can also contribute to sustainability (Chen et al., 2020). These partnerships can provide resources, expertise, and support that can enhance the program's effectiveness and longevity. They can also help advocate for the program and its importance, attracting more funding and support (Reinhard et al., 2020).

For a program to be scalable, its design should be flexible and adaptable (Li et al., 2022). It should be able to accommodate an increase in the number of caregivers served without compromising the quality of the services provided. This might involve training more staff, securing additional resources, or expanding the program's geographic coverage (Tretteteig et al., 2021).

Monitoring and evaluation are also key to scalability (Dam et al., 2016). By regularly assessing the program's effectiveness and identifying areas for improvement, the program can adapt and grow in a way that best serves caregivers' needs. Feedback from caregivers and other stakeholders should be actively sought and incorporated into the program's development (Bom et al., 2019).

Sustainability and scalability are crucial considerations in the development and planning of caregiver support programs (Kent et al., 2020). By securing stable funding, forming strategic partnerships, designing adaptable programs, and regularly monitoring and evaluating, caregiver support programs can continue to serve and grow with their communities (Chen et al., 2020).

4.2: Stakeholder Engagement and Collaboration

The Key to Effective Caregiver Support Programs

Caregiver support programs are fundamental to the well-being of those who shoulder the responsibility of caring for the elderly, chronically ill, or disabled loved ones. These programs provide essential resources and emotional support, alleviate caregiver stress, and improve overall care quality (Li et al., 2022). However, the planning and development of these programs require careful consideration and strategic collaboration to ensure their effectiveness and sustainability. A critical aspect of this development process is stakeholder engagement and collaboration (Tretteteig et al., 2021).

Stakeholder engagement involves the active participation of individuals or groups with a personal stake in or potential impact from a particular project or program (Dam et al., 2016). In the context of caregiver support services, stakeholders include family caregivers, healthcare professionals, community organizations, and policymakers. Their involvement can enhance the integration and efficiency of these programs, ensuring they align with the needs of the intended beneficiaries (Bom et al., 2019).

Furthermore, successful collaboration among these stakeholders can leverage their unique strengths and expertise, creating a synergistic effect that results in more effective and sustainable programs. It provides a platform for shared decision-making and resource allocation, leading to better outcomes (Kent et al., 2020).

The importance of stakeholder engagement and collaboration becomes more evident when viewed through the lens of caregiver support. Caregivers often face high levels of stress, depression, and burnout due to their demanding roles. They require a comprehensive support system that addresses their emotional, physical, and practical needs. Stakeholder collaboration can ensure that these needs are adequately addressed, providing caregivers with the support they need to thrive (Chen et al., 2020).

Let us focus on the importance of stakeholder engagement and collaboration in developing impactful caregiver support programs. It will provide insights into understanding stakeholder engagement, the power of collaboration, their significance in caregiver support, and how to implement these practices effectively (Reinhard et al., 2020).

Understanding Stakeholder Engagement

Stakeholder engagement is a pivotal aspect of any successful project or program. It refers to the systematic inclusion of individuals or groups who have a stake in or may be affected by a particular initiative. The spectrum of stakeholders for caregiver support programs is broad, encompassing family caregivers, healthcare professionals, community organizations, and policymakers (Li et al., 2022).

Engaging these stakeholders is not a one-off event but rather an ongoing process. It begins with identifying potential stakeholders, understanding their interests, needs, and expectations, and then involving them in the planning, development, and implementation stages of the program. This level of engagement ensures that the program is tailored to meet the needs of the caregivers and the recipients of care (Tretteteig et al., 2021).

Family caregivers, as direct users of these programs, provide invaluable perspectives and ideas that can enhance the program's effectiveness. Their experiences and challenges can guide the development of support services that directly tackle their pain points, thereby increasing the program's impact (Dam et al., 2016).

Healthcare professionals, on the other hand, bring a wealth of expertise and knowledge in caregiving. Their insights can inform the program's content, ensuring it adheres to best practices and addresses the caregivers' health and well-being aspects (Bom et al., 2019).

Community organizations and policymakers play an integral role in shaping the program's structure and sustainability. They can provide resources, endorse policies that support caregiving, and ensure the program's integration into the community (Kent et al., 2020).

Stakeholder engagement allows for a comprehensive understanding of the caregiving landscape. It ensures the development of a program that is relevant, practical, and effective in supporting caregivers (Chen et al., 2020).

The Power of Collaboration

Collaboration is the cornerstone of stakeholder engagement. It entails working together to achieve a common goal, often by sharing resources, expertise, and knowledge (Reinhard et al., 2020). This collective effort leverages the strengths and expertise of diverse stakeholders to create effective and sustainable programs.

In the context of caregiver support programs, collaboration can manifest in various ways. For instance, family caregivers and healthcare professionals can collaborate to identify the most pressing issues faced by caregivers. They can jointly develop strategies to address these issues, combining the caregivers' lived experiences with the professionals' expertise (Li et al., 2022).

Community organizations can collaborate with healthcare professionals and caregivers to provide resources that support these strategies. This could include educational materials, counseling services, or respite care facilities. They can also collaborate with policymakers to advocate for legislation that supports caregivers, creating a more conducive environment for caregiving (Tretteteig et al., 2021).

Collaboration also fosters innovation. By bringing together different perspectives and ideas, it can lead to the development of novel solutions that address the unique challenges faced by caregivers (Dam et al., 2016).

Moreover, collaboration promotes a sense of shared responsibility and ownership among stakeholders. This can enhance commitment to the program, ensuring that it is not only started but also maintained over time (Bom et al., 2019).

Collaboration converts the collective knowledge, experience, and resources of stakeholders into a robust support system for caregivers. It is the driving force behind impactful and sustainable caregiver support programs (Kent et al., 2020).

The Significance of Stakeholder Engagement and Collaboration in Caregiver Support

Stakeholder engagement and collaboration hold particular significance in the context of caregiver support programs. As caregivers often face high levels of stress, depression, and burnout due to their demanding roles, they require a multifaceted support system that addresses their emotional, physical, and practical needs (Chen et al., 2020). This comprehensive approach can only be achieved through effective stakeholder engagement and collaboration (Reinhard et al., 2020).

Family caregivers, as the primary beneficiaries of these programs, can provide first-hand insights into their needs and challenges. Their involvement in the program development process ensures that the services offered are relevant, practical, and responsive to their needs. They also function as ambassadors for the program, promoting its use among other caregivers in their network (Li et al., 2022).

Healthcare professionals bring their technical knowledge and expertise to the table. They can help identify the health and well-being needs of caregivers, recommend evidence-based strategies to address these needs, and evaluate the program's effectiveness. Their involvement enhances the program's credibility and ensures that it adheres to best practices in caregiver support (Tretteteig et al., 2021).

Community organizations can provide resources and links to various services that caregivers may need. They can also play a critical role in embedding the program within the community, enhancing its accessibility and uptake (Dam et al., 2016).

Policymakers, meanwhile, can enact supportive policies that provide the necessary legal and financial groundwork for the program. Their involvement ensures that the program can be sustained over time and adapt to changing needs and circumstances (Bom et al., 2019).

Stakeholder engagement and collaboration in caregiver support programs ensure a holistic approach to caregiver support. They ensure that the programs address the comprehensive needs of caregivers, leading to better outcomes for caregivers and those they care for (Kent et al., 2020).

Implementing Stakeholder Engagement and Collaboration

The implementation of stakeholder engagement and collaboration in caregiver support programs requires careful planning and execution. It is a multi-step process that involves conducting a needs assessment, developing a program plan, building partnerships, securing funding, and fostering effective communication and trust among stakeholders (Chen et al., 2020).

Conducting a needs assessment involves identifying and understanding the needs of caregivers and the resources available to meet these needs. This forms the basis for the program plan, which outlines the program's goals, strategies, and evaluation measures. The plan should be developed in consultation with stakeholders to ensure it is responsive to their needs and leverages their expertise and resources (Reinhard et al., 2020).

Building partnerships is another critical step in this process. Partnerships should be formed with a diverse range of stakeholders, each bringing unique strengths and resources to the table. These partnerships can enhance the program's capacity to provide comprehensive support to caregivers (Li et al., 2022).

Securing diverse funding sources is also essential to ensure the program's financial sustainability. This can involve exploring various funding options, such as grants, donations, and government funding. Stakeholders can play a key role in identifying and securing these funding sources (Tretteteig et al., 2021).

Fostering effective communication and trust among stakeholders is critical to the success of the program. Regular meetings, open communication channels, and transparent decision-making processes can enhance trust and cooperation among stakeholders. When stakeholders trust each other and feel heard and valued, they are more likely to collaborate effectively and create impactful programs (Dam et al., 2016).

Stakeholder engagement and collaboration are fundamental to the development of effective caregiver support programs. By involving a diverse group of stakeholders, leveraging their strengths and expertise, and fostering effective communication and trust, caregiver support programs can be tailored to meet the unique needs of caregivers, ensuring their effectiveness and sustainability (Bom et al., 2019).

4.3: Funding and Resource Allocation

Caregiver support programs play an essential role in providing much-needed resources and assistance to caregivers. These programs provide a lifeline for caregivers, helping to alleviate their stress, enhance their skills, and improve their overall well-being (Li et al., 2022). However, the development, implementation, and sustainability of these programs require significant financial resources and strategic resource allocation. Attaining the necessary funding and efficiently allocating resources can be challenging, but it is crucial to ensure the longevity and effectiveness of these programs (Tretteteig et al., 2021).

The funding landscape for caregiver support programs is multifaceted, encompassing a range of potential sources from government funding to private donations. Each source of funding brings with it its own set of advantages, challenges, and requirements. Therefore, it is critical for organizations to explore and understand the various funding options available to them (Dam et al., 2016).

Similarly, resource allocation within caregiver support programs requires careful consideration and strategic planning. It is a delicate balancing act, ensuring that resources are directed where they're most needed, while also taking into account the long-term sustainability of the program. Effective resource allocation strategies can make a significant difference in the success and longevity of caregiver support programs (Bom et al., 2019).

Here, we will delve into the diverse funding options available for caregiver support programs and discuss strategies for efficient and effective resource allocation. Our goal is to provide a comprehensive look for those involved in the development and implementation of caregiver support programs, helping them navigate the complexities of funding and resource allocation (Kent et al., 2020).

Diverse Funding Options

Funding is the cornerstone of any caregiver support program, ensuring the continuation of their vital work in providing resources and aid to caregivers. With a multitude of funding options available, each comes with its own unique set of advantages and potential challenges (Chen et al., 2020).

The first step towards understanding the diverse funding options is to recognize the different types of available funding sources. These can broadly be categorized into government funding, private donations, corporate sponsorship, and grants. Each of these categories offers different avenues for obtaining financial support for caregiver programs and services (Reinhard et al., 2020).

However, one must also consider that each funding source comes with its own set of requirements and constraints. For instance, government funding may have strict eligibility criteria and require extensive reporting and compliance with regulations. Similarly, while private donations may offer greater flexibility, they also demand a considerable amount of effort in fundraising and donor relationship management (Li et al., 2022).

Aside from understanding the advantages and constraints of each funding source, it is also crucial to consider the sustainability of the funding. Some sources, such as government funding, may be subject to political and economic changes, while others, like private donations, may fluctuate based on the economy and the personal circumstances of donors. Therefore, a balanced and diversified funding strategy is often the most resilient approach (Tretteteig et al., 2021).

The targeted use of funding should be considered. Some funding sources may be more suitable for certain types of programs or specific aspects of a program. For example, grants are often project-specific, while corporate sponsorship can be useful for initiatives that align with a company's corporate social responsibility goals (Dam et al., 2016).

Government Funding

Government funding represents a significant source of support for caregiver programs. Federal, state, and local government agencies often allocate funds for health and social service programs, including those that support caregivers. For example, in the United States, agencies such as the National Institute on Aging and the Administration for Community Living provide funding for research and programs aimed at supporting caregivers of older adults (Bom et al., 2019).

Government funding can be a substantial source of financial support, capable of funding large-scale programs and initiatives. Moreover, government support can also lend legitimacy to a caregiver support program, which can be beneficial for the program's public image and for attracting additional funding sources (Kent et al., 2020).

Nevertheless, government funding often comes with strict requirements. These can include detailed reporting on how the funds are used, compliance with specific regulations, and meeting certain performance benchmarks. Fulfilling these requirements can be time-consuming and may require additional administrative resources (Chen et al., 2020).

In addition, the availability of government funding can be unpredictable and subject to changes in political and economic conditions. Budget cuts or policy changes can lead to reductions in funding, which can pose challenges for programs that rely heavily on government support (Reinhard et al., 2020).

Despite these challenges, government funding remains a crucial source of support for many caregiver support programs. Understanding how to navigate the application process, comply with requirements, and adapt to changes in funding levels can help programs maximize their benefit from this funding source (Li et al., 2022).

Private Donations

Private donations are another key financial resource for caregiver support programs. These donations can come from individuals, corporations, or foundations that are interested in supporting the cause of caregivers (Li et al., 2022). Private donors can contribute in various ways, including one-time donations, regular contributions, or even endowments (Tretteteig et al., 2021).

Unlike government funding, private donations often come with fewer restrictions. This allows programs to use the funds more flexibly, whether it is for general operating expenses, specific projects, or innovative initiatives that may not be eligible for other types of funding (Dam et al., 2016).

However, securing private donations requires a great deal of effort in fundraising and donor management. This includes activities such as developing fundraising campaigns, building relationships with potential donors, demonstrating the impact of the program to attract and retain donors, and managing donations and donor information (Bom et al., 2019).

Private donations can also be unpredictable, as they can be influenced by a variety of factors, including the economy, the personal circumstances of donors, and competition with other causes and organizations for donations (Kent et al., 2020).

Despite these potential challenges, private donations can provide crucial support for caregiver programs. By developing a robust fundraising strategy and investing in donor management, programs can maximize the benefits of this funding source (Chen et al., 2020).

Corporate Sponsorship

Corporate sponsorship is a form of funding where businesses provide financial support to caregiver support programs in return for recognition and positive publicity. It is a mutually beneficial relationship, wherein the business can build goodwill and enhance its corporate social responsibility profile, while providing essential funding for caregiver programs (Reinhard et al., 2020).

Corporate sponsorships can range from financial contributions to donations of products or services. They can also involve partnerships on specific projects or initiatives, such as awareness campaigns, educational programs, or fundraising events (Li et al., 2022).

However, to attract corporate sponsors, caregiver programs need to demonstrate the value of the sponsorship to the business. This could involve highlighting the positive impact of the program, the alignment of the program's mission with the company's values, or the potential for positive publicity (Tretteteig et al., 2021).

Like other types of funding, corporate sponsorships can pose challenges. They often require a significant amount of time and resources to secure and manage. In addition, the interests of the corporate sponsor may not always align perfectly with those of the caregiver program, which can lead to complications (Dam et al., 2016).

Despite these potential challenges, corporate sponsorships can provide a valuable source of support for caregiver programs. They not only offer financial resources but can also provide opportunities for increased visibility and public awareness, which can be beneficial for the program's overall mission and goals (Bom et al., 2019).

Grants

Grants are a major source of funding for caregiver support programs, offering financial support without the expectation of repayment. They can be sourced from various entities, including foundations, corporations, and government agencies (Kent et al., 2020). The grant-making entity usually provides funding for a specific purpose or project, providing a unique opportunity for caregiver support programs to implement or expand particular initiatives (Chen et al., 2020).

The process of applying for grants can be time-consuming and requires a significant level of detail regarding the proposed use of funds. Grant proposals must typically outline the purpose, methods, timeline, and expected outcomes of the project or initiative for which funding is sought. It is essential that these proposals align closely with the funding entity's goals and objectives, as they are often highly competitive (Reinhard et al., 2020).

Once a grant is received, there are stringent requirements and reporting obligations attached to it. These obligations can include regular updates on the project's progress, detailed financial reports demonstrating how the funds have been used, and evidence of the project's outcomes and impact (Li et al., 2022).

However, the potential benefits of grants are substantial. They can provide significant funding for the development, implementation, and evaluation of caregiver support programs. This can enable programs to undertake new initiatives, expand existing services, or conduct research and evaluation to improve their effectiveness (Tretteteig et al., 2021).

One of the key challenges with grant funding is its project-specific nature. This means that it may not be used to cover general operational costs or other initiatives outside the specified project. This can place constraints on flexibility and may require the program to seek additional funding sources for other needs (Dam et al., 2016).

Implementing Resource Allocation Strategies

Resource allocation is a critical aspect of managing caregiver support programs. It involves deciding how to distribute resources—both financial and non-financial—to ensure the program's goals are achieved (Bom et al., 2019).

Funding and resource allocation are critical aspects of developing and maintaining effective caregiver support programs. Diverse funding options—including government funding, private donations, corporate sponsorships, and grants—provide multiple avenues for securing the necessary financial resources (Kent et al., 2020). Meanwhile, strategic resource allocation, through needs assessment, prioritization, collaboration, and volunteerism, ensures that these resources are used efficiently and effectively (Chen et al., 2020).

By understanding and effectively navigating these complexities, caregiver support programs can secure their longevity and maximize their impact, providing crucial support for caregivers in their most challenging times (Reinhard et al., 2020).

4.4: Program Evaluation and Quality Improvement

Caregivers perform a crucial role in society, often sacrificing their time, resources, and emotional well-being to support those in their care. They may be tending to the needs of young children, individuals with disabilities, or elderly family members. Regardless of their circumstances, caregivers often need support themselves. This is where caregiver support programs come in, acting as a lifeline to these selfless individuals (Li et al., 2022).

These programs offer resources, guidance, and assistance to caregivers, aiming to lighten their load and enhance their caregiving capacities (Tretteteig et al., 2021). However, the existence of such programs is not enough. It is essential to ensure their effectiveness and the quality of support they provide. This is where program evaluation and quality improvement become vital (Dam et al., 2016).

Program evaluation and quality improvement are twin processes that ensure caregiver support programs are not just operational, but optimally effective and continually improving (Bom et al., 2019). Their roles are interwoven, with program evaluation providing the evidence base for quality improvement efforts and quality improvement feeding back into more targeted and effective program evaluation (Kent et al., 2020).

Program evaluation assesses the effectiveness of a program, providing insights into whether a program is achieving its predetermined goals and objectives (Chen et al., 2020). On the other hand, quality improvement is a systematic, data-driven approach to improving the efficiency and effectiveness of a program. It involves identifying areas for improvement, implementing changes, and monitoring the results (Reinhard et al., 2020).

To delve deeper into these processes, let us break down the steps involved in both program evaluation and quality improvement.

Program Evaluation

Setting Goals and Objectives

Setting goals and objectives is a fundamental step in program evaluation. Clear and well-defined goals provide a roadmap for the program and a benchmark against which its effectiveness can be measured (Li et al., 2022). The goals of a caregiver support program could range from reducing caregiver stress, increasing caregiver self-efficacy, to improving the quality of life for both caregivers and the individuals they care for (Tretteteig et al., 2021).

When setting goals and objectives, it is important to use the SMART criteria—Specific, Measurable, Achievable, Relevant, and Time-bound (Dam et al., 2016). For example, a specific goal could be to reduce the incidence of caregiver burnout by 20% within a year. This goal is measurable (20% reduction), achievable (with the right resources and interventions), relevant (burnout is a major issue for caregivers), and time-bound (within a year) (Bom et al., 2019).

Goals and objectives should be informed by understanding the needs and experiences of caregivers. This might involve conducting surveys or interviews with caregivers to identify their challenges and needs (Kent et al., 2020). It is also important to consider the broader context in which the program operates, including the availability of resources, the characteristics of the caregiver population, and the prevailing social, economic, and political conditions (Chen et al., 2020).

Once the goals and objectives are set, they should be communicated to all stakeholders. This includes the caregivers themselves, program staff, funders, and any other relevant parties. Clear communication ensures everyone understands what the program is trying to achieve and their role in helping to achieve it (Reinhard et al., 2020).

Data Collection

Data collection is the cornerstone of program evaluation. It involves gathering information about the program's inputs (resources used), processes (activities carried out), outputs (products or services delivered), and outcomes (changes resulting from the program) (Li et al., 2022).

In a caregiver support program, inputs might include staff time, funding, and materials; processes might include training sessions, support groups, and counseling; outputs might include the number of caregivers served or sessions delivered; and outcomes might include changes in caregiver stress levels, skills, and quality of life (Tretteteig et al., 2021).

Data can be collected using a variety of methods, including surveys, interviews, focus groups, and direct observation. For example, surveys might be used to measure caregivers' stress levels and skills before and after participating in the program. Interviews or focus groups could provide more in-depth insights into caregivers' experiences and perceptions of the program (Dam et al., 2016).

When collecting data, it is important to consider issues of validity (are you measuring what you intend to measure?) and reliability (would you get the same results if you measured the same thing again?) (Bom et al., 2019). It is also crucial to ensure that data collection is ethical, respecting participants' privacy and confidentiality (Kent et al., 2020).

Data Analysis

Data analysis involves examining and interpreting the data collected to draw conclusions about the program's effectiveness. This may involve descriptive statistics (e.g., averages, frequencies), inferential statistics (e.g., testing hypotheses, identifying relationships), or qualitative analysis (e.g., identifying themes or patterns in interview or focus group data) (Chen et al., 2020).

In the context of a caregiver support program, data analysis might involve comparing caregivers' stress levels before and after participating in the program to see if there's been a significant reduction. Or it might involve analyzing interview data to understand caregivers' perceptions of the program and their suggestions for improvement (Reinhard et al., 2020).

Data analysis should be guided by the program's goals and objectives. For example, if one of the objectives is to reduce caregiver burnout, the analysis should focus on whether and to what extent this objective has been achieved (Li et al., 2022).

Making Recommendations

Based on the data analysis, the evaluators can make recommendations for program improvement. These recommendations should be evidence-based, concrete, and actionable (Tretteteig et al., 2021). They should identify areas where the program can improve and provide clear strategies for doing so.

For example, if the data shows that caregivers are still experiencing high levels of stress despite participating in the program, the evaluators might recommend introducing additional stress management interventions, such as mindfulness training or peer support groups (Dam et al., 2016).

When making recommendations, it's important to consider their feasibility and implications for the program. This might involve considering the availability of resources, the needs and preferences of caregivers, and the potential impacts on program operations and outcomes (Bom et al., 2019).

Follow-up

Follow-up is the final stage of program evaluation. This involves monitoring whether the recommendations are implemented and assessing their impact on the program's effectiveness (Kent et al., 2020). This stage is crucial for ensuring that the evaluation leads to tangible improvements.

Follow-up might involve regular check-ins with program staff to see how they're implementing the recommendations, or it could involve a follow-up evaluation to measure the program's effectiveness after the recommendations have been implemented (Chen et al., 2020).

It's important that the follow-up process is supportive and constructive, rather than punitive. The goal is to help the program improve, not to penalize it for any shortcomings (Reinhard et al., 2020). To this end, the evaluators should be available to provide ongoing support and guidance as needed (Li et al., 2022).

Quality Improvement

Needs Assessment

A needs assessment is an indispensable starting point in the process of quality improvement. This systematic process involves identifying, understanding, and addressing gaps in a program or system (Li et al., 2022). In the context of a caregiver and care support program, a needs assessment is utilized to understand what caregivers need and how the program can better fulfill those needs (Tretteteig et al., 2021).

A needs assessment begins by collecting and analyzing data. This could involve surveying caregivers to understand their experiences and needs, observing program operations to identify potential areas of improvement, or reviewing program records to identify trends and patterns (Dam et al., 2016). This data provides a comprehensive picture of the program's current state and highlights areas where changes may be required (Bom et al., 2019).

For a caregiver support program, the needs assessment may reveal gaps in service provision—for example, a lack of support for caregivers of individuals with specific conditions, or services not available in certain geographic areas (Kent et al., 2020). Caregivers may also express feeling unsupported in certain areas, such as managing the emotional stress of caregiving or navigating the healthcare system (Chen et al., 2020).

Additionally, the needs assessment should also include an analysis of the program's current goals and objectives. It's important to evaluate whether these goals are being met and, if not, to understand why. This component of the needs assessment can shed light on systemic issues that might be hindering the program's success (Reinhard et al., 2020).

Upon completion, the needs assessment provides a roadmap for improvements. It highlights the areas that need to be addressed and provides the basis for developing a targeted, effective quality improvement plan (Li et al., 2022).

Prioritization

Following the identification of areas for improvement through a needs assessment, the next step in the quality improvement process is prioritization. Prioritization is a key step to ensuring that resources are used effectively and that the most pressing issues are addressed first (Tretteteig et al., 2021).

Factors to consider during the prioritization process include the urgency of the need, the potential impact of addressing the issue, and the resources required (Dam et al., 2016). For example, a problem that significantly impacts many caregivers and can be addressed with minimal resources would likely be given a high priority. Conversely, a less urgent issue that would require significant resources might be given a lower priority (Bom et al., 2019).

Prioritization is not a one-size-fits-all process. Different programs and contexts will necessitate different approaches (Kent et al., 2020). For instance, in a caregiver support program with limited resources, the focus might be on addressing the issues that are most feasible to address. In a larger program with more resources, there might be more scope to tackle larger, more systemic issues (Chen et al., 2020).

Regardless of the specific approach, the goal of prioritization is to ensure that resources are used wisely and that the most important issues are addressed first (Reinhard et al., 2020). Prioritization should be a collaborative process, involving input from all stakeholders to ensure that the areas identified as priorities align with the needs and goals of the caregiver community (Li et al., 2022).

Collaboration

Collaboration is crucial in the quality improvement process. It involves working together with all relevant stakeholders, including caregivers, program staff, and other parties (Tretteteig et al., 2021). This collective approach helps ensure that the changes proposed are feasible, acceptable, and beneficial to all involved.

Involving caregivers in the quality improvement process is particularly important (Dam et al., 2016). As the individuals who are directly impacted by the program, caregivers can provide valuable insights into what works, what doesn't, and what changes could be most beneficial. Their firsthand experience can inform the development of changes that are both effective and relevant to their needs (Bom et al., 2019).

Collaboration with program staff is also crucial (Kent et al., 2020). As the individuals responsible for implementing the changes, staff need to understand the reasons for the changes, how to implement them, and what benefits they are expected to bring. Staff can also provide insights into the feasibility of proposed changes and help identify potential challenges and solutions (Chen et al., 2020).

Furthermore, collaboration should extend beyond the immediate program to include other relevant stakeholders (Reinhard et al., 2020). This might include other organizations in the caregiving sector, funders, policymakers, and the broader community. These stakeholders can provide additional perspectives, resources, and support, and their engagement can help build broader support for the changes (Li et al., 2022).

Volunteerism

While professional staff drive the core functions of a caregiver support program, volunteers can play an invaluable role in supporting and enhancing the program's work (Tretteteig et al., 2021). The utilization of volunteers in the quality improvement process can provide a range of benefits, from increasing capacity to bringing fresh perspectives and ideas.

Volunteers can contribute a range of skills and expertise that may not exist within the existing staff team (Dam et al., 2016). For example, a volunteer with a background in data analysis could support the needs assessment process, while a volunteer with experience in project management could assist with implementing changes. Volunteers can also bring new ideas and perspectives, which can be particularly valuable in the innovation-driven quality improvement process (Bom et al., 2019).

Moreover, volunteers can help increase the program's capacity, allowing it to address more areas of improvement or to implement changes more quickly (Kent et al., 2020). This can be particularly valuable in resource-constrained settings, where staff may not have the capacity to undertake all aspects of the quality improvement process on their own (Chen et al., 2020).

Engaging volunteers in the quality improvement process also has benefits for the volunteers themselves. It can provide opportunities for skill development, networking, and personal satisfaction. Moreover, volunteers who are also caregivers can develop a sense of ownership and investment in the program, which can enhance their satisfaction and engagement with the program (Reinhard et al., 2020).

However, it's important to note that engaging volunteers requires resources and management (Li et al., 2022). Effective volunteer engagement involves recruiting, training, and supporting volunteers. Therefore, before engaging volunteers in the quality improvement process, programs should ensure they have the resources and structures in place to effectively manage and support these volunteers (Tretteteig et al., 2021).

Continuous Monitoring

The final step in the quality improvement process is continuous monitoring. This involves regularly assessing the program's performance, ensuring that improvements are maintained, and identifying new areas for improvement (Dam et al., 2016). It's a crucial element of the quality improvement cycle, allowing for adjustments and refinements to be made as necessary and ensuring the program continues to strive for excellence (Bom et al., 2019).

Continuous monitoring involves the regular collection and analysis of data related to the program's performance. This could include data on service provision, caregiver outcomes, and program operations. This data should be compared to the program's goals and objectives, as well as to previous data, to assess whether improvements have been made and whether they are being maintained (Kent et al., 2020).

In the context of a caregiver support program, continuous monitoring could involve tracking metrics such as the number of caregivers served, caregiver satisfaction levels, and caregiver outcomes such as stress levels or quality of life (Chen et al., 2020). By regularly monitoring these metrics, programs can identify trends, assess whether their interventions are having the desired impact, and identify areas where further improvements are needed (Reinhard et al., 2020).

Continuous monitoring should be a shared responsibility amongst all stakeholders. Caregivers, program staff, volunteers, and other stakeholders should all be involved in monitoring the program's performance and identifying areas for improvement (Li et al., 2022). This collaborative approach ensures a wide range of perspectives are considered and that all stakeholders are invested in the program's continuous improvement (Tretteteig et al., 2021).

Evidence-based Practices

Evidence-based practices are interventions that have been proven effective through rigorous scientific research (Dam et al., 2016). They are grounded in empirical evidence, often derived from randomized controlled trials or systematic reviews of such trials. In the context of caregiver support programs, evidence-based practices could include specific therapeutic techniques, educational programs, or resources that have been shown to improve caregiver well-being or the quality of care they provide (Bom et al., 2019).

The use of evidence-based practices ensures that caregiver support programs are using interventions that have been proven to work (Kent et al., 2020). This can increase the likelihood of positive outcomes for caregivers and the individuals they care for. It also ensures that resources are being used effectively and not wasted on interventions that may not be effective (Chen et al., 2020).

However, implementing evidence-based practices is not a simple matter of just adopting a proven intervention. It requires careful consideration of the context in which the intervention will be implemented (Reinhard et al., 2020). For example, an intervention that works well in a clinical setting might not work as well in a community-based caregiver support program. Similarly, an intervention that works well for one population of caregivers might not be as effective for another population with different characteristics or needs (Li et al., 2022).

Translating Research into Practice

Translating research into practice involves taking evidence-based interventions and adapting them for use in a specific context (Tretteteig et al., 2021). This step is crucial to ensure that the interventions are effective in the specific context of the caregiver support program and are culturally sensitive and accessible to all caregivers (Dam et al., 2016).

Adapting interventions for a specific context can involve a range of considerations. For example, the intervention may need to be modified to fit the resources available to the program (Bom et al., 2019). It may also need to be adapted to fit the cultural context of the caregivers being served. Language, literacy levels, and cultural norms and values can all impact the effectiveness of an intervention and should be considered when adapting an intervention (Kent et al., 2020).

Training program staff in the intervention is also a key component of translating research into practice (Chen et al., 2020). Staff need to understand the intervention, why it works, and how to implement it effectively. Training should be ongoing, with opportunities for staff to refresh their knowledge and skills and to discuss any challenges they are facing in implementing the intervention (Reinhard et al., 2020).

Evaluating the Impact

The use of evidence-based practices should be continuously evaluated to ensure they are having the desired impact (Li et al., 2022). This involves collecting data on the outcomes of these practices, such as improvements in caregiver well-being or reductions in caregiver burnout. Evaluating the impact of evidence-based practices helps ensure that they continue to be effective in the context of the caregiver support program and allows for adjustments to be made if necessary (Tretteteig et al., 2021).

Evaluation should be rigorous, using valid and reliable measures to assess outcomes (Dam et al., 2016). It should also be ongoing, with data collected at regular intervals to track progress and identify trends. Feedback from caregivers and program staff should also be included in the evaluation process to provide a more comprehensive picture of the impact of the interventions (Bom et al., 2019).

Evidence-informed Practices

While evidence-based practices are grounded in rigorous scientific research, evidence-informed practices consider the best available evidence alongside the unique needs and preferences of the population being served (Kent et al., 2020). In other words, they balance scientific evidence with practical considerations, ensuring that the interventions are not only effective but also feasible and acceptable to caregivers (Chen et al., 2020).

Evidence-informed practice acknowledges that while randomized controlled trials and systematic reviews provide valuable information about what works on average, they may not capture the full complexity of real-world practice (Reinhard et al., 2020).

Factors such as the characteristics of the caregivers, the context in which the program operates, and the resources available can all impact the effectiveness of an intervention. Evidence-informed practices take these factors into account, tailoring interventions to the specific context and population (Li et al., 2022).

For example, an evidence-informed practice in a caregiver support program might involve adapting a proven stress management intervention to better fit the needs and preferences of caregivers. This could involve modifying the delivery mode (e.g., offering the intervention online for caregivers who can't attend in-person sessions), adjusting the content (e.g., including information relevant to caregivers of individuals with specific conditions), or considering cultural adaptations (e.g., ensuring the intervention is culturally sensitive and accessible to caregivers from diverse backgrounds) (Tretteteig et al., 2021).

The development of evidence-informed practices requires a thorough understanding of the evidence base, the population being served, and the context in which the program operates (Dam et al., 2016). It involves a process of continual learning, reflection, and adaptation to ensure that the interventions remain effective and relevant (Bom et al., 2019).

Continuous Quality Improvement

Continuous Quality Improvement (CQI) is a philosophy and approach that encourages ongoing efforts to improve products, services, or processes (Kent et al., 2020). It works on the premise that quality can always be improved and that small, incremental changes can lead to significant improvements over time (Chen et al., 2020).

In the context of a caregiver support program, CQI could involve regularly reviewing and refining program operations, services, and outcomes. This might involve regular staff meetings to discuss potential improvements, ongoing training and development opportunities for staff, regular surveys or feedback sessions with caregivers, and routine data collection and analysis to monitor program performance (Reinhard et al., 2020).

The goal of CQI is not to find faults or assign blame, but rather to identify opportunities for improvement and to encourage a culture of continual learning and improvement (Li et al., 2022). It involves all stakeholders, including caregivers, program staff, volunteers, and others, in a collaborative process of identifying, planning, implementing, and evaluating improvements (Tretteteig et al., 2021).

CQI is a cyclical process. It begins with the identification of an area for improvement, followed by planning and implementing changes. The impact of these changes is then evaluated, and the results are used to inform further improvements. This cycle repeats continuously, ensuring that the program is always striving to improve and adapt to the changing needs and preferences of caregivers (Dam et al., 2016).

The quality improvement process in the context of a caregiver support program involves a range of steps, including needs assessment, prioritization, collaboration, volunteerism, continuous monitoring, the use of evidence-based and evidence-informed practices, translating research into practice, evaluating the impact, and continuous quality improvement (Bom et al., 2019). Each of these steps is crucial for ensuring that the program is effective, relevant, and continually improving to meet the needs of caregivers (Kent et al., 2020).

Tailoring Interventions

The concept of tailoring interventions is a critical element in providing effective support for caregivers. It underscores the need to provide care that is not only evidence-informed, but also sensitive to the unique circumstances, needs, and preferences of the individuals being served (Chen et al., 2020). This process entails customizing or adapting available evidence-based interventions to match the specific conditions of caregivers in real-world settings.

For instance, an evidence-based stress management technique such as mindfulness meditation might be of great value to some caregivers. However, it's equally important to recognize that this technique may not be universally applicable or equally effective for all caregivers (Reinhard et al., 2020). Some caregivers may have cultural beliefs or practices that resonate more with other forms of stress management. In such cases, it's crucial to adapt the evidence-based practice or combine it with traditional or culturally specific practices to make it more relevant and effective for those caregivers (Li et al., 2022).

Similarly, a caregiver with a specific health condition might require a modified intervention approach. For instance, a caregiver with chronic pain might benefit from an evidence-based pain management strategy integrated into their stress management plan (Tretteteig et al., 2021). Therefore, tailoring interventions is not merely about implementing evidence-based practices verbatim; it's about integrating these practices into the caregivers' unique context in a meaningful and effective way (Dam et al., 2016).

Tailoring interventions also require a deep understanding of the caregivers' environment, their sociocultural context, their values, beliefs, and preferences. This understanding is often achieved through a collaborative relationship between the caregiver, the practitioner, and other relevant stakeholders, such as family members or community support groups (Bom et al., 2019).

Ultimately, the goal of tailoring interventions is to enhance the relevance, acceptability, and effectiveness of caregiver support programs. This approach acknowledges and respects the individuality, autonomy, and expertise of caregivers, thereby fostering a more empowering and person-centered model of care (Kent et al., 2020).

Learning from Experience

Learning from experience is a fundamental aspect of practice-based evidence and continuous quality improvement (Li et al., 2022). It involves reflecting on the outcomes of different interventions and strategies, identifying what works, and what doesn't work in the specific context of the caregiver support program. This process should be inclusive and collaborative, involving all stakeholders, including caregivers, program staff, and volunteers, to ensure a comprehensive understanding of the program's effectiveness (Tretteteig et al., 2021).

Learning from experience begins with observing and documenting the process and outcomes of interventions. This could involve quantitative measures such as caregiver stress levels or quality of life scores, as well as qualitative measures such as caregiver feedback or case notes (Dam et al., 2016). This data provides a basis for reflecting on the effectiveness of different interventions and strategies (Bom et al., 2019).

Reflection involves analyzing the data, interpreting the results, and drawing conclusions about the effectiveness of the interventions. This process should be collaborative, involving conversations and discussions among all stakeholders. These discussions can provide diverse perspectives, stimulate critical thinking, and foster collective understanding of the program's effectiveness (Kent et al., 2020).

Learning from experience also involves applying the insights gained from reflection to future interventions (Chen et al., 2020). This could involve modifying existing interventions, developing new interventions, or changing the way interventions are delivered. This application of learning ensures that the program continually evolves and improves, based on the insights gained from experience (Reinhard et al., 2020).

However, learning from experience is not a one-time process; it's a continuous cycle of observation, reflection, and application. This cycle ensures that the program continually learns from its experiences, adapts to changing circumstances, and strives for continuous improvement. In this way, learning from experience forms the backbone of evidence-informed practice and continuous quality improvement in caregiver support programs (Li et al., 2022).

The Wisdom of Practitioners

The wisdom of practitioners is a crucial element in the realm of caregiver support. Years of hands-on experience and direct interaction with caregivers bestow practitioners with a rich accumulation of knowledge, skills, and insights (Tretteteig et al., 2021). This wisdom extends beyond theoretical understanding and clinical expertise to include empathy, compassion, and a deep understanding of the nuanced challenges caregivers face. It is a holistic understanding that encompasses the physical, emotional, and psychological aspects of caregiving (Dam et al., 2016).

Practitioners' wisdom can offer valuable insights into the needs of caregivers. These insights are informed by the lived experiences of countless interactions, observations, and feedback from caregivers themselves (Bom et al., 2019). This can include understanding the emotional toll caregiving can take, the importance of self-care for caregivers, and practical strategies for managing common challenges such as stress, burnout, or managing complex care tasks (Kent et al., 2020).

Moreover, practitioner wisdom provides a rich source of effective strategies for supporting caregivers. These strategies are often grounded in practical experience and fine-tuned through trial and error. They can include strategies for building caregiver resilience, providing emotional support, improving communication with the care recipient, and navigating healthcare systems (Chen et al., 2020).

The value of practitioner wisdom in caregiver support is not limited to the knowledge practitioners possess. It also lies in their ability to adapt and apply their wisdom to each unique caregiving situation. Caregiving is inherently individualistic and context-dependent, and practitioners' wisdom can provide the necessary flexibility to tailor caregiver support approaches to individual needs and circumstances (Reinhard et al., 2020).

Therefore, in program evaluation and quality improvement efforts, the wisdom of practitioners should be respected and valued. Their experience-driven insights can identify gaps in caregiver support programs, suggest improvements and provide a reality check on the feasibility and relevance of potential strategies (Li et al., 2022).

Incorporating Practitioner Wisdom

Incorporating practitioner wisdom into the evaluation and improvement process of caregiver support programs is a multi-faceted endeavor. At its core, it involves recognizing and valuing the expertise that practitioners bring to the table (Tretteteig et al., 2021). This acknowledgement of the importance of practitioner wisdom is the first step in creating an environment where their insights are sought and their input is appreciated (Dam et al., 2016).

Engaging practitioners in the evaluation and improvement process is one practical way of incorporating their wisdom. This can involve regular consultations, feedback sessions, and making practitioners an integral part of decision-making processes (Bom et al., 2019). By encouraging their active participation, a two-way dialogue is created where practitioners can voice their insights, concerns, and suggestions (Kent et al., 2020).

Furthermore, providing opportunities for practitioners to learn from each other is another effective way of incorporating their wisdom. Peer learning groups, workshops, and forums can serve as platforms for practitioners to share experiences, insights, and effective strategies (Chen et al., 2020). This collaborative learning process can help in the cross-pollination of ideas, facilitating the spread of best practices and innovative solutions across the caregiver support landscape (Reinhard et al., 2020).

Incorporating practitioner wisdom also involves integrating their insights into the design and implementation of caregiver support programs. Rather than simply relying on theoretical models or research findings, the practical wisdom of practitioners can guide the creation of more relevant, effective, and adaptable support strategies (Li et al., 2022).

Incorporating practitioner wisdom is an ongoing process. It requires continuous engagement with practitioners, regular updates on their insights, and a willingness to adapt and refine strategies based on their feedback (Tretteteig et al., 2021). This ongoing integration of practitioner wisdom helps ensure that caregiver support programs remain responsive to changing needs and contexts (Dam et al., 2016).

Practice-based Evidence and the Wisdom of Practitioners

The value of practice-based evidence and the wisdom of practitioners cannot be overstated in the realm of caregiver support. These components bring in the critical dimensions of experiential knowledge and practical wisdom, which bridge the gap between theoretical knowledge and real-world application (Bom et al., 2019). They add depth, context, and practicality to the theoretical and empirical insights provided by evidence-based practices (Kent et al., 2020).

Practice-based evidence is derived from the everyday experiences, observations, and reflections of practitioners in real-world settings. It provides a practical, ground-level perspective of what works and what doesn't work in specific contexts (Chen et al., 2020). For example, a practitioner working with caregivers in a rural community might discover that certain interventions, which are theoretically sound and evidence-based, do not work well in that specific context due to cultural, socioeconomic, or logistical reasons (Reinhard et al., 2020).

Such insights, although they may not have been generated through formal research, are invaluable in providing contextualized, practical knowledge. They help in customizing and adapting evidence-based interventions to match the unique needs and circumstances of the caregivers being served. Moreover, practice-based evidence can also stimulate new research questions, thus contributing to the evolution of evidence-based practices (Li et al., 2022).

The wisdom of practitioners, on the other hand, refers to the experiential knowledge and insights gained through years of practical experience (Tretteteig et al., 2021). This wisdom, often honed through trial and error, success and failure, and continuous learning and adaptation, provides a rich and nuanced understanding of caregiver needs, challenges, and effective strategies for support (Dam et al., 2016).

Practitioners, over the years, develop a keen sense of intuition and insight, which enables them to understand and respond to the subtleties and complexities inherent in caregiving situations. They often develop innovative and effective strategies that are deeply rooted in their practical wisdom and contextual understanding. This wisdom is an invaluable resource in program evaluation and quality improvement (Bom et al., 2019).

Collaborative Learning and Shared Wisdom

Collaborative learning and shared wisdom are also critical elements of learning from experience. Collaborative learning involves engaging all stakeholders, including caregivers, practitioners, program staff, and volunteers, in the process of reflection and learning (Kent et al., 2020). This collaborative approach ensures a diverse range of perspectives, enriches the learning process, and fosters a sense of shared ownership and commitment to the program's success (Chen et al., 2020).

Shared wisdom involves leveraging the collective knowledge and insights of all stakeholders to inform program improvement. This could involve sharing success stories, lessons learned, and best practices. It could also involve collaborative problem-solving, where stakeholders work together to address challenges and develop solutions (Reinhard et al., 2020).

This process of collaborative learning and shared wisdom fosters a culture of continuous learning and improvement, where everyone is a learner and everyone is a teacher. It fosters a culture where wisdom is not confined to a few experts but is shared and cultivated by all (Li et al., 2022).

The Role of Feedback Loops

Feedback loops play a pivotal role in learning from experience. A feedback loop is a mechanism that allows the program to gather input about its operations and outcomes, analyze the data, and use the insights to improve future actions (Tretteteig et al., 2021). These loops create a continuous cycle of information flow that enables the program to adapt and evolve based on data-driven insights.

In the context of caregiver support, feedback loops could involve various types of data, such as caregiver satisfaction surveys, outcome measures, process indicators, and anecdotal reports from caregivers and practitioners (Dam et al., 2016). This data provides valuable insights into the strengths and weaknesses of the program and the impact of different interventions on caregiver well-being (Bom et al., 2019).

Feedback loops also support a culture of openness, where caregivers, practitioners, and other stakeholders feel comfortable sharing their experiences, ideas, and concerns (Kent et al., 2020). This openness fosters a collaborative environment where everyone is invested in the program's success and feels empowered to contribute to its continuous improvement (Chen et al., 2020).

Adaptive Learning and Iterative Improvement

Adaptive learning and iterative improvement are key components of learning from experience. Adaptive learning involves using the insights gained from feedback loops to make informed decisions about program improvement (Reinhard et al., 2020). This could involve making adjustments to existing interventions, developing new interventions, or changing the way interventions are delivered (Li et al., 2022).

Iterative improvement, on the other hand, involves implementing these changes in a gradual, step-by-step manner, while continuously monitoring the impact of these changes (Tretteteig et al., 2021). This iterative approach allows the program to test different strategies, learn from the results, and continually refine the strategies based on the learning (Dam et al., 2016).

This cycle of adaptive learning and iterative improvement ensures that the program is not static but continually evolving and improving (Bom et al., 2019). It ensures that the program is responsive and adaptive to the changing needs of caregivers and the emerging evidence in the field (Kent et al., 2020).

The Learning Organization

Fostering a culture of learning is key to embedding learning from experience into the fabric of a caregiver support program (Chen et al., 2020). This involves cultivating a learning organization, where learning is not confined to sporadic training events or formal evaluations, but is ingrained into everyday practice (Reinhard et al., 2020).

A learning organization continuously focuses on increasing its capabilities and performance through ongoing learning and adaptation (Li et al., 2022). It involves developing systems and processes that promote inquiry, reflection, knowledge sharing, and collective problem solving (Tretteteig et al., 2021).

For a caregiver support program, this could mean providing regular opportunities for staff to come together and reflect on program outcomes, share insights on effective practices, analyze challenges, and brainstorm solutions (Dam et al., 2016). It could also involve cross-training staff and encouraging peer-to-peer learning to enhance skills and perspective taking (Bom et al., 2019).

Moreover, a learning organization empowers people to actively question the status quo, seek new knowledge, and propose improvements (Kent et al., 2020). It recognizes that valuable insights can come from anywhere within the organization, not just formal leadership roles. This culture of continuous learning is key to ongoing improvement and innovation (Chen et al., 2020).

At its core, a learning organization in the context of caregiver support is driven by a shared vision to provide the best possible support for caregivers (Reinhard et al., 2020). By embedding learning into everyday practice through inquiry, reflection and knowledge sharing, the program can fulfill this vision while continually evolving and improving (Li et al., 2022).

Continuous Quality Improvement

Continuous quality improvement is an essential aspect of effective caregiver support programs (Li et al., 2022). It is a proactive approach that aims to ensure that caregiver support programs not only meet the needs of caregivers but also evolve and improve over time. This process requires a commitment to regular assessment, feedback, and refinement of program strategies and practices (Tretteteig et al., 2021).

The heart of continuous quality improvement lies in regular program evaluation. This involves assessing the effectiveness of the program, identifying areas of strength and areas in need of improvement (Dam et al., 2016). Evaluation can take many forms, including caregiver feedback, practitioner input, and quantitative measures of program outcomes (Bom et al., 2019). Through this process, caregiver support programs can gain a clear understanding of their performance and where improvements are needed (Kent et al., 2020).

Evidence-based and evidence-informed practices are key tools in the continuous quality improvement process (Chen et al., 2020). These practices, derived from rigorous research and validated by empirical evidence, provide a solid foundation for effective caregiver support. However, while important, they are not the only source of knowledge for improvement. The wisdom of practitioners, as discussed earlier, also plays a crucial role, providing practical, experience-based insights that complement and enrich evidence-based practices (Reinhard et al., 2020).

In continuous quality improvement, these elements - program evaluation, evidence-based and evidence-informed practices, and practitioner wisdom – are not standalone components but interconnected pieces of a larger system. They inform and reinforce each other, creating a dynamic, iterative process of improvement (Li et al., 2022).

The continuous quality improvement process is not a linear, one-time effort but an ongoing cycle. This cycle involves planning, doing, studying, and acting - a process commonly known as the PDSA cycle. This cycle ensures that improvements are not just made but also monitored, assessed, and refined over time, securing the effectiveness and relevance of caregiver support programs (Tretteteig et al., 2021).

By embracing continuous quality improvement, caregiver support programs can ensure they are providing the most effective and high-quality support to caregivers (Dam et al., 2016). It enables these programs to adapt to the changing needs of caregivers and to the evolving landscape of care. This adaptability is crucial in a field as dynamic and complex as caregiving, where new challenges and opportunities continually emerge (Bom et al., 2019).

Program Evaluation and Quality Improvement

Program evaluation and quality improvement are critical components of effective caregiver support. They serve as key mechanisms for understanding how well a program is working, where it can do better, and how it can adapt to the changing needs and aspirations of caregivers (Kent et al., 2020).

Program evaluation is more than just a measure of effectiveness; it's a tool for learning and improvement. It involves systematically collecting and analyzing information about program activities, characteristics, and outcomes to understand its effectiveness and make informed decisions (Chen et al., 2020). Feedback from caregivers, insights from practitioners, and analysis of program data all contribute to a comprehensive understanding of the program's strengths and areas needing improvement (Reinhard et al., 2020).

The evaluation process should be designed to capture the nuances of the caregiving experience. This requires a combination of quantitative and qualitative methods. Quantitative methods, such as surveys and data analysis, provide a broad overview of program outcomes and trends. Qualitative methods, like interviews and focus groups, can provide deeper insights into caregivers' experiences, perceptions, and needs (Li et al., 2022).

Quality improvement is the natural follow-up to program evaluation. Once areas needing improvement have been identified, a plan can be developed to address these issues. This plan should be specific, measurable, achievable, relevant, and time-bound (SMART) (Tretteteig et al., 2021). It should outline clear steps for how improvements will be implemented and how success will be measured (Dam et al., 2016).

Quality improvement should be a continuous, cyclical process. It involves implementing changes, monitoring the effects of these changes, refining and adjusting as necessary, and then starting the cycle again. This iterative process promotes ongoing learning and adaptation, ensuring that caregiver support programs continually evolve to meet the changing needs of caregivers (Bom et al., 2019).

Both program evaluation and quality improvement are essential for ensuring caregiver support programs are as effective as possible (Kent et al., 2020). They provide the tools for understanding what works, what doesn't, and how to make meaningful, lasting improvements. Through this process, caregiver support programs can ensure they are providing the best possible support to caregivers, today and in the future (Chen et al., 2020).

Harnessing Technology for Learning

Technology can greatly enhance the process of learning from experience. Technological tools such as digital surveys, data analytics, and collaborative platforms can make the process of data collection, analysis, and collaborative learning more efficient and effective (Reinhard et al., 2020).

Digital surveys can provide a convenient and efficient way for caregivers and practitioners to provide feedback (Li et al., 2022). Data analytics can help analyze large volumes of data and generate actionable insights (Tretteteig et al., 2021). Collaborative platforms can facilitate discussions, idea sharing, and collective learning among stakeholders (Dam et al., 2016).

In addition, technology can also support the dissemination of learning. Through webinars, online training programs, and digital libraries, the program can share its learning with a wider audience, thereby contributing to the broader field of caregiver support (Bom et al., 2019).

Learning from experience, underpinned by feedback loops, adaptive learning, iterative improvement, collaborative learning, shared wisdom, and technology, forms the backbone of evidence-informed practice and continuous quality improvement in caregiver support programs (Kent et al., 2020). It ensures that these programs are not only grounded in evidence but also responsive to the lived experiences of caregivers and practitioners, thereby ensuring the most effective and high-quality support to caregivers (Chen et al., 2020).

Chapter 5- Educational Needs of Caregiver Families

5.1: Understanding the Educational Needs of Caregiver Families

Caregiving, an act of profound love and compassion, necessitates not only physical strength but also emotional resilience and cognitive preparedness (Pearlin et al., 1990). It often falls upon family members, who might find themselves in the role of caregivers without adequate knowledge or skills to manage the complex medical and social needs of their loved ones (Family Caregiver Alliance, 2020). This lack of preparedness can lead to stress, burnout, and diminished care quality (Adelman et al., 2014).

Recognizing the unique challenges family caregivers face, the role of education in their journey is pivotal (Coleman, 2016). Through education, caregiver families can be empowered to navigate the labyrinth of caregiving, ensuring better outcomes for both the caregiver and the care recipient (Sinclair et al., 2020). This article aims to delve into the multifaceted educational needs of caregiver families and the transformative potential of education in caregiving outcomes.

Multifaceted Educational Needs of Caregiver Families

Family caregivers often find themselves thrust into a complex web of responsibilities that stretch beyond their pre-existing knowledge and skills (Reinhard et al., 2020). These responsibilities can range from managing the medical aspects of a loved one's condition to providing emotional support and navigating social and legal dynamics (Family Caregiver Alliance, 2012). The key to successfully handling these challenges lies within the realms of knowledge, skills, and attitudes (Coleman, 2016).

Knowledge: Medical Aspects

The medical domain of caregiving encompasses a wide array of subjects (Reinhard et al., 2020). First and foremost, caregivers must understand the nature of their loved one's illness. This comprehension requires a basic understanding of the illness's symptoms, the course it typically follows, and its potential complications (Coleman, 2016). For instance, if their loved one has Alzheimer's disease, the caregiver should be familiar with the cognitive and behavioral changes that occur as the disease progresses (Alzheimer's Association, 2022). This understanding can help caregivers anticipate changes and adapt their care strategies as needed.

In addition to understanding the disease itself, caregivers need to know about the various treatment options that are available (Reinhard et al., 2020). This includes understanding the purpose and desired outcomes of different treatments, as well as the potential side effects (Family Caregiver Alliance, 2020). For example, a caregiver may need to know what to do if the care recipient experiences side effects from their medication, such as nausea or fatigue (Coleman, 2016).

Caregivers often perform medical tasks at home, such as administering medication, changing dressings, or monitoring vital signs (Reinhard et al., 2020). Therefore, they need to acquire the necessary skills to perform these tasks and understand when to seek professional help (Family Caregiver Alliance, 2020). This includes knowing how to recognize signs of a medical emergency and how to respond appropriately (Coleman, 2016).

Knowledge about pain management is also essential (Reinhard et al., 2020). Caregivers should be aware of the different ways to manage pain, whether through medication, non-pharmacological techniques, or a combination of both (Family Caregiver Alliance, 2020). They should also be able to distinguish between typical discomfort and severe or unusual pain that requires immediate medical attention (Coleman, 2016).

Finally, caregivers should understand the benefits of palliative and end-of-life care (Reinhard et al., 2020). They need to be aware of the options for ensuring the comfort and dignity of their loved ones during this challenging time (Family Caregiver Alliance, 2020). This knowledge can help them make informed decisions about end-of-life care when the time comes (Coleman, 2016).

Knowledge: Social Aspects

Understanding the social aspects of caregiving is of equal importance (Reinhard et al., 2020). Caregivers should be aware of the significant role that lifestyle factors such as diet and exercise play in promoting health and well-being (Family Caregiver Alliance, 2020). A balanced diet can help maintain the care recipient's physical health and optimize their body's ability to recover and fight off disease (Coleman, 2016). Regular physical activity, adapted to the care recipient's abilities, can also have positive effects on both physical and mental health (Reinhard et al., 2020).

Caregivers should also consider the importance of social interactions for their loved ones (Family Caregiver Alliance, 2020). Regular contact with friends and family can boost the care recipient's mood and help prevent feelings of isolation (Coleman, 2016). Additionally, mental stimulation, such as engaging in hobbies or intellectual activities, can have beneficial effects on cognitive health (Reinhard et al., 2020). For example, someone with dementia may benefit from activities that stimulate memory and cognitive function, such as puzzles or reminiscence therapy (Family Caregiver Alliance, 2020).

Understanding the impact of the caregiving role on their own social life is also crucial for caregivers (Coleman, 2016). Caregiving can be isolating, and caregivers may need to seek out support groups or counseling services to cope with the emotional strain (Reinhard et al., 2020). They should also learn to accept help when offered and to ask for help when needed (Family Caregiver Alliance, 2020).

Caregivers should also be aware of the importance of maintaining their health and well-being (Coleman, 2016). This includes recognizing the signs of caregiver stress or burnout and taking steps to address it, such as seeking respite care, practicing self-care, and validating their own feelings and experiences (Reinhard et al., 2020).

Knowledge: Legal and Financial Aspects

The legal and financial aspects of caregiving can be complex, but they are crucial for ensuring the rights and welfare of the care recipient (Family

Caregiver Alliance, 2020). Caregivers should be knowledgeable about patient rights, including the right to privacy, dignity, and informed consent (Coleman, 2016). Understanding these rights can protect the care recipient from potential exploitation or abuse (Reinhard et al., 2020).

Caregivers should also be aware of the legal documents that may be necessary for managing their loved one's care (Family Caregiver Alliance, 2020). This includes power of attorney documents, advance healthcare directives, and wills (Coleman, 2016). These documents can ensure that the care recipient's wishes are respected and that any medical or financial decisions made on their behalf are in their best interest (Reinhard et al., 2020).

Financial knowledge is also crucial for caregiver families (Family Caregiver Alliance, 2020). This includes understanding the costs associated with long-term care, such as home care services, medical supplies, and medication (Coleman, 2016). Caregivers should be aware of any insurance coverage their loved one has, including what is covered and what is not (Reinhard et al., 2020).

Knowledge of financial planning and resource management for long-term care is essential for caregiver families (Family Caregiver Alliance, 2020). This includes understanding how to budget for care costs, how to protect the care recipient's assets, and how to plan for potential changes in financial circumstances (Coleman, 2016).

Caregivers should be aware of the community resources available to them (Family Caregiver Alliance, 2020). This may include local agencies that provide services such as respite care, meal delivery, or transportation (Coleman, 2016). Additionally, there may be financial assistance programs or subsidies available to help cover the costs of care (Reinhard et al., 2020). By understanding these resources, caregivers can make informed decisions about how best to manage their loved one's care.

Skills: Practical Abilities and Competencies

The second domain involves developing practical skills and competencies (Coleman, 2016). This includes mastering daily tasks such as medication management, wound care, and mobility assistance (Reinhard et al., 2020). These tasks often require specific techniques and precautions to ensure safety and effectiveness (Family Caregiver Alliance, 2020).

Effective communication with healthcare professionals is another vital skill (Coleman, 2016). Caregivers need to articulate their concerns clearly, understand medical jargon, and actively participate in healthcare decision-making (Reinhard et al., 2020). This can help ensure that the care recipient's needs are accurately communicated and adequately addressed (Family Caregiver Alliance, 2020).

Caregivers must acquire problem-solving skills to navigate unexpected challenges (Coleman, 2016). This can involve creative thinking, adaptability, and decision-making under pressure (Reinhard et al., 2020). Time-management skills and the ability to delegate responsibilities can also be invaluable in preventing caregiver burnout (Family Caregiver Alliance, 2020).

Lastly, self-care skills are essential for caregivers (Coleman, 2016). They need to recognize their own physical and emotional needs, and take proactive measures to maintain their health (Reinhard et al., 2020). This can involve regular exercise, adequate rest, balanced nutrition, and seeking emotional support when needed (Family Caregiver Alliance, 2020).

Attitudes: Shaping Perspectives and Approaches

The third domain pertains to attitudes, which can shape caregivers' perspectives and approaches toward their role (Coleman, 2016). Caregivers need to cultivate empathy, compassion, patience, and resilience (Reinhard et al., 2020). These attitudes can help them navigate the emotional roller coaster that accompanies caregiving and manage their emotions effectively (Family Caregiver Alliance, 2020).

Understanding the emotional journey of caregiving can help caregivers maintain a positive outlook even in challenging situations (Coleman,

2016). They need to recognize that feelings of stress, sadness, and frustration are normal and valid (Reinhard et al., 2020). Developing coping strategies, such as seeking support, practicing mindfulness, or engaging in hobbies, can help manage these emotions (Family Caregiver Alliance, 2020).

Also, caregivers need to adopt a patient-centered approach to caregiving (Coleman, 2016). This involves respecting the autonomy and preferences of the care recipient, promoting their dignity, and aiming to improve their quality of life (Reinhard et al., 2020). This attitude can foster a more harmonious caregiving relationship and enhance the care recipient's mental well-being (Family Caregiver Alliance, 2020).

Transformative Impact of Education on Caregiving Outcomes

The power of education to transform lives is well-recognized, and its impact is no less significant in the context of caregiving (Coleman, 2016). Education can equip caregiver families with the knowledge, skills, and attitudes necessary to navigate their caregiving journey confidently and compassionately (Reinhard et al., 2020). It can also have a broader impact on societal attitudes toward caregiving, fostering empathy and recognition for caregivers (Family Caregiver Alliance, 2020).

Empowerment and Autonomy

Education plays a crucial role in fostering a sense of empowerment among caregivers (Coleman, 2016). Empowerment in a caregiving context implies the ability to effectively manage the multifaceted demands of caregiving (Reinhard et al., 2020). This can range from understanding the medical condition of their loved ones, administering medication properly, managing diet and exercise routines, to handling emergency situations (Family Caregiver Alliance, 2020). Through education, caregivers can acquire these necessary skills and knowledge, hence enhancing their self-efficacy in caregiving (Coleman, 2016).

A well-informed caregiver can make decisions about care with confidence (Coleman, 2016). They can assess the pros and cons of different treatment

SCHIELOH WOLFE, M.S. AND NAOMI LATINI WOLFE, M.S.

options and make choices that best fit the needs and preferences of their loved ones (Reinhard et al., 2020). By being actively involved in the decision-making process, caregivers can ensure that the care provided aligns with the values and wishes of their care recipients (Family Caregiver Alliance, 2020). This active role not only improves the quality of care but also fosters a sense of agency and autonomy in caregivers (Coleman, 2016).

With the right knowledge and skills, caregivers can reduce their reliance on healthcare professionals (Coleman, 2016). While medical professionals provide essential support, caregivers equipped with the right knowledge can handle day-to-day care tasks more effectively (Reinhard et al., 2020). This reduced dependence can alleviate some of the healthcare system's burden and provide caregivers with a greater sense of control over their caregiving situation (Family Caregiver Alliance, 2020).

The sense of empowerment and autonomy can have a profound impact on caregivers' mental well-being (Coleman, 2016). Caregiving, especially long-term, can induce feelings of helplessness and burnout (Reinhard et al., 2020). However, when caregivers feel capable and confident, they are less likely to experience these negative emotions (Family Caregiver Alliance, 2020). Instead, they can derive a sense of accomplishment and satisfaction from their role, leading to improved self-esteem and overall mental health (Coleman, 2016).

With a deep understanding of the disease process, the potential complications, and coping strategies, caregivers can better navigate the uncertainties and challenges of caregiving (Coleman, 2016). They can develop a holistic and realistic view of their role, which can help them adapt to changing circumstances and maintain their well-being (Reinhard et al., 2020)..

Communication and Advocacy

Effective communication skills. Effective communication is crucial in the caregiving journey. Education can enhance caregivers' communication skills, enabling them to articulate their concerns and needs clearly and effectively. With a better understanding of medical terms and conditions, caregivers can communicate more efficiently with healthcare professionals. They can ask relevant questions, clarify doubts, and better comprehend the information provided by doctors and nurses (Beder, 2013).

Active participation in healthcare. Furthermore, education empowers caregivers to actively participate in healthcare decision-making. By understanding the medical condition of their loved ones and the implications of different treatment options, caregivers can contribute meaningfully to discussions about care (Rosland et al., 2018). This active involvement can lead to more informed decisions and better healthcare outcomes for the care recipient.

Advocacy. Education can also transform caregivers into advocates for their loved ones. Armed with knowledge, caregivers can ensure that the rights and needs of their loved ones are respected in the healthcare system. They can negotiate with healthcare providers, challenge decisions when necessary, and ensure that the care provided aligns with the preferences of their loved ones (Carbonneau et al., 2010).

Impact on dignity and autonomy. This advocacy role can have a significant impact on the dignity and autonomy of care recipients. It can ensure that they are treated as individuals with unique needs and preferences, rather than just patients. This can lead to more personalized, compassionate, and dignified care (Bastawrous, 2013).

Raising awareness. Moreover, caregivers can use their knowledge and experiences to raise awareness about caregiving issues. They can advocate for better policies and support systems for caregivers, contributing to societal change (Burghardt et al., 2013). By doing so, caregivers can help create a more caregiver-friendly society, where their roles are recognized and valued, and their needs are adequately addressed.

Shaping Societal Attitudes

Promoting empathy and reducing stigma. Education can also play a crucial role in shaping societal attitudes towards caregiving. By raising awareness about the role and challenges of caregivers, education can foster empathy, respect, and support for them in society. This can help reduce the stigma associated with caregiving, and recognize it as an act of profound love and compassion (Bergmann, 2020).

Practical support. Awareness and understanding can also lead to practical support for caregivers. This can take the form of more supportive policies, better access to resources, and more flexible work arrangements (Reinhard et al., 2008). Such societal support can significantly reduce the burden on caregivers, and improve their emotional well-being and quality of life.

Inclusion in community. Additionally, education can help normalize caregiving as a part of life, and promote the inclusion of caregiver families in social activities and community life. This can reduce feelings of isolation among caregivers, and provide them with opportunities for relaxation and social connection (Hill et al., 2009).

Evidence-Based Educational Programs

The Savvy Caregiver Program. There are various evidence-based educational programs designed to address the educational needs of caregiver families. Two such programs include the Savvy Caregiver Program and the SHARE program (Support, Health, Activities, Resources, and Education). The Savvy Caregiver Program is a comprehensive six-week program that focuses on equipping caregivers with the knowledge and skills needed to manage the challenges of caregiving effectively (Hepburn et al., 2007). It provides learning on understanding dementia, developing communication skills, problem-solving techniques, and self-care strategies.

The SHARE program. The SHARE program is a community-based initiative that offers educational workshops and support groups for caregiver families (Clay et al., 2013). It creates a safe and supportive platform where caregivers can learn from each other, share experiences, and build a network of support.

Education plays a crucial role in equipping caregiver families to navigate this journey successfully. Not only does it empower caregivers with the necessary knowledge and skills, but it also fosters a sense of autonomy and confidence in their caregiving abilities. Furthermore, education enables caregivers to advocate for their loved ones effectively and helps shape societal attitudes towards caregiving. The Savvy Caregiver Program and the SHARE program are examples of how education can be tailored to address the unique needs of caregiver families. They offer a beacon of hope, lighting the path towards a future where caregiving is recognized and celebrated as an act of love, compassion, and resilience.

5.2: Developing Educational Programs for Caregiver Families

Ensuring Efficient and Effective Care

Developing Educational Programs for Caregiver Families: Ensuring Efficient and Effective Care

Caring for a loved one is often a labor of love that requires immense emotional strength and dedication. It can be a rewarding experience, but it also comes with its unique set of challenges, particularly for family caregivers who often must juggle caring responsibilities with their personal and professional lives. This delicate balancing act can lead to stress, burnout, and feelings of isolation, which may impact the quality of care provided. Therefore, it becomes critical to empower these caregiver families with the knowledge and skills to navigate the complex landscape of caregiving.

Educational programs tailored to the needs of caregiver families can play a transformative role in this context. They can provide vital practical information, emotional support, and coping strategies to manage the demands of caregiving effectively. However, developing these programs requires a deep understanding of the multifaceted needs of the caregivers, from managing the medical requirements of their loved ones to overseeing the emotional and psychological challenges that come with caregiving.

The development of such educational programs must be driven by a comprehensive approach that addresses the caregivers' unique challenges and equips them with the necessary tools to provide efficient and effective care. The following sections delve into critical aspects to consider when developing educational programs for caregiver families, from content selection and delivery methods to addressing emotional challenges and ensuring continuous program evaluation and adaptation.

Content Selection

Medication management. The selection of content for educational programs aimed at caregiver families is a crucial aspect that can significantly influence the effectiveness of the program. A well-curated content selection should address the unique challenges and responsibilities that caregivers face, providing them with comprehensive knowledge and strategies to manage their roles effectively. One of the critical areas that programs should cover is medication management. Caregivers often find themselves in the role of managing their loved ones' medications, which can be complex and daunting. Content should include understanding distinct types of medications, potential side effects, interactions, and proper administration techniques (Reinhard et al., 2019). Additionally, information on maintaining medication schedules and organizing medication regimens can be of major help to caregivers.

Nutrition guidance. Nutritional guidance is another essential component of the program. The right nutrition can significantly impact the health and well-being of the care recipient. Therefore, providing caregivers with a solid understanding of nutritional needs, dietary restrictions, and meal preparation strategies is vital (Vaitkeviciute et al., 2018). This information can be especially beneficial when caring for individuals with specific dietary needs related to chronic diseases like diabetes, heart disease, or dementia.

Safety precautions. Safety precautions form the bedrock of day-to-day caregiving. This involves understanding how to prevent falls, manage emergencies, and ensure a safe living environment (Huang et al., 2015). It is also important to include content on recognizing signs of physical, emotional, or financial abuse, as elderly people are often vulnerable to these forms of exploitation.

Legal and financial guidance. Legal and financial issues are often an overlooked aspect of caregiving. Caregivers may need to navigate complex legal systems to maintain or take control of their loved one's affairs. Offering resources and guidance on topics such as power of attorney, guardianship, healthcare directives, and estate planning can provide much-needed support (Reinhard et al., 2019).

Self-care strategies. The content must cater to the needs of both the caregiver and the care recipient. This includes information on self-care for caregivers, understanding the emotional toll of caregiving, and strategies to maintain mental and physical health (Ugalde et al., 2018). Furthermore, resources on support services available for caregivers and how to access them can be invaluable.

Delivery Methods

In-person workshops. The delivery methods of the educational programs should be tailored to the varying needs and preferences of caregiver families. The methods need to be flexible, accessible, and engaging to ensure optimal learning and retention. In-person workshops can be highly beneficial for caregivers. They offer a chance for direct interaction with experts and a firsthand learning experience (Goyal et al., 2019). These workshops can cover a range of topics, from practical skills like wound care or mobility assistance, to softer skills like communication or stress management. Moreover, the real-time feedback and clarification provided during these workshops can enhance learning outcomes.

Online resources. Online resources offer flexibility and convenience, which can be especially beneficial for caregivers juggling multiple responsibilities. Webinars can provide in-depth knowledge on specific topics, while video tutorials can demonstrate practical skills (Parra-Vidales et al., 2017). Articles and blogs can offer quick access to information and advice. Furthermore, interactive forums can create a sense of community, where caregivers can pose questions, share experiences, and learn from one another.

Support groups. Support groups can be a boon for caregivers, offering emotional support and practical advice. These groups can exist in both physical and online spaces, catering to different preferences (Chan et al., 2019). They provide a safe environment for caregivers to express their feelings, fears, and frustrations, and receive comfort and advice from others in similar situations.

Addressing Emotional and Psychological Challenges

Stress management. Caregiving can be a highly emotionally charged experience, often leading to feelings of guilt, sadness, stress, and burnout.

Educational programs must acknowledge these challenges and equip caregivers with coping strategies. Stress management workshops can provide caregivers with practical strategies to manage their stress levels (Cooper et al., 2016). This can include techniques like mindfulness exercises, deep breathing, and progressive muscle relaxation. It can also involve training on time management and setting boundaries to prevent caregiver burnout.

Communication skills training. Communication skills training can help caregivers effectively communicate their needs and concerns, both to the care recipient and to other family members or healthcare professionals (Judge et al., 2011). It can also help caregivers manage difficult conversations, such as discussing care plans, changes in health status, or end-of-life decisions.

Self-care strategies. Self-care is another critical area that programs should focus on. Caregivers often neglect their own health and well-being, which can have a detrimental effect on both their physical and mental health. Workshops on self-care can teach caregivers the importance of maintaining their own health, and provide strategies for physical exercise, balanced nutrition, adequate rest, and mental health care (Acton, 2002).

Support groups. Support groups play a vital role in managing emotional challenges. The shared experience of caregiving can foster a powerful sense of community and empathy among group members (Sun et al., 2010). These groups can offer emotional support, reassurance, and practical advice, reducing feelings of isolation and helplessness.

Continuous Evaluation and Adaptation

Caregiver feedback. Continuous evaluation and adaptation are crucial for maintaining the relevance and effectiveness of educational programs. As the needs and challenges of caregiver families evolve, so should the programs that aim to support them. Feedback from caregivers, care recipients, and healthcare professionals can provide valuable insights into the program's effectiveness. Surveys, interviews, and focus group discussions can be used to collect this feedback (Montgomery et al., 2009). These methods can highlight areas of success, identify gaps, and suggest improvements.

Content and delivery adaptation. This feedback can be used to revise and update the program content and delivery methods. For example, if feedback indicates that caregivers are struggling with a particular topic, such as understanding complex medication regimes, the program can be revised to include more in-depth information and practical examples on this topic (Nichols et al., 2011).

Similarly, if caregivers express a preference for a particular delivery method, such as online webinars over in-person workshops, the program can be adapted to provide more online learning opportunities. The convenience and accessibility of online resources can be a significant advantage for many caregivers, particularly those who are balancing caregiving with other responsibilities.

Outcomes measurement. Continuous evaluation also allows for the measurement of program outcomes. This can include assessments of knowledge gained, skills developed, and changes in attitudes or behaviors (Elliott et al., 2010). These outcomes can provide valuable evidence of the program's effectiveness and can be used to justify continued funding or support for the program.

Updating for new developments. Moreover, continuous adaptation ensures that the program remains current and relevant. As new research emerges, best practices evolve, and healthcare policies change, the program must adapt to reflect these changes (Samia et al., 2012). For example, if new guidelines for dementia care are published, these should be incorporated into the program content.

Flexibility for changing needs. Lastly, considering the dynamic nature of caregiving, where the care recipient's health status can change rapidly, the program content needs to be flexible and adaptable (Sörensen et al., 2002). It should provide resources and support for caregivers at all stages of the caregiving journey, from the initial diagnosis to advanced stages of illness and end-of-life care.

Educational programs for caregiver families play a vital role in providing the necessary knowledge, skills, and support to navigate the complex challenges of caregiving. By ensuring relevant content selection, flexible delivery methods, addressing emotional and psychological challenges, and providing continuous evaluation and adaptation, these programs can significantly enhance the caregiving experience, improving the quality of care provided and the well-being of both the caregiver and the care recipient.

5.3: Engaging Caregiver Families in Educational Initiatives

Empowering Caregiver Families and Promoting a Culture of Continuous Learning

The journey of family caregivers is one marked by love, resilience, and often, complexity. Caregivers play a crucial role in healthcare, offering both physical and emotional support to their loved ones. However, they often face a myriad of challenges, such as navigating intricate healthcare systems, managing medications, and providing emotional support, all while balancing their personal life (Reinhard et al., 2020). These challenges underscore the importance of engaging caregiver families in educational initiatives, which can empower them to effectively navigate their unique journeys and promote optimal caregiver outcomes (Family Caregiver Alliance, 2022).

Engaging caregiver families in educational initiatives is not just about providing information; it is about empowerment, building capacity, and fostering resilience. It is about recognizing the caregiver's role, valuing their contribution, and equipping them with the tools they need to provide the best possible care (Family Caregiver Alliance, 2022). It is about creating a culture of continuous learning, where caregivers are encouraged to learn, grow, and adapt in their caregiving journey (Reinhard et al., 2020).

Understanding and addressing caregivers' needs necessitates an approach that is holistic, adaptive, and responsive (Family Caregiver Alliance, 2022). It calls for initiatives that are inclusive and collaborative, and which value the lived experiences and insights of caregivers (Kent et al., 2016). It demands the development and implementation of strategies that harness the power of technology to provide flexible, accessible, and personalized educational resources (Reinhard et al., 2020).

By engaging caregiver families in educational initiatives, we can create a nurturing environment where caregivers feel supported, heard, and empowered (Family Caregiver Alliance, 2022). This, in turn, can enhance the caregiver's well-being, reduce caregiver burnout, and improve the quality of care provided to their loved one (Kent et al., 2016). This article delves into the various strategies for engaging caregiver families in educational initiatives, exploring how these strategies can empower caregiver families and promote a culture of continuous learning.

Empowering Caregiver Families

Empowerment is a critical component when collaborating with caregiver families in educational programs. Caregiving, whether for an elderly parent, a spouse with a chronic illness, a child with special needs, or another family member, can be a complex and demanding journey (Reinhard et al., 2019). The empowerment of caregivers is about enhancing their abilities to manage their caregiving roles confidently and independently (Bauer et al., 2021).

The cornerstone of empowerment lies in personalized support. Every caregiving situation is unique, shaped by a variety of factors including the nature of the care recipient's needs, the caregiver's personal attributes, and the resources available to them (Beach et al., 2021). Personalized support recognizes these individual nuances and tailors' assistance accordingly. This could mean providing emotional support, practical advice, or helping caregivers navigate healthcare systems (Kent et al., 2016). Personalized support can lessen the burden of caregiving, enabling caregivers to be more effective and resilient in their roles (Chen et al., 2020).

Capacity building is another key aspect of caregiver empowerment. This involves equipping caregivers with the knowledge, skills, and resources they need to fulfill their caregiving roles (Li et al., 2019). It may involve training in practical care skills, like how to safely lift and transfer a care recipient or managing complex medication regimes. It also includes building soft skills such as problem-solving, communication, and stress management (McCarron et al., 2019). Capacity building empowers caregivers to manage their caregiving tasks more skillfully and confidently, improving the quality of care provided and their own well-being (Rodakowski et al., 2017).

The provision of educational resources is also a critical part of empowering caregiver families. This could include written materials, online resources, and workshops that provide information about the care recipient's condition, treatment options, and available support services (Barbabella et al., 2019). Educational resources can demystify the caregiving process, help caregivers make informed decisions, and connect them with a broader community of caregivers for peer support and shared learning (Brown et al., 2016).

Empowering caregiver families is not a one-off event but a continuous process that evolves with the changing needs and circumstances of the caregivers. It requires a supportive and responsive system that recognizes and respects the invaluable work caregivers do and is committed to providing them with ongoing support and learning opportunities (Greenwood et al., 2019). Caregivers empowered in such a manner are not only better equipped to provide care but are also more likely to find fulfillment and satisfaction in their caregiving roles (Samson et al., 2016).

Personalized Support

Personalized support is a cornerstone in the empowerment of caregiver families. The caregiving journey is an intensely personal one, with every caregiver facing different challenges and circumstances (Dionne-Odom et al., 2019). Recognizing and addressing these unique needs can make a significant difference in the caregiver's experience.

Personalized support initiatives may include one-on-one consultations, which provide caregivers with a safe space to discuss their concerns, ask questions, and receive advice tailored to their specific needs (Adams et al., 2019). Healthcare professionals, social workers, or experienced caregivers can facilitate these consultations. They can cover a broad range of topics, from managing the physical aspects of caregiving to coping with emotional stress.

338 SCHIELOH WOLFE, M.S. AND NAOMI LATINI WOLFE, M.S.

In addition to individual consultations, personalized support can also involve targeted workshops and support groups (Robinson et al., 2019). These initiatives can provide caregivers with a sense of community, helping them to feel less alone in their journey. They can also offer practical advice and tips tailored to specific caregiving situations, such as caring for a loved one with dementia or managing end-of-life care.

Furthermore, personalized support recognizes the importance of catering to the caregiver's preferences. This means that support initiatives should be flexible, allowing caregivers to choose the types of support they want and need (Sinclair et al., 2020). For instance, some caregivers may prefer online support groups, while others may benefit more from in-person workshops.

Personalized support also involves connecting caregivers with relevant resources and services (Anastasia et al., 2020). This could include referring caregivers to financial assistance programs, legal services, or respite care options. By doing so, personalized support can help to alleviate the practical burdens of caregiving, empowering caregivers to navigate their journey with greater confidence and autonomy.

Capacity Building

Capacity building is another crucial aspect of empowering caregiver families. It involves equipping caregivers with the skills and abilities they need to effectively care for their loved ones (Dam et al., 2019).

One key component of capacity building is training caregivers in specific caregiving skills. This could involve teaching caregivers how to manage medications, provide wound care, assist with mobility, or manage behavioral issues (Vandepitte et al., 2019). Such training can be delivered through workshops, online courses, or firsthand sessions with healthcare professionals.

Beyond physical caregiving skills, capacity building also encompasses emotional and mental health skills. Caregivers often face elevated levels of stress and emotional burden, making it vital to equip them with coping strategies (Lilly et al., 2019). This could involve training in stress management techniques, mindfulness practices, or counselling skills.

Capacity building also involves teaching caregivers how to navigate the healthcare system (Czaja et al., 2019). This could include understanding medical jargon, communicating effectively with healthcare professionals, making informed decisions about treatment options, and advocating for their loved ones' rights.

Importantly, capacity building should also focus on empowering caregivers to take care of their own health and well-being (Parveen et al., 2017). This could involve educating caregivers about the importance of self-care, providing them with strategies for maintaining their physical health, and connecting them with resources to support their mental well-being.

By building their capacity in these various areas, caregivers can provide better care for their loved ones and feel more confident and competent in their caregiving roles (Van Houtven et al., 2020).

Educational Resources

Educational resources are vital tools in empowering caregiver families. They provide caregivers with the knowledge they need to understand and manage the complexities of caregiving (Samson et al., 2016). These resources can come in various forms, including books, online articles, webinars, and training modules.

Resources that offer information about specific illnesses or conditions can be immensely helpful (Greenwood et al., 2019). They can help caregivers understand what their loved one is going through, anticipate potential challenges, and learn about treatment options. This knowledge can empower caregivers to make informed decisions and provide more effective care.

At the same time, educational resources can also provide practical advice for managing the day-to-day aspects of caregiving (Sinclair et al., 2020).

This could include tips for managing medications, advice on modifying the home environment for safety, or strategies for handling difficult behaviors.

In addition to providing information and advice, educational resources can also serve as sources of emotional support (Dionne-Odom et al., 2019). They can include personal stories from other caregivers, offering reassurance that others have faced similar challenges and overcome them. These stories can serve as a source of inspiration and hope, helping caregivers to feel less alone in their journey.

Educational resources can also help caregivers manage their own well-being (Czaja et al., 2019). They can provide information about stress management techniques, advice on balancing caregiving with other responsibilities, and strategies for seeking help when needed.

By equipping caregivers with knowledge and practical tips, educational resources can empower them to navigate their caregiving journey with greater confidence and resilience (Van Houtven et al., 2020).

Promoting a Culture of Continuous Learning

Promoting a culture of continuous learning among caregiver families is pivotal. Caregiving is a dynamic journey, with new challenges and situations continually emerging. As such, caregivers must be prepared to continually adapt and grow (Bauer et al., 2021).

One way to promote continuous learning is through a trauma-informed care approach. This approach recognizes that many caregivers have experienced trauma, either through their caregiving experiences or in other areas of their lives (Beach et al., 2021). It involves creating a safe and supportive environment where caregivers can learn and grow, while also addressing their trauma-related needs.

Caregiver education and training programs are another crucial component of promoting continuous learning (Parveen et al., 2017). These programs should be ongoing, allowing caregivers to continually update their skills and knowledge. In addition to providing information about specific illnesses and conditions, these programs should also cover a broad range of topics, such as effective communication with healthcare professionals, legal and financial planning, and self-care strategies for caregivers (Rodakowski et al., 2017). This comprehensive approach to education ensures that caregivers are well-equipped to manage the multi-faceted challenges of caregiving.

Promoting a culture of continuous learning also involves recognizing and validating the experiential knowledge that caregivers acquire through their caregiving journey (Kent et al., 2016). Caregivers often develop a wealth of practical knowledge and insights through their experiences. Recognizing this knowledge and incorporating it into educational initiatives can help to validate caregivers' experiences, boost their confidence, and enhance the relevance and effectiveness of the education provided.

Caregiver research is another key element in promoting continuous learning (Dam et al., 2019). This involves conducting research to understand the experiences, needs, and challenges of caregivers. The findings from this research can be used to inform the development of educational initiatives, ensuring that they are responsive to caregivers' actual needs. By incorporating research into caregiver education, we can ensure that our efforts to empower caregivers are evidence-based and effective.

Finally, promoting a culture of continuous learning also necessitates creating opportunities for caregivers to learn from each other (Lilly et al., 2019). Peer support groups, online forums, and caregiver conferences can provide valuable platforms for caregivers to share their experiences, insights, and tips. These peer learning opportunities can help caregivers to feel less isolated, enhance their critical thinking skills, and foster a sense of empowerment and community (Robinson et al., 2019).

Empowering caregiver families requires a multi-faceted approach, encompassing personalized support, capacity building, the provision of educational resources, and the promotion of a culture of continuous learning (Reinhard et al., 2019). By taking this holistic approach, we can empower caregivers to navigate their caregiving journey with greater confidence, resilience, and autonomy.

Trauma-Informed Care Approach

A trauma-informed care approach recognizes that the physical and emotional health of individuals can be profoundly influenced by traumatic experiences. This approach requires a shift in the perspective of healthcare providers, from asking "what's wrong with you?" to "what happened to you?" It is a model that aims to understand, recognize, and respond to the effects of all types of traumas (Substance Abuse and Mental Health Services Administration, 2014).

Trauma-informed care is not a therapy or intervention; rather, it is an organizational structure and treatment framework that involves understanding, recognizing, and responding to the effects of trauma (Muskett, 2014). It emphasizes physical, psychological, and emotional safety for both patients and providers, and helps survivors rebuild a sense of control and empowerment (Butler et al., 2017). It is important to note that trauma-informed care is not about treating the trauma itself, but rather about providing services in a manner that is accessible and appropriate to those who may have experienced trauma, and does no further harm (Branson et al., 2017).

For caregivers, having a trauma-informed approach means understanding that trauma can affect the individuals they are caring for and their families (Beach et al., 2021). It can impact the way they interact with the healthcare system, their responses to care, and their engagement with healthcare providers. A trauma-informed approach can also help caregivers understand their own responses and reactions, which may be influenced by their own experiences of trauma (Fry-Bowers et al., 2020).

In terms of practical applications, a trauma-informed care approach could involve implementing screening processes for identifying trauma, providing ongoing education, and training for staff on trauma and its impacts, and developing policies that acknowledge and address the role of trauma in patients' lives (Marsac et al., 2016). It could also involve creating environments that are physically and emotionally safe, ensuring that patients have a voice and choice in their care, and providing trauma-specific services and referrals where needed (Keesler, 2018).

The goal of a trauma-informed care approach is to create a system that is more supportive and effective for all involved. This involves promoting a culture of safety, empowerment, and healing – a culture that recognizes the pervasiveness of trauma and promotes resilience and recovery rather than simply managing symptoms (Sweeney et al., 2018).

Caregiver Education and Training

Caregiver education and training are essential components of promoting a culture of continuous learning. They provide caregivers with necessary skills and knowledge, thereby empowering them to provide effective care for their loved ones (Reinhard et al., 2019). Education and training can take many forms, ranging from formal classes to informal support groups, and can cover a range of topics, including practical caregiving skills, understanding medical conditions, managing medications, and navigating the healthcare system (Vandepitte et al., 2016).

Effective caregiver education should also focus on the caregiver's own needs, equipping them with strategies for self-care, stress management, and coping with the emotional challenges of caregiving. This can help prevent caregiver burnout and ensure the sustainability of care (Beach et al., 2021). Furthermore, education and training can provide caregivers with strategies to advocate for their loved ones in healthcare settings, ensuring that their needs and preferences are respected and met (Samson et al., 2016).

Training can also help caregivers build a sense of competence and self-efficacy, boosting their confidence in their caregiving abilities (Rodakowski et al., 2017). This can improve the quality of care provided and enhance the caregiver's relationship with their loved one. Moreover, caregiver education can help reduce feelings of isolation by connecting caregivers with others in similar situations, fostering a sense of community and shared understanding (Lilly et al., 2019).

Research has consistently shown that caregiver education and training can lead to better outcomes for both caregivers and the people they care for. These outcomes can include improved physical and mental health, higher quality of care, and better patient satisfaction (Dam et al., 2019). Thus, caregiver education and training are not just beneficial but critical to promoting a culture of continuous learning and improving the caregiving experience.

Caregiver Research

Caregiver research is a vital aspect of promoting a culture of continuous learning. It involves the systematic investigation of caregiving, with the aim of gaining a deeper understanding of caregivers' experiences, needs, and challenges (National Academies of Sciences, Engineering, and Medicine, 2016). Through this research, we can uncover patterns, identify gaps in support, and inform the development of more effective services, policies, and interventions (Family Caregiver Alliance, 2012).

Research can take many forms, from large-scale surveys and longitudinal studies to qualitative interviews and case studies (Levine et al., 2010). Regardless of the methodology used, it is vital that research is conducted ethically and with the full consent and involvement of caregivers (Sinclair et al., 2020). This includes ensuring that caregivers understand the purpose of the research, how their information will be used, and what benefits they may receive from participating.

Caregiver research can provide valuable insights into the unique experiences and needs of diverse groups of caregivers, such as those caring for individuals with specific conditions, caregivers from diverse cultural backgrounds, and those in different caregiving roles (e.g., spouses, children, friends) (Barnes et al., 2015). This can help ensure that services and support are tailored to meet the diverse needs of all caregivers.

Importantly, caregiver research also offers an opportunity for caregivers themselves to be heard (Beach et al., 2021). Too often, caregivers' voices are overlooked in discussions about healthcare and social services. By involving caregivers in research, we can ensure that their perspectives, concerns, and aspirations inform the services and policies that affect them.

Caregiver research contributes to a culture of continuous learning by driving evidence-based practice (Van Houtven et al., 2020). It helps us understand what works, what does not, and why, and it provides the knowledge base needed to continually improve and innovate in the field of caregiving.

Harnessing the Power of Technology

Technology has an immense potential to support caregiver families. It provides new avenues for delivering services, facilitating communication, and providing education (Reinhard et al., 2019). The use of technology in caregiving has been accelerated by the COVID-19 pandemic, which has made remote support and digital resources more important than ever (Van Houtven et al., 2020).

Telehealth is one such technology that has become increasingly prevalent. Telehealth involves the use of digital information and communication technologies to access health care services remotely. For caregivers, this can mean being able to consult with healthcare professionals, access educational resources, and receive emotional support without having to leave their homes (Jiang et al., 2021). This can be particularly beneficial for caregivers who live in rural areas, or those who have difficulty leaving their homes due to their caregiving responsibilities.

Digital educational resources are another aspect of technology that can support caregivers (Boltz et al., 2019). These resources can provide caregivers with flexible and convenient access to information and training. They can include online courses, webinars, videos, podcasts, and e-books, covering a wide range of topics from understanding a loved one's health condition to managing the caregiver's own stress and well-being.

Health monitoring and management tools are another technology that can support caregivers (Reeder et al., 2013). These tools can provide caregivers with valuable insights into their loved ones' health, enabling them to provide better care. These can include apps that track medication regimens, devices that monitor vital signs, and platforms that provide personalized health recommendations.

While technology has incredible potential to support caregivers, it is important to remember that not all caregivers have the same level of access to or comfort with technology (Boltz et al., 2019). Care must be taken to ensure that digital resources and services are accessible and user-friendly, and that support is available for those who need help navigating these tools.

Inclusion and Collaboration

Inclusion and collaboration are central to engaging caregiver families in educational initiatives (Greenwood et al., 2019). This involves not just providing services to caregivers, but actively involving them in the design, delivery, and evaluation of these services. By involving caregivers in these processes, we can ensure that services are responsive to their needs, and that caregivers feel valued and heard (Dam et al., 2019).

Involving caregivers in service design and delivery can lead to more effective and tailored services. Caregivers have unique insights into what works and what does not in their caregiving journey, and these insights can be invaluable in shaping services (Sinclair et al., 2020). This can involve caregivers in decision-making processes, soliciting their feedback on proposed services, and incorporating their insights into the final design and delivery of services.

In addition, involving caregivers in the evaluation of services can provide valuable feedback on the effectiveness of these services (Lilly et al., 2019). This can help identify areas for improvement and inform the development of future services. Methods for involving caregivers in evaluation can include surveys, interviews, focus groups, and other forms of feedback.

Promoting diversity and representation is key to inclusion and collaboration (Beach et al., 2021). This means ensuring that caregivers from diverse backgrounds, cultures, and experiences are represented in educational initiatives. It also means making resources accessible and inclusive, such as by providing resources in multiple languages, or in formats that are accessible to people with disabilities.

Promoting a culture of continuous learning among caregivers involves a multi-faceted approach. It requires acknowledging and addressing the impacts of trauma, providing education and training, conducting research, harnessing the power of technology, and fostering inclusion and collaboration (Reinhard et al., 2019). By adopting this approach, we can ensure that caregivers are empowered, supported, and valued, and that they have the resources and knowledge they need to provide the best possible care for their loved ones.

Involving Caregivers in Service Design and Delivery

Involving caregivers directly in the design and delivery of services is essential for creating responsive, tailored support (Dam et al., 2019). As the primary users and experts of these services, caregivers have invaluable insights that can shape more effective programs. Their meaningful engagement should occur across all stages of service development.

In the design phase, caregivers can identify unmet needs, challenges, and gaps through surveys, interviews, and focus groups (Sinclair et al., 2020). Their input helps set priorities and objectives. Caregivers can provide feedback on proposed program models to enhance relevance. Mock-ups and pilots allow them to trial services and suggest improvements pre-implementation.

During implementation, caregivers should have ongoing opportunities to evaluate and refine services (Beach et al., 2021). Advisory panels, user experience testing, and satisfaction surveys can elicit their assessment of what works well versus potential changes needed. Caregivers also play a key role in service delivery through peer facilitation of support groups, helplines, and mentoring programs.

Beyond formal mechanisms, an organizational culture valuing caregiver expertise should infuse all interactions (Reinhard et al., 2019). Staff should actively listen and respond to caregiver perspectives shared in casual conversations, comments, and complaints. Applying a "nothing about us without us" philosophy ensures caregivers are respected as equal partners.

Effectively engaging caregivers requires dedicated resources and relational approaches to build trust and accessibility (Greenwood et al., 2019). Compensation, transportation, respite care and language/cultural support may be needed for participatory programs. Systems must be transparent and accountable.

While investment is required, the benefits of embedding caregivers' first-hand experiences into services justify the effort (Lilly et al., 2019). Caregivers feel valued, programs become more user-centered, and efficiencies emerge as services better align with families' realities (Van Houtven et al., 2020). Most importantly, engagement leads to optimal outcomes for caregivers' and care recipients' health and well-being.

Involving Caregivers in Service Evaluation

Promoting a Culture of Continuous Learning

Continuous learning is an essential aspect of caregiving. Given the dynamic nature of caregiving, with its changing needs and challenges, caregivers must be equipped with the knowledge and skills to adapt and evolve (Reinhard et al., 2019). Promoting a culture of continuous learning is, therefore, central to engaging caregiver families in educational initiatives.

A culture of continuous learning recognizes that caregivers, just like the individuals they support, are in a constant state of growth and development (Beach et al., 2021). It acknowledges that every experience, challenge, or change in caregiving circumstances is an opportunity to gain experience and grow. It encourages caregivers to take initiative-taking in seeking knowledge, skill acquisition, and personal development, thereby enhancing their capacity to provide effective care (Dam et al., 2019).

One way to foster a culture of continuous learning is through a trauma-informed care approach. This approach recognizes the impact of trauma on individuals and promotes practices that are sensitive to this reality (Fry-Bowers et al., 2020). For caregivers, a trauma-informed approach can provide insights into the behaviors and needs of those they support, helping them to provide more compassionate, effective care.

Caregiver education and training are also key to promoting continuous learning (Vandepitte et al., 2016). This can take many forms, from formal courses and workshops to online resources and peer support groups. These initiatives can help caregivers to build their knowledge and skills, stay up to date with the latest research and best practices in caregiving, and learn from the experiences of others.

Finally, involving caregivers in research can also contribute to a culture of continuous learning (Sinclair et al., 2020). Participating in research not only provides caregivers with access to the latest information in the caregiving field, but it also allows them to contribute to the development of knowledge in this area. This active involvement can empower caregivers, making them feel valued and respected for their unique experiences and insights.

Promoting a culture of continuous learning is a multifaceted effort that requires commitment from all stakeholders (Lilly et al., 2019). It necessitates a proactive approach to caregiver education and development, a sensitivity to the impact of trauma, and an openness to learning from caregivers' experiences. By fostering this culture, we can enhance the capacity of caregivers, improve the quality of care, and contribute to a more compassionate and effective care support system (Van Houtven et al., 2020).

Involving Caregivers in Research

Involving caregivers in research can promote continuous learning and growth. As the primary providers of care and support, caregivers have invaluable insights and experiences that can inform research aimed at improving care practices, programs, policies, and interventions (Dam et al., 2019). However, caregivers have traditionally been overlooked as partners in research. Actively engaging them can yield significant benefits.

Participating in research can empower caregivers by valuing their knowledge and giving them an active voice (Beach et al., 2021). It can provide education and skills in research methodology, ethics, data analysis, and communication that caregivers can apply beyond the research itself. Involvement also allows caregivers to network with peers, professionals, and advocates (Reinhard et al., 2019).

For researchers, partnering with caregivers enhances relevance, acceptability, and adoption of findings by reflecting caregivers' priorities and perspectives (Van Houtven et al., 2020). Caregivers can inform research aims, methodologies, instruments, recruitment, analysis plans, and dissemination strategies. Their insights improve contextualization and interpretation of data.

Effective engagement requires promoting a culture of respect, diversity, transparency, and shared power (Lilly et al., 2019). Caregivers should be involved in meaningful ways at all stages, from conceptualization to reporting. Compensation, accommodations, training, and ongoing communication and feedback mechanisms must be provided.

While involving caregivers in research requires commitment and resources, the benefits warrant the investment (Sinclair et al., 2020). The outcomes include richer data, new discoveries, and research that truly translates into improved support for caregivers and those they care for. Most importantly, it recognizes caregivers as equal partners in the pursuit of knowledge, care, and compassion.

Peer Support and Mentorship

Peer support and mentorship provide powerful avenues for promoting continuous learning among caregiver families. Connecting caregivers to peers who are on similar journeys can foster ongoing exchange of knowledge, insights, and emotional support (Greenwood et al., 2019). This can occur through informal networks or more structured programs.

Informal peer connections can develop through support groups, online communities, or social events for caregivers (Boltz et al., 2019). These platforms allow caregivers to freely share advice, resources, and encouragement based on their lived experiences. Mutual understanding helps normalize challenges and reduces isolation.

Formal peer mentorship initiates experienced caregivers providing guidance to newer caregivers (Beach et al., 2021). Mentors can share practical tips learned through their own caregiving journey and provide empathetic support. Mentees gain knowledge and confidence in their new role.

Peer support models should promote diversity and representation by tailoring programs to specific populations and caregiving contexts (Reinhard et al., 2019). This ensures relevancy of shared experiences while also broadening perspectives.

Training for peers and ongoing coordination by program staff help maintain quality engagement and minimize misinformation. Confidentiality and secure platforms provide safe spaces for connection. Evaluation mechanisms can guide program improvement.

Overall, peer sharing combats helplessness by reframing caregivers as active providers and seekers of knowledge. The insights of experienced caregivers are invaluable resources. Supporting platforms for connection and exchange fosters continuous reciprocal learning essential for effective caregiving.

5.4: Evaluating the Effectiveness of Educational Programs for Caregiver Families

The demographic shift towards an aging population has significant implications, particularly concerning the increase in older adults with dementia. As the disease progresses, patients require increasing levels of care, and the burden often falls on family members who assume the role of caregivers (Schulz & Martire, 2004). To support these caregivers, various education and support programs have been developed, aiming to enhance their knowledge and skills necessary for providing dementia care (Gitlin et al., 2010). However, the effectiveness of these programs needs to be rigorously evaluated to ensure they are achieving their intended outcomes and meeting the needs of caregiver families (Jensen et al., 2015).

The evaluation process of these programs should not be a mere formality, but a rigorous, evidence-based activity aimed at continuous improvement (Bass et al., 2013). It should be conducted systematically, using both quantitative and qualitative data, and guided by the principles of evidence-based and evidence-informed practice. Furthermore, the evaluation process should include multiple stakeholders' perspectives, including those of caregivers and care recipients, healthcare professionals, and program facilitators (Dam et al., 2019).

Evaluating the effectiveness of these programs is not only about ensuring resources are used efficiently but also about making a positive impact on caregivers and care recipients' lives (Van Houtven et al., 2020). Successful programs can reduce caregiver burden, improve the quality of care for dementia patients, and enhance caregivers' well-being. By providing them with the necessary knowledge and skills and ongoing support, these programs can make a significant positive impact (Lilly et al., 2019).

Defining Effectiveness

When evaluating educational programs for caregiver families, effectiveness can be defined as the degree to which these programs achieve their intended outcomes (Bass et al., 2013). These outcomes may vary depending on the specific program and the needs of the caregiver families it aims to serve.

The primary intended outcome of these programs is to improve caregivers' knowledge and skills related to dementia care (Hepburn et al., 2003). This can include understanding the nature of dementia, managing behavioral symptoms, and navigating the healthcare system. Through the program, caregivers should become more knowledgeable and confident in their ability to provide care.

Another important outcome is reducing caregiver burden (Van Houtven et al., 2020). Caregiving can be emotionally and physically demanding, leading to stress, burnout, and other negative health outcomes. Effective programs should help caregivers manage these demands, providing them with strategies to cope with stress and prevent burnout.

Improving the quality of care provided to dementia patients is another critical outcome (Lilly et al., 2019). This can be assessed by evaluating changes in patient health and well-being, instances of hospitalization, or use of emergency services. Additionally, patient feedback can provide valuable insights into the quality of care they are receiving.

Enhancing the well-being of caregivers and care recipients is a vital outcome (Reinhard et al., 2019). This can include improvements in mental health, physical health, and quality of life. A holistic approach to well-being should be taken, considering both physical and emotional aspects.

Evidence-Based and Evidence-Informed Practice

Evaluating the effectiveness of educational programs for caregiver families should be guided by the principles of evidence-based and evidence-informed practice (Bass et al., 2013). These complementary approaches integrate scientific research, clinical expertise, and patient values and preferences to inform decision-making and practice.

Evidence-based practice is the use of current best evidence from rigorous scientific research to guide decision-making and practice (Sackett et al., 1996). In the context of evaluating caregiver education programs, this means using reliable and valid measures to assess outcomes, conducting rigorous analyses, and interpreting the findings considering the existing scientific literature.

Evidence-informed practice, on the other hand, takes a broader view (Regehr, 2010). While it recognizes the importance of scientific research, it also acknowledges that other types of evidence can be valuable. In this context, it means considering the experiences and perspectives of caregivers and care recipients, as well as the expertise of healthcare professionals and program facilitators.

In both approaches, the goal is to ensure that the evaluation process is rigorous, transparent, and accountable (Glasgow et al., 2005). This means clearly defining the intended outcomes, using appropriate methods to assess these outcomes, and interpreting and reporting the findings honestly and accurately.

In the context of caregiver education programs, this means using a combination of quantitative and qualitative methods to assess the effectiveness of the program (Gitlin et al., 2010). Quantitative measures, such as pre-and post-tests of caregiver knowledge and skills, can provide objective evidence of the program's impact. Meanwhile, qualitative data, such as interviews or focus groups with caregivers, can provide insights into their experiences and the perceived benefits of the program.

Gathering and Analyzing Data

The process of gathering and analyzing data to evaluate the effectiveness of caregiver education programs should be systematic and rigorous (Bass et al., 2013). This involves defining the outcomes of interest, choosing appropriate measures to assess these outcomes, collecting, and analyzing the data, and interpreting the findings.

The first step in this process is defining the outcomes of interest. These should be linked to the intended outcomes of the program, as discussed in the previous section. They might include caregivers' knowledge and skills, caregiver burden, quality of care, and caregiver and care recipient well-being (Sörensen et al., 2002).

Next, appropriate measures should be chosen to assess these outcomes. These measures should be reliable (i.e., they measure what they are supposed to measure consistently) and valid (i.e., they measure what they are supposed to measure) (Streiner et al., 2015). They might include standardized tests or scales, surveys, interviews, or observational measures.

The data collection process should be structured and systematic (Creswell & Creswell, 2017). Depending on the measures used, this might involve administering pre-and post-tests, conducting interviews or focus groups, or observing caregiver interactions with care recipients. Care should be taken to ensure that the data collection process is ethical and respects the rights and privacy of participants (Grady et al., 2017).

Once the data has been collected, it needs to be analyzed. The specific methods used will depend on the nature of the data (Braun & Clarke, 2006). Quantitative data might be analyzed using statistical methods, while qualitative data might be analyzed using thematic analysis or other qualitative methods. The aim of the analysis is to determine whether the program has achieved its intended outcomes, and to identify any areas where improvement may be needed.

The findings need to be interpreted and reported (APA, 2010). This involves making sense of the data in light of the existing literature and the aims of the program. The findings should be reported honestly and transparently, acknowledging both the strengths and weaknesses of the program.

Continuous Improvement

The aim of evaluating the effectiveness of caregiver education programs is not just to assess whether they have achieved their intended outcomes, but also to identify areas for improvement (Deming, 1986). This is where the principle of continuous improvement comes in.

Continuous improvement involves using the findings from the evaluation process to identify areas where the program can be improved, and then making changes accordingly (Jensen et al., 2015). This requires a commitment to learning and improvement from all stakeholders, including program developers, facilitators, and funders.

The first step in this process is to review the findings from the evaluation process and identify areas where improvement is needed (Van Houtven et al., 2020). This might involve looking at the data for each intended outcome and seeing whether the program has met its targets. It might also involve looking at feedback from caregivers and care recipients to identify areas where they feel the program could be better.

Next, strategies for improvement should be developed (Lilly et al., 2019). These might involve making changes to the program content, delivery, or support structures. For example, if the data shows that caregivers are still struggling with certain aspects of dementia care, the program may need to be modified to provide more support in these areas.

Once changes have been made, the impact of these changes should be monitored (Reinhard et al., 2019). This involves repeating the evaluation process to assess whether the changes have led to improvements in the intended outcomes. This process of continuous improvement should be ongoing, with regular reviews and updates to ensure the program remains effective and relevant.

Evaluating the effectiveness of educational programs for caregiver families is a complex but essential process. It requires a systematic and rigorous approach, guided by the principles of evidence-based and evidence-informed practice, and a commitment to continuous improvement. By doing so, these programs can effectively improve the knowledge and skills of caregivers, reduce caregiver burden, improve the quality of care, and enhance the well-being of caregivers and care recipients.

Chapter 6: Role and Function of Caregivers

6.1: Understanding the Role of Caregivers

The role of caregivers is a critical aspect of healthcare management, influencing not only the well-being of the individuals they care for but also their own health, financial stability, and social connections (Reinhard et al., 2019). Considering their profound impact, it is imperative to gain a deeper understanding of the multifaceted role that caregivers play within care management programs. This chapter seeks to shed light on the complexities of direct care provision, coordination of services, and the importance of caregivers' well-being. In doing so, we aim to provide a comprehensive understanding of the responsibilities and roles of caregivers in health and care management.

The role of a caregiver is like a multi-faceted jewel, each aspect reflecting a diverse set of responsibilities and skills (Van Houtven et al., 2020). This includes the direct provision of care, acting as a compassionate catalyst for healing, orchestrating the coordination of services, and shouldering the emotional and physical toll of caregiving. Each facet is vital, contributing to the overall quality of care received by the dependent individual and influencing the caregiver's ability to fulfill their duties (Lilly et al., 2019).

Beyond the tasks they perform, caregivers also serve as an emotional anchor for their care recipients. In their capacity as compassionate care catalysts, they foster genuine, healing relationships that motivate individuals to actively participate in their own health management (Beach et al., 2021). In providing direct care, they assist with daily living activities, manage medications, and tackle other healthcare tasks, necessitating a deep understanding of the care recipient's needs and a skill set to match (Dam et al., 2019).

In addition, caregivers are often called upon to function as the nexus of a vast network of healthcare providers, family members, and other support services. They coordinate and ensure that all necessary services are delivered promptly and efficiently, making the navigation of the healthcare system, communication with providers, and advocacy for care recipients' needs an essential part of their role (Sinclair et al., 2020). The physical and emotional demands of caregiving can be high, leading to caregiver burnout if not addressed (Stall et al., 2019).

We will look at the path to excellence in caregiving, which requires continuous learning and improvement. Caregiver training programs, workshops, and continuing education opportunities are vital to maintaining the highest standards of care (Rodakowski et al., 2017). By staying abreast of the latest trends and best practices in caregiving, caregivers can ensure they provide top-notch care to their recipients.

Caregivers as Compassionate Care Catalysts

The role of caregivers extends beyond the physical provision of care. They serve as compassionate catalysts for healing, providing emotional support and motivation for care recipients to actively manage their health (Beach et al., 2021). They establish genuine, healing relationships characterized by security and continuity, which are crucial to the care recipient's overall well-being.

Caregivers, in their capacity as empathetic confidants, are uniquely positioned to foster a sense of security in their care recipients (Van Houtven et al., 2020). The creation of a secure environment involves building trust and demonstrating reliability, which can enhance the care recipient's mental and emotional health. Caregivers must prioritize trust-building to ensure that recipients feel safe and supported.

Continuity is another key aspect of these relationships (Lilly et al., 2019). Care recipients often face numerous changes in their health condition, which can be disorienting and distressing. Caregivers provide a constant presence, offering comfort and stability amid the flux. Continuity in care also enhances the caregiver's understanding of the recipient's condition and needs, enabling them to provide more personalized care.

Caregivers also have the opportunity to motivate their care recipients to take an active role in managing their health (Sinclair et al., 2020). By fostering a strong, supportive relationship and providing appropriate health education, caregivers can empower recipients, enhancing their self-efficacy and motivation to adhere to their care plan.

The depth of the relationship between the caregiver and care recipient significantly influences the latter's overall health outcomes (Kent et al., 2016). Research suggests that strong caregiver-recipient relationships can improve the recipient's mental health, increase treatment adherence, and enhance overall satisfaction with care. Therefore, building these relationships should be a top priority for caregivers.

Direct Care Provision

Direct care provision is the most visible aspect of a caregiver's role. It involves assistance with a range of activities that ensure the care recipient's well-being and comfort (Reinhard et al., 2019). These activities encompass daily living tasks, medication management, and other healthcare tasks, all of which necessitate a deep understanding of the recipient's needs and a robust skill set.

Daily living tasks form a large part of direct care. These tasks can range from meal preparation and personal hygiene to transportation and household chores (Van Houtven et al., 2020). Caregivers often need to adapt to the specific needs and preferences of the care recipient, necessitating flexibility and a compassionate, patient approach.

Medication management is a critical aspect of direct care, especially for care recipients with complex medical conditions (Lilly et al., 2019). Caregivers must ensure that medications are taken correctly and on time, monitor for side effects, and communicate any issues to healthcare providers. This responsibility requires a solid understanding of medications, keen observational skills, and clear communication.

Beyond routine tasks, caregivers often need to perform healthcare tasks traditionally undertaken by medical professionals, such as wound care, injections, or assisting with medical equipment (Dam et al., 2019). These responsibilities require specific training and competency to ensure they are performed safely and effectively.

Understanding the unique needs and preferences of care recipients is pivotal to providing personalized, effective care (Beach et al., 2021). Caregivers should continuously assess the care recipient's condition, needs, and responses to interventions. This ongoing assessment allows caregivers to adapt their approaches and strategies, ensuring optimal care.

Coordination of Services

As part of their role, caregivers often find themselves acting as the central hub in a network of healthcare providers, family members, and other support services (Reinhard et al., 2019). In this capacity, they coordinate care, ensuring that all necessary services are provided promptly and efficiently. This coordination role involves navigating the healthcare system, communicating effectively with various stakeholders, and advocating for care recipients' needs.

Navigating the healthcare system can be complex and challenging (Van Houtven et al., 2020). Caregivers must understand how to access the necessary services, schedule appointments, manage insurance issues, and handle paperwork. They need to be resourceful, organized, and proactive to ensure that care recipients receive the right care at the right time.

Effective communication is key in coordinating care (Lilly et al., 2019). Caregivers must convey information accurately and clearly among healthcare providers, family members, and the care recipient. They need to ask the right questions, relay medical information, and facilitate discussions about the care recipient's condition and care plan.

Advocacy is another fundamental aspect of the caregiver's role in coordinating care (Sinclair et al., 2020). They must ensure that the care recipient's needs and preferences are heard and respected. This involves speaking up for the care recipient during healthcare encounters, making sure their wishes are considered in decision-making processes, and seeking second opinions or alternative options when necessary.

Coordinating care often involves negotiating and managing relationships with various stakeholders (Beach et al., 2021). Caregivers need to balance the needs and preferences of the care recipient, the recommendations of healthcare providers, and the expectations of family members. This can require diplomacy, conflict resolution skills, and a deep commitment to the care recipient's best interests.

Recognizing Caregiver Burnout

The role of a caregiver is not without its challenges. The emotional and physical demands of caregiving can sometimes be overwhelming, leading to a state of emotional, physical, and mental exhaustion known as caregiver burnout (Stall et al., 2019). Recognizing the signs of burnout and implementing strategies to prevent its onset is crucial for the well-being of both the caregiver and the care recipient.

Physically, caregiving can be demanding (Van Houtven et al., 2020). It often involves long hours, heavy lifting, and little time for rest or relaxation. Over time, these physical demands can lead to fatigue, sleep disturbances, and other health problems. It is important for caregivers to recognize these physical signs of burnout and seek help when needed.

Emotionally, caregivers may experience feelings of sadness, frustration, and guilt (Lilly et al., 2019). The constant worry for the care recipient's well-being, coupled with the often-thankless nature of the job, can lead to emotional exhaustion (Schulz & Sherwood, 2008). Caregivers need to be aware of these emotional symptoms and seek support from counseling or support groups as necessary (Beach et al., 2021).

Mentally, burnout can manifest as a sense of depersonalization – a feeling of detachment or a lack of personal accomplishment (Tremolada et al., 2016). Caregivers may feel as though they are merely going through the motions, rather than actively engaging in their roles. Recognizing these feelings and seeking help is crucial for the caregiver's mental health (Lilly et al., 2019).

Preventing caregiver burnout involves implementing self-care strategies, setting boundaries, and seeking support. Caregivers must prioritize their own health and well-being, taking time to rest, eat healthily, and engage in activities they enjoy (Reinhard et al., 2019). It is also important to set realistic expectations, delegate tasks when possible, and seek help from caregiver support services (Dam et al., 2019).

Caregiver support services play a crucial role in preventing burnout. They provide respite care, counseling, and other resources that can help caregivers manage the demands of their role (Van Houtven et al., 2020). Utilizing these services can make a significant difference in the well-being and effectiveness of caregivers.

The Path to Excellence in Caregiving

Continuous learning and improvement are key to excellence in caregiving. Caregivers must remain up to date with the latest trends and best practices in their field, and take advantage of training programs, workshops, and continuing education opportunities (Beach et al., 2021). This commitment to lifelong learning benefits both the caregiver and the care recipient.

Training programs provide caregivers with the necessary skills and knowledge to provide high-quality care (Gitlin et al., 2010). These programs cover a range of topics, from basic care skills to more complex healthcare tasks. By participating in these programs, caregivers can improve their competence and confidence in their role.

Workshops offer opportunities for caregivers to learn new strategies and techniques (Van Houtven et al., 2020). These can range from hands-on training sessions to discussions on the latest research in caregiving. Workshops also provide a platform for caregivers to share experiences and learn from each other, fostering a supportive community.

Continuing education is essential for keeping caregivers up to date with the latest developments in healthcare and caregiving (Reinhard et al., 2019). This can involve attending conferences, reading research articles, or participating in online courses. By staying informed, caregivers can adapt their practices to reflect the latest evidence-based approaches.

A commitment to self-improvement and professional development is a hallmark of excellence in caregiving (Lilly et al., 2019). This involves seeking feedback, reflecting on one's own practices, and setting goals for improvement. A caregiver who is committed to learning and growth is better equipped to provide exceptional care.

Caregivers play a critical role in care management programs, providing direct care, coordinating services, and establishing authentic healing relationships with care recipients. Recognizing the signs of caregiver burnout and taking steps to prevent it is crucial for their well-being and effectiveness (Dam et al., 2019).

Through continuous learning and improvement, caregivers can ensure they provide exceptional care and improve the quality of life for care recipients and their families (Greenwood et al., 2019). This comprehensive understanding of the caregiver's role and responsibilities forms the foundation on which exceptional care is built.

6.2: Challenges Faced by Caregivers

Caring for a loved one is a monumental responsibility that comes with a myriad of challenges. From the emotional toll to physical strain, financial burdens, and impacts on personal relationships, being a caregiver is a role that demands resilience, patience, and immense strength (Family Caregiver Alliance, 2012). While it is a role often filled with a deep sense of purpose and love, it is also a job that can feel overwhelming and isolating. Understanding these challenges is the first step towards finding effective solutions and support to navigate the caregiving journey (Reinhard et al., 2019).

The role of caregiving is often thrust upon individuals unexpectedly, without any formal training or preparation. It could be an aging parent who suddenly needs help with daily activities, a spouse who falls ill, or a child who has special needs (Family Caregiver Alliance, 2012). Regardless of the circumstances, caregivers must quickly adapt to new responsibilities, which can be stressful and demanding (Adelman et al., 2014).

Moreover, caregivers often juggle their caregiving role with other responsibilities like work, parenting, and managing their own health. This can lead to an elevated level of stress and physical exhaustion. The stress associated with caregiving is often referred to as caregiver stress syndrome, characterized by chronic stress that can lead to significant health problems, including depression and burnout (Schulz & Sherwood, 2008).

Yet, despite these challenges, caregivers continue to provide care for their loved ones. They do so out of love, duty, or necessity, often without seeking help or acknowledging their struggles (Family Caregiver Alliance, 2012). This is why understanding the challenges faced by caregivers is so crucial, not only for the caregivers themselves but also for health professionals, policymakers, and society as a whole (Reinhard et al., 2019).

Recognizing and addressing these challenges can lead to better support for caregivers, improved health outcomes for the people they care for, and a stronger, more compassionate society (Quinn et al., 2019). The following sections detail the primary challenges faced by caregivers.

Emotional Challenges

Caregiving is an emotionally intense role. Caregivers frequently navigate through a vast spectrum of emotions, from love and fulfillment to guilt, frustration, and sadness (Family Caregiver Alliance, 2012). The emotional toll of caregiving is often heightened as caregivers watch their loved one's struggle with illness or disability (Schulz & Sherwood, 2008).

These emotional challenges can also be exacerbated by the constant demand for attention and responsiveness. Caregivers often must be on high alert, anticipating the needs of their loved ones. This constant state of alertness can lead to emotional exhaustion, making it difficult for caregivers to manage their own emotions effectively (Adelman et al., 2014).

Guilt is another common emotional challenge for caregivers. They may feel guilty for feeling frustrated or resentful, or for not doing enough for their loved ones (Family Caregiver Alliance, 2012). Moreover, caregivers often must make difficult decisions about their loved ones' care, which can lead to feelings of guilt and second-guessing (Reinhard et al., 2019).

Anxiety and depression are also common among caregivers. The uncertainty associated with their loved ones' health, the financial strain, and the overall burden of caregiving can cause significant anxiety (Schulz & Sherwood, 2008). In addition, caregivers may feel isolated and alone, leading to feelings of sadness and depression (Family Caregiver Alliance, 2012).

Despite these emotional challenges, caregivers often neglect their emotional well-being. They may suppress their emotions to focus on their caregiving duties or feel guilty for prioritizing their emotional needs (Adelman et al., 2014). However, neglecting their emotional well-being can lead to emotional burnout and have detrimental effects on their overall health (Schulz & Sherwood, 2008). Therefore, it is crucial for caregivers to acknowledge their emotional challenges and seek support when needed (Reinhard et al., 2019).

Physical Challenges

In addition to emotional challenges, caregivers also face significant physical challenges. Providing care can be physically taxing, with tasks ranging from assisting with personal care to doing household chores and managing medical care (Family Caregiver Alliance, 2012).

Caregivers often must assist their loved ones with personal care tasks such as bathing, dressing, and feeding. These tasks can be physically demanding, especially for caregivers who are older or have their own health issues (Reinhard et al., 2019). Over time, this can lead to physical strain and related health issues like back pain, fatigue, and sleep disturbances (Family Caregiver Alliance, 2012).

Caregiving also involves managing medical care, which can include administering medication, coordinating healthcare appointments, and managing medical emergencies. This can be physically demanding and stressful, especially for caregivers without formal medical training (Schulz & Sherwood, 2008).

Additionally, caregiving often requires doing additional household chores, from cleaning and cooking to shopping for groceries and managing finances. These additional tasks can add to the physical burden of caregiving, leading to physical exhaustion (Adelman et al., 2014).

Furthermore, the constant stress and anxiety associated with caregiving can also take a toll on caregivers' physical health. Chronic stress can lead to various health issues, including heart disease, high blood pressure, and weakened immune system (Schulz & Sherwood, 2008).

Therefore, maintaining physical health is crucial for caregivers. This involves taking care of their diet, getting regular exercise, enough sleep, and seeking regular medical check-ups (Reinhard et al., 2019). By prioritizing their physical well-being, caregivers can ensure they have the physical stamina to provide care effectively (Family Caregiver Alliance, 2012).

Financial Challenges

Caregiving can also place a significant financial burden on caregivers. Medical expenses, caregiving supplies, and the potential loss of income due to caregiving responsibilities can lead to financial stress (Adelman et al., 2014).

Medical expenses are often a significant part of the financial burden of caregiving. This can include the cost of medications, medical equipment, home modifications, and healthcare services (Reinhard et al., 2019). In addition, caregivers often must bear the cost of transportation for medical appointments, which can add to the financial strain (Family Caregiver Alliance, 2012).

Purchasing caregiving supplies and equipment is another part of the financial burden. These items can range from personal care items like adult diapers and bathing aids to mobility aids like wheelchairs and walkers (Schulz & Sherwood, 2008). The cost of these items can quickly add up, putting additional financial stress on caregivers (Adelman et al., 2014).

Loss of income is another significant financial challenge for caregivers. They often must reduce their work hours or leave their jobs entirely to provide care (Family Caregiver Alliance, 2012). This loss of income, combined with the increased expenses associated with caregiving, can lead to substantial financial stress (Reinhard et al., 2019).

Furthermore, caregivers often face financial uncertainty, not knowing how long they will need to provide care and how their financial situation will change over time. This uncertainty can exacerbate the financial stress associated with caregiving (Adelman et al., 2014).

Despite these financial challenges, there are resources available to help caregivers. From financial assistance programs to tax credits for caregivers, it is important for caregivers to explore all available options to mitigate the financial burden of caregiving (Reinhard et al., 2019).

Impact on Personal Relationships

Caregiving can have a significant impact on caregivers' personal relationships. This includes their relationships with the person they are caring for, their relationships with other family members, and their relationships with friends and social networks (Family Caregiver Alliance, 2012).

The relationship between the caregiver and the care recipient can be deeply affected by the caregiving role. The dynamic often shifts from a mutual relationship to one where the caregiver has more control and responsibility (Schulz & Sherwood, 2008). This shift can lead to tension and conflicts, impacting the quality of the relationship (Reinhard et al., 2019).

Caregiving can also strain relationships with other family members. This can occur when caregiving responsibilities are unevenly distributed, leading to resentment and conflict (Adelman et al., 2014). In addition, the time and energy devoted to caregiving can make it difficult for caregivers to maintain their relationships with other family members (Family Caregiver Alliance, 2012).

Friends and social networks are also impacted by caregiving. Caregivers often have less time and energy to socialize and maintain their social relationships (Reinhard et al., 2019). This can lead to social isolation, which can exacerbate the emotional challenges of caregiving (Schulz & Sherwood, 2008).

Furthermore, the strain on personal relationships can add to the stress and emotional burden of caregiving (Adelman et al., 2014). Therefore, maintaining strong and supportive personal relationships is crucial for caregivers' emotional well-being (Family Caregiver Alliance, 2012).

Despite these challenges, open communication, setting boundaries, and seeking support can help caregivers manage the impact of caregiving on their personal relationships (Reinhard et al., 2019). By acknowledging these challenges and seeking solutions, caregivers can maintain strong relationships while fulfilling their caregiving responsibilities (Quinn et al., 2019).

Caregiving is a journey filled with unique challenges, encompassing emotional, physical, financial, and relational aspects (Family Caregiver Alliance, 2012). Regardless of the difficulties, caregivers continue to provide unwavering care for their loved ones (Schulz & Sherwood, 2008). By acknowledging these challenges and seeking support, caregivers can navigate this journey with resilience and strength (Reinhard et al., 2019). It is crucial that society recognize the invaluable role that caregivers play and provide the necessary resources and support to help them in their journey (Quinn et al., 2019).

6.3: Impact of Caregivers on Care Recipients

The role of caregivers, often overlooked in the healthcare sector, is pivotal in shaping the quality of life for those in need of care. Caregiving, a multifaceted and demanding responsibility, influences both the physical and emotional well-being of care recipients and caregivers. The balance of this symbiotic relationship is critical, as it often dictates the overall health outcomes of the individuals involved (Schulz & Sherwood, 2008).

Caregivers, whether professional or family members, provide more than just physical assistance. They offer emotional support, companionship, and a sense of security that can drastically enhance the life of care recipients (Family Caregiver Alliance, 2012). However, the responsibilities associated with caregiving can also impose a significant burden on the caregivers themselves, manifesting in emotional and physical strain (Adelman et al., 2014).

The knowledge and skills possessed by caregivers play an essential role in this dynamic. The better equipped a caregiver is, the more effectively they can meet the needs of their care recipients (Reinhard et al., 2019). With the right knowledge, skills, and resources, caregivers can effectively manage their responsibilities and mitigate potential adverse outcomes (Family Caregiver Alliance, 2012).

Moreover, caregiving is not a one-sided process. It is a reciprocal relationship that can bring fulfillment and satisfaction to caregivers, while also enhancing the quality of life for care recipients (Quinn et al., 2019). Recognizing the complexity and reciprocal nature of this relationship is crucial to providing adequate support to caregivers and, in turn, ensuring the well-being of care recipients (Schulz & Sherwood, 2008).

Emotional Impact

Emotional Impact: Caregivers on Care Recipients

The role of a caregiver often extends beyond the provision of physical care. They are also a crucial source of emotional support for their care recipients. This emotional support can range from offering a listening ear, providing comforting words, or simply being present to share moments of joy, sadness, fear, and hope (Family Caregiver Alliance, 2012).

The emotional support caregivers provide is particularly essential for individuals dealing with chronic illnesses or disabilities. The constant strain of managing a chronic condition, coupled with the potential loss of independence, can lead to increased levels of stress, anxiety, and depression (Schulz & Sherwood, 2008). A caregiver's presence and continued support can serve as a beacon of hope and stability, helping care recipients navigate the emotional turmoil associated with their condition (Family Caregiver Alliance, 2012).

Moreover, the companionship that caregivers offer can significantly reduce feelings of loneliness and isolation that care recipients may experience, particularly those who live alone or have limited social interactions (Hansen & Slagsvold, 2013). Companionship can stimulate positive emotions and provide a much-needed distraction from the physical discomfort or limitations associated with their condition (Kramer, 2017).

Caregivers are often able to understand their care recipient's needs, moods, and emotions in a way that others may not. This deep understanding, born out of time spent together and shared experiences, can lead to a unique bond between caregiver and care recipient (Quinn et al., 2019). This bond can enhance the care recipient's emotional well-being, providing a sense of being understood and valued (Kramer, 2017).

The emotional support provided by caregivers can significantly improve the mood and overall emotional health of care recipients. It offers comfort, companionship, and a sense of security that is invaluable to individuals in need of care, contributing to their overall quality of life (Schulz & Sherwood, 2008).

Emotional Impact: Care Recipients on Caregivers

While caregivers play an undeniably critical role in supporting the emotional welfare of care recipients, the emotional impact of caregiving on the caregiver is equally significant and must not be overlooked. Caregiving, though rewarding, can also be emotionally draining. The constant need to be supportive, empathetic, and patient can lead to emotional fatigue (Adelman et al., 2014).

One of the primary emotional challenges caregivers often face is stress. This stress can stem from numerous sources, ranging from the physical demands of caregiving to the emotional strain of seeing a loved one in pain or distress (Schulz & Sherwood, 2008). For family caregivers, there can also be the additional stress of balancing caregiving responsibilities with their personal life, work, and other commitments (Reinhard et al., 2019).

Anxiety is another common emotional challenge for caregivers. The constant worry about the health and well-being of their care recipient, coupled with the uncertainty that often accompanies chronic illnesses or disabilities, can lead to heightened anxiety levels (Family Caregiver Alliance, 2012). This anxiety can be particularly intense when the caregiver must make difficult decisions related to the care recipient's health or care plan (Adelman et al., 2014).

Moreover, caregivers may also experience feelings of sadness or depression. Witnessing the pain, suffering, or decline of a loved one can be emotionally devastating (Schulz & Sherwood, 2008). Furthermore, the demands of caregiving can often lead to social isolation, as caregivers may find little time or energy to maintain social connections or engage in activities they enjoy, which can further contribute to feelings of sadness or depression (Reinhard et al., 2019).

Despite these challenges, it is important to acknowledge the emotional fulfillment that caregivers can derive from their role. The knowledge that they are providing vital support to a loved one, the bond that develops between caregiver and care recipient, and the personal growth that often results from overcoming challenges can all contribute to a sense of purpose and emotional satisfaction (Quinn et al., 2019).

Mitigating Negative Emotional Impact

While caregiving can be emotionally challenging, there are several strategies that caregivers can employ to manage and mitigate the negative emotional impact. One of the primary ways to manage the emotional stress associated with caregiving is through emotional support. This support can come from various sources, including counselling services, support groups, or even trusted friends and family members (Family Caregiver Alliance, 2012).

Professional counselling services can provide a safe space for caregivers to express their feelings, fears, and frustrations. Counselors can offer strategies for managing stress and anxiety, coping mechanisms for dealing with sadness or depression, and techniques to improve communication with care recipients (Zarit et al., 2014).

Support groups can also be incredibly beneficial. They provide a platform for caregivers to share their experiences, challenges, and victories with others in similar situations. The sense of community and understanding that comes from support groups can help alleviate feelings of isolation and provide practical advice and emotional support (Quinn et al., 2019).

Taking regular breaks from caregiving duties can also help manage emotional stress. Respite care services or other family members can step in to allow caregivers some time to rest, recharge, and engage in activities they enjoy. Ensuring a balance between personal life and caregiving responsibilities can prevent burnout and promote emotional well-being (Reinhard et al., 2019).

Practices such as mindfulness, meditation, and regular exercise can also help manage stress and anxiety. These practices promote relaxation, improve mood, and can provide a much-needed distraction from the demands of caregiving (Waelde et al., 2004).

Role of Emotional Intelligence

Emotional intelligence, defined as the ability to understand, use, and manage emotions in positive ways, plays a significant role in caregiving. Caregivers with high emotional intelligence are better equipped to manage the emotional challenges associated with their role (Goleman, 2005).

A key aspect of emotional intelligence is self-awareness, the ability to recognize and understand one's own emotions. This skill can be particularly beneficial for caregivers, as it can help them identify signs of stress or burnout and take steps to manage their emotional health before it becomes overwhelming (Parveen et al., 2017).

Emotional intelligence also involves empathy, the ability to understand and share the feelings of others. Empathetic caregivers are often more effective in their role, as they can better understand the emotions, needs, and concerns of their care recipients (Kramer, 2017). This understanding can lead to improved communication, better conflict resolution, and a more supportive care environment (Goleman, 2005).

Additionally, emotional intelligence encompasses the ability to manage emotions, both one's own and others. This skill is invaluable for caregivers, as it allows them to stay calm and composed in stressful situations, manage their own emotional responses, and provide appropriate emotional support to their care recipient. It can also help caregivers navigate difficult conversations about health, care, and end-of-life decisions (Parveen et al., 2017).

Emotional intelligence can enhance the caregiving experience for both the caregiver and the care recipient. It can lead to a more supportive and nurturing care environment, improve communication, and help manage the emotional challenges associated with caregiving (Goleman, 2005).

Importance of Emotional Support

The emotional support provided by caregivers is invaluable to care recipients. It goes beyond merely performing routine tasks and enters the realm of companionship, shared experiences, and mutual understanding (Kramer, 2017).

Emotional support can significantly contribute to the mental well-being of care recipients. It can alleviate feelings of loneliness, provide comfort during times of stress or anxiety, and promote a sense of belonging and understanding (Hansen & Slagsvold, 2013). This emotional support can be particularly beneficial for individuals dealing with chronic illnesses or disabilities, as it can provide a counterbalance to the challenges and stress associated with their condition (Schulz & Sherwood, 2008).

Moreover, the emotional support provided by caregivers can improve the overall quality of life of care recipients. It can enhance their mood, boost their self-esteem, and provide a sense of security and stability (Family Caregiver Alliance, 2012). This emotional uplift can have a positive impact on their physical health as well, as emotional well-being is intricately linked to physical health (Reinhard et al., 2019).

However, it is important to note that the benefits of emotional support are not limited to care recipients. Providing emotional support can also be rewarding for caregivers. It can strengthen the bond between caregiver and care recipient, provide a sense of purpose, and contribute to the caregiver's emotional fulfillment (Quinn et al., 2019).

Emotional support should be recognized and valued as a critical component of caregiving. It enhances the well-being of both the caregiver and the care recipient, contributing to a more fulfilling and effective care relationship (Kramer, 2017).

Physical Impact

Physical Impact of Caregivers on Care Recipients

The physical labor undertaken by caregivers can have a profound impact on improving the health and well-being of care recipients. This impact can be seen in the assistance they provide with activities of daily living (ADLs), such as bathing, dressing, and eating (Reinhard et al., 2019). In many cases, these tasks may be challenging or impossible for the care recipient to perform independently due to illness, disability, or age-related decline (Family Caregiver Alliance, 2012). By assisting with these tasks, caregivers enable care recipients to maintain their personal hygiene and nutritional health, which are crucial for overall well-being (Schulz & Sherwood, 2008).

In addition to these basic tasks, caregivers often help with more complex activities, such as medication management. This might involve organizing medication schedules, ensuring that drugs are taken on time and in the correct dosages, and monitoring for any adverse reactions (Adelman et al., 2014). This aspect of caregiving is particularly crucial for care recipients with chronic conditions or multiple health issues, where mismanagement of medication can have serious, even life-threatening consequences (Reinhard et al., 2019).

Caregivers also play a significant role in facilitating the mobility of care recipients. This can involve anything from providing minor assistance with walking or transferring to a chair, to more substantial support such as lifting or moving the care recipient (Family Caregiver Alliance, 2012). This assistance can enhance the physical capabilities of care recipients, helping them maintain their mobility and independence (Schulz & Sherwood, 2008).

Improved mobility can have a ripple effect on other aspects of a care recipient's life. It can lead to improved physical fitness and strength, better mental health through a greater ability to engage with the world, and increased independence and quality of life (Reinhard et al., 2019). It can also help prevent falls and other injuries, which are a major health risk for people with limited mobility (Adelman et al., 2014).

Despite the significant role they play, caregivers' contributions to the physical health and well-being of care recipients are often overlooked or undervalued. Recognizing and supporting these contributions is crucial in ensuring the health and well-being of both caregivers and care recipients (Quinn et al., 2019).

Physical Impact of Care Recipients on Caregivers

While the physical tasks undertaken by caregivers can improve the lives of care recipients, they can also have a significant impact on the caregivers themselves. The physical demands of caregiving, including lifting or moving the care recipient, can be strenuous, and over time can lead to physical health issues for the caregiver (Reinhard et al., 2019).

One of the most common physical issues faced by caregivers is back pain. This can arise from improper lifting techniques or from the cumulative strain of regularly lifting or moving the care recipient (Family Caregiver Alliance, 2012). Back pain can be debilitating, affecting the caregiver's ability to perform their duties, and impacting their quality of life (Adelman et al., 2014).

In addition to back pain, caregivers often face fatigue. This can result from the physical exertion involved in caregiving tasks, but also from the emotional and mental strain of caregiving (Schulz & Sherwood, 2008). Fatigue can impact a caregiver's physical health, reduce their effectiveness in their role, and increase their risk of accidents or errors (Reinhard et al., 2019).

Extended periods of caregiving without adequate rest can also contribute to sleep disturbances. Caregivers may find themselves waking up multiple times in the night to assist the care recipient or lying awake worrying about their responsibilities (Family Caregiver Alliance, 2012). Over time, chronic sleep deprivation can lead to serious health issues, including cardiovascular disease, diabetes, and depression (Adelman et al., 2014).

The physical demands of caregiving can also contribute to a general decline in the physical well-being of caregivers. They may have less time and energy for physical exercise or may neglect their own health needs in favor of those of the care recipient (Reinhard et al., 2019). This can lead to a gradual decline in their physical health, impacting their ability to provide care and further reducing their quality of life (Schulz & Sherwood, 2008).

Mitigating Negative Physical Impact

Despite the physical challenges of caregiving, there are strategies that can be implemented to mitigate these effects. One of the most effective strategies is proper training in safe and efficient techniques for physical tasks (Family Caregiver Alliance, 2012). This can include training in safe lifting and transferring techniques, which can significantly reduce the risk of back pain and other injuries (Reinhard et al., 2019).

Regular breaks and adequate rest are also crucial in maintaining the physical health of caregivers (Adelman et al., 2014). This can involve taking short breaks throughout the day to rest and recharge, as well as ensuring adequate sleep at night (Schulz & Sherwood, 2008). For caregivers who are caring for a loved one around the clock, respite care can provide a much-needed break and opportunity to rest (Reinhard et al., 2019).

Exercise and proper nutrition are also important for maintaining the physical well-being of caregivers (Family Caregiver Alliance, 2012). Regular physical activity can help manage stress, improve sleep, and maintain physical strength and endurance (Adelman et al., 2014). A balanced diet can provide the energy and nutrients needed to cope with the physical demands of caregiving (Reinhard et al., 2019).

Support from healthcare professionals can also be invaluable in managing the physical impact of caregiving. This can include regular health check-ups to monitor the caregiver's physical health, as well as interventions such as physical therapy or pain management for issues like back pain or fatigue (Schulz & Sherwood, 2008).

Emotional and social support can also have a significant impact on the physical well-being of caregivers (Quinn et al., 2019). Feeling valued and supported can reduce stress and improve mental health, which in turn can have a positive impact on physical health (Reinhard et al., 2019).

Role of Physical Therapy and Rehabilitation

For care recipients with mobility issues, physical therapy and rehabilitation can be a critical part of their care plan. These interventions can help care recipients regain lost abilities, maintain their current level of function, and prevent further physical decline (Kasven-Gonzalez et al., 2010). A caregiver who is trained in these areas can play a significant role in this process.

Physical therapy can involve a range of techniques and exercises designed to improve strength, flexibility, and balance (Reinhard et al., 2019). These might include stretching exercises, resistance training, and balance exercises. With the assistance of a caregiver, these exercises can often be done at home, making them more accessible and convenient for the care recipient (Kasven-Gonzalez et al., 2010).

Rehabilitation can also include assistive devices such as walkers or wheelchairs. A caregiver can assist with training the care recipient in the safe and effective use of these devices, as well as providing ongoing assistance as needed (Family Caregiver Alliance, 2012). This can significantly enhance the care recipient's mobility and independence, as well as reducing the physical strain on the caregiver (Reinhard et al., 2019).

In addition to physical therapy and rehabilitation, caregivers can also assist with other aspects of physical health care. This might include wound care, monitoring for signs of illness or infection, and assisting with other medical tasks (Adelman et al., 2014). This can help ensure the overall physical health of the care recipient, as well as reducing the risk of complications or hospitalization (Schulz & Sherwood, 2008).

While the role of physical therapy and rehabilitation in caregiving can be demanding, it can also be rewarding. Assisting a care recipient in improving their physical capabilities can lead to significant improvements in their quality of life, as well as increased independence (Kasven-Gonzalez et al., 2010). It can also provide a sense of achievement and satisfaction for the caregiver (Quinn et al., 2019).

Importance of Physical Assistance

Physical assistance is often a central aspect of caregiving, particularly for care recipients with significant physical limitations (Reinhard et al., 2019). This assistance can take many forms, from help with basic tasks such as bathing and dressing, to more substantial support such as lifting or moving the care recipient (Family Caregiver Alliance, 2012). In all cases, the physical support provided by caregivers can enhance the daily lives of care recipients.

By assisting with basic tasks, caregivers enable care recipients to maintain their personal hygiene, nutritional health, and overall well-being (Adelman et al., 2014). This can help them feel more comfortable, healthy, and dignified, as well as reducing the risk of complications such as infections or malnutrition (Schulz & Sherwood, 2008).

Physical assistance can also enable care recipients to engage in activities that they enjoy (Reinhard et al., 2019). This might include hobbies such as gardening or painting, or simply getting out of the house for a walk or a visit to a friend. These activities can provide mental stimulation, social interaction, and a sense of purpose, all of which can significantly enhance the care recipient's quality of life (Family Caregiver Alliance, 2012).

In addition, physical assistance can help maintain the dignity and independence of care recipients (Adelman et al., 2014). Being able to do things for themselves, even with assistance, can provide a sense of control and self-worth (Reinhard et al., 2019). This can be particularly important for care recipients who are struggling with the loss of independence associated with illness or age-related decline (Schulz & Sherwood, 2008).

Despite its importance, the physical assistance provided by caregivers is often overlooked or undervalued (Quinn et al., 2019). Recognizing and supporting this critical aspect of caregiving is crucial for the health and well-being of both caregivers and care recipients (Family Caregiver Alliance, 2012). This can involve providing training and support for caregivers, ensuring they have the resources they need to provide physical assistance safely and effectively, and recognizing their contributions to the health and well-being of care recipients (Reinhard et al., 2019).

Knowledge and Skills of Caregivers

Caregivers play a crucial role in providing support and care for individuals who are unable to fully care for themselves due to age, illness, or disability (Family Caregiver Alliance, 2012). The knowledge and skills that caregivers possess directly affect the quality of care they can provide to care recipients (Reinhard et al., 2019).

One of the most principal elements of caregiving is knowing and understanding the specific health conditions of the care recipient (Adelman et al., 2014). This knowledge can drastically affect the care and support one provides. For example, the care required for an Alzheimer's patient differs from the care needed for a patient with heart disease (Schulz & Sherwood, 2008). Understanding the specific health condition, its symptoms, complications, and common treatment plans can help caregivers anticipate and meet care recipients' needs (Reinhard et al., 2019).

Further, understanding medications and their side effects is a crucial part of caregiving. This includes knowledge of when and how to administer medications, understanding the purpose of each medication, and being aware of potential side effects or interactions (Family Caregiver Alliance, 2012). This knowledge can help prevent medication errors and can facilitate prompt response to any adverse reactions (Adelman et al., 2014).

Managing medical equipment also requires specific skills. From using a wheelchair to operating a home dialysis machine, these skills ensure the safety and comfort of care recipients (Reinhard et al., 2019). Training in CPR and other emergency procedures is also valuable (Schulz & Sherwood, 2008).

Effective communication skills are necessary for caregivers. They need to communicate clearly and compassionately with care recipients, understand their needs and concerns, and communicate effectively with other healthcare providers (Quinn et al., 2019). This skill enhances the overall care process, ensuring that all parties are informed and involved in the care of the recipient (Reinhard et al., 2019).

Training and Education for Caregivers

The role of a caregiver often comes without a handbook, and it can be a steep learning curve (Family Caregiver Alliance, 2012). Training and education are vital to equip caregivers with the necessary knowledge and skills, and to ensure the best possible care for the recipient (Reinhard et al., 2019).

Formal caregiver training programs are available and can provide comprehensive knowledge and practical skills (Adelman et al., 2014). These programs often cover a range of topics, such as understanding common health conditions, medication management, emergency procedures, and use of medical equipment (Schulz & Sherwood, 2008). They may also include modules on nutrition, personal care, and mobility assistance (Reinhard et al., 2019).

Training is not limited to formal programs. Informal training provided by healthcare professionals, such as nurses, doctors, and therapists, is also invaluable (Family Caregiver Alliance, 2012). This type of training often occurs during hospital stays or outpatient appointments, and it is tailored to the specific needs of the care recipient (Adelman et al., 2014).

Managing the emotional aspects of caregiving is another critical area of training (Schulz & Sherwood, 2008). Caregiving can be emotionally demanding, and caregivers need strategies to cope with stress, prevent burnout, and manage their own mental and emotional well-being (Reinhard et al., 2019). This training might include stress management techniques, self-care strategies, and resources for mental health support (Quinn et al., 2019).

Education also plays a significant role in caregiver training (Family Caregiver Alliance, 2012). This can include self-guided learning through reading books, articles, and reputable online resources. It also involves staying updated on the latest research and advancements related to the care recipient's condition (Reinhard et al., 2019).

Utilizing Resources

The role of a caregiver can be overwhelming, and it is important for caregivers to know they are not alone. Numerous resources are available to support caregivers in their significant role, and being adept at utilizing these resources can significantly enhance the quality of care provided (Reinhard et al., 2019).

One of the most important resources is information. This can be found in medical books, online resources, and through healthcare professionals (Family Caregiver Alliance, 2012). This information can help caregivers understand the care recipient's condition, learn about treatment options, and stay updated on new research and advancements (Adelman et al., 2014).

Support services are another crucial resource. These can include respite care services, home health services, and support groups (Schulz & Sherwood, 2008). Respite care services provide temporary relief for caregivers, while home health services can provide professional medical care in the home setting (Reinhard et al., 2019). Support groups offer a space for caregivers to share experiences, learn from others in similar situations, and receive emotional support (Quinn et al., 2019).

Navigating the healthcare system is a skill in itself. This involves understanding insurance coverage, coordinating with multiple healthcare providers, and advocating for the care recipient's needs (Family Caregiver Alliance, 2012). Knowing how to effectively navigate this complex system can ensure the care recipient receives the necessary care and can help reduce the caregiver's stress and burden (Reinhard et al., 2019).

Role of Experience

Experience is often said to be the best teacher, and this is especially true in caregiving (Adelman et al., 2014). As caregivers gain experience, they become more adept at managing their responsibilities, understanding their care recipient's needs, and navigating challenges that arise (Schulz & Sherwood, 2008).

Experience helps caregivers refine their skills and deepen their understanding of the care recipient's condition (Reinhard et al., 2019). It also helps them become more efficient in their tasks, develop routines, and anticipate problems before they arise (Family Caregiver Alliance, 2012).

Experience also provides a deeper understanding of the care recipient as an individual. Caregivers learn their preferences, habits, and unique ways of communicating (Quinn et al., 2019). This understanding can lead to more personalized care and a better quality of life for the care recipient (Adelman et al., 2014).

However, experience also comes with challenges. Caregivers may face emotional exhaustion, physical strain, and potential burnout (Reinhard et al., 2019). It is crucial for caregivers to take care of their own health and well-being, seek support when needed, and recognize the signs of caregiver stress and burnout (Schulz & Sherwood, 2008).

Importance of Ongoing Learning

The field of healthcare is ever evolving, with new research, treatments, and protocols emerging regularly (Reinhard et al., 2019). Thus, caregivers must commit to ongoing learning to stay updated and provide the best possible care (Family Caregiver Alliance, 2012).

New treatments and interventions may become available that could significantly impact the care recipient's health and quality of life (Adelman et al., 2014). It is important for caregivers to stay informed about these advancements and discuss them with the healthcare team to determine if they are applicable (Schulz & Sherwood, 2008).

Changes in care protocols also require ongoing learning. For example, guidelines for managing chronic conditions like diabetes or hypertension may change based on new research (Reinhard et al., 2019). Caregivers who are up to date with these changes can ensure that care recipients are receiving the most current and effective care (Family Caregiver Alliance, 2012).

Ongoing learning also allows caregivers to implement best practices in their care. This can include strategies for managing challenging behaviors in dementia patients, techniques for safely transferring mobility-impaired individuals, or methods for managing medication side effects (Adelman et al., 2014).

In addition, ongoing learning can help caregivers better understand and navigate the healthcare system. This can include learning about changes in healthcare laws, insurance coverage, or available support services (Schulz & Sherwood, 2008).

Finally, continuous learning is crucial for caregiver's self-care. They can learn new strategies for managing stress, preventing burnout, and promoting their own physical and mental health (Reinhard et al., 2019). This not only benefits caregivers themselves but also allows them to provide better care for their recipients (Quinn et al., 2019).

The role of a caregiver is multifaceted and requires a wide range of knowledge and skills. Through education, training, utilizing resources, gaining experience, and committing to ongoing learning, caregivers can provide high-quality, personalized care, leading to improved health outcomes for care recipients and a rewarding caregiving experience (Family Caregiver Alliance, 2012).

The Reciprocal Nature of Caregiving

Fulfillment and Satisfaction for Caregivers

Caregiving is a role that is frequently fraught with difficulties, yet it can also be a profoundly rewarding and satisfying experience (Quinn et al., 2019). It provides caregivers with a sense of purpose, allowing them to derive meaning from the act of helping others (Kramer, 2017). This sense of purpose can be a powerful motivator, driving caregivers to face the challenges associated with caregiving with resilience and perseverance (Reinhard et al., 2019).

The bond formed between caregivers and care recipients can often lead to deep emotional satisfaction (Family Caregiver Alliance, 2012). This bond is often formed on mutual trust, respect, and a shared understanding of the situation (Adelman et al., 2014). It is a unique relationship that can offer a sense of connection and belonging, which can be particularly significant in situations where the caregiver and care recipient are family members (Kramer, 2017).

The satisfaction derived from seeing the positive impact of their efforts on the well-being of their care recipients can also be a source of gratification for caregivers (Reinhard et al., 2019). Observing improvements in the physical or mental state of care recipients can serve as a tangible reminder of the importance of their role, reinforcing their commitment and dedication (Quinn et al., 2019).

However, it is important to note that this fulfillment does not negate the challenges associated with caregiving. The role can be physically and emotionally demanding, often leading to stress and burnout (Schulz & Sherwood, 2008). Therefore, it is crucial for caregivers to take care of their own well-being as well, engaging in self-care activities and seeking support when necessary (Reinhard et al., 2019).

The fulfillment and satisfaction derived from caregiving can serve as a powerful counterbalance to the inherent challenges of the role (Kramer, 2017). They can empower caregivers to navigate their caregiving journey with resilience and fortitude, contributing positively to their emotional well-being and overall quality of life (Quinn et al., 2019).

Improved Quality of Life for Care Recipients

Care recipients often experience significant improvements in their quality of life because of the care and support provided by caregivers (Reinhard et al., 2019). This is particularly true for those who are living with chronic illnesses or disabilities, where the constant support provided by caregivers can make a substantial difference in their daily lives (Schulz & Sherwood, 2008).

The physical assistance provided by caregivers is an essential aspect of care. This can range from help with daily tasks such as bathing, dressing, and meal preparation, to more medical-oriented tasks such as medication management and physical therapy (Family Caregiver Alliance, 2012). By providing this assistance, caregivers reduce the physical strain on care recipients, allowing them to live more comfortably and independently (Adelman et al., 2014).

Emotional support is another crucial aspect of caregiving. Caregivers often play a significant role in providing companionship and emotional comfort to care recipients (Kramer, 2017). They can help alleviate feelings of loneliness, anxiety, and depression that care recipients may experience, contributing to their emotional well-being (Reinhard et al., 2019).

The presence of a caregiver can provide a sense of security and reassurance for care recipients (Quinn et al., 2019). Knowing that there is someone they can rely on in times of need can significantly reduce stress and anxiety, promoting a more positive overall outlook (Schulz & Sherwood, 2008).

The care and support provided by caregivers can drastically enhance the quality of life for care recipients (Reinhard et al., 2019). They provide physical assistance, emotional support, and companionship, all of which are essential for the well-being of care recipients (Family Caregiver Alliance, 2012). This underscores the reciprocal nature of caregiving, where both caregivers and care recipients can benefit from the relationship (Kramer, 2017).

Balancing the Caregiving Relationship

Understanding the reciprocal nature of caregiving is crucial for maintaining a balanced caregiving relationship (Reinhard et al., 2019). While caregivers play an essential role in supporting care recipients, they also require support to manage their responsibilities effectively. This can come from various sources, including family, friends, healthcare professionals, and community resources (Family Caregiver Alliance, 2012).

Caregivers often bear a significant amount of responsibility, which can lead to physical and emotional exhaustion (Schulz & Sherwood, 2008).

6.4: Enhancing Caregiver-Care Recipient Relationship- Strategies for Strengthening the Emotional Connection

The role of a caregiver involves a complex interplay of physical and emotional tasks aimed at improving the well-being of the care recipient. While the physical aspects of this role are often more visible, the emotional connection between the caregiver and the care recipient forms the underpinning of the caregiving relationship (Schulz & Sherwood, 2008). This emotional bond can significantly impact the care recipient's outlook, overall health, and quality of life (Reinhard et al., 2019). For caregivers, a strong emotional connection can provide a sense of fulfillment and mitigate the stresses associated with their role (Quinn et al., 2019).

The importance of this emotional bond is underscored by research indicating that a closer caregiver-care recipient relationship is associated with improved health outcomes. This includes better cognitive and functional abilities, improved ability to conduct daily activities, and reduced severity of neuropsychiatric symptoms in individuals with dementia (Fauth et al., 2021).

Understanding the dynamics of this relationship is crucial for both caregivers and care recipients (Kramer, 2017). A supportive, empathetic, and understanding approach can significantly enhance the caregiving experience and improve the overall well-being of both parties involved (Family Caregiver Alliance, 2012). However, nurturing this relationship requires a clear set of strategies aimed at strengthening emotional connections and fostering a supportive caregiving environment (Adelman et al., 2014).

In this discourse, we will delve into the intricacies of the caregiver-care recipient relationship and explore strategies to fortify and nurture this relationship. The strategies include active listening, empathy, effective communication, and self-care (Reinhard et al., 2019). Each of these elements plays a unique role in enhancing the emotional bond between caregiver and care recipient and improving the caregiving experience (Quinn et al., 2019).

Active Listening

Understanding Through Listening

Active listening is a crucial skill for caregivers that extends far beyond hearing the words that care recipients say (Kramer, 2017). It involves fully focusing on the speaker, avoiding internal and external distractions, and responding to the speaker in a way that demonstrates understanding and engagement. This means not only hearing the words, but also noticing non-verbal cues such as body language, tone of voice, and facial expressions (Family Caregiver Alliance, 2012).

In the caregiving context, active listening can help caregivers to better understand the needs, experiences, and emotions of the care recipients (Reinhard et al., 2019). This greater understanding can guide caregivers in providing care that is more personalized and empathetic, meeting the care recipients' needs in a holistic and individualized way (Quinn et al., 2019).

Active listening also aids in identifying and addressing any concerns or issues the care recipient might be facing (Adelman et al., 2014). By paying close attention to what is being said and not said, caregivers can notice subtle hints of discomfort, distress, fear, or any other emotions that the care recipient might not be explicitly expressing (Schulz & Sherwood, 2008).

Active listening affirms to the care recipient that their thoughts, feelings, and experiences are valued (Kramer, 2017). This can enhance their sense of self-worth and dignity, aspects that are critical for their overall well-being and satisfaction with the care they receive (Reinhard et al., 2019).

Active listening provides an opportunity for caregivers to learn more about the care recipient's life, enriching their understanding of the person they are caring for (Quinn et al., 2019). This can deepen the caregiver-care recipient relationship, fostering a sense of connection and mutual respect (Family Caregiver Alliance, 2012).

Building Trust

Trust is a fundamental pillar in the caregiver-care recipient relationship (Reinhard et al., 2019). It is the glue that holds the relationship together and the lubricant that keeps it moving smoothly. Active listening plays a key role in building this trust (Kramer, 2017).

When caregivers actively listen, they demonstrate to care recipients that they are genuinely interested in their thoughts and feelings (Quinn et al., 2019). This can make care recipients feel valued and understood, fostering a sense of safety and security in the relationship (Family Caregiver Alliance, 2012).

Trust built through active listening can also enhance cooperation in care tasks (Adelman et al., 2014). When care recipients trust their caregivers, they are more likely to follow their advice and cooperate with the care plan. This can lead to improved health outcomes and a better quality of life for the care recipient (Schulz & Sherwood, 2008).

Moreover, trust can make it easier for caregivers to address difficult issues with care recipients (Reinhard et al., 2019). For instance, conversations about end-of-life care or changes in care plans can be challenging and emotionally charged. However, if there is a strong foundation of trust, these conversations can be conducted in a more open and respectful manner (Kramer, 2017).

Trust can also reduce stress and conflict in the caregiver-care recipient relationship (Quinn et al., 2019). When both parties trust each other, they can communicate more effectively, solve problems more efficiently, and enjoy a more harmonious relationship (Family Caregiver Alliance, 2012).

Expression of Empathy

Empathy is the capacity to understand and share the feelings of others (Kramer, 2017). For caregivers, empathy is not only about understanding the care recipient's feelings but also about conveying this understanding in a compassionate and supportive manner (Reinhard et al., 2019).

Through active listening, caregivers can show empathy to care recipients (Quinn et al., 2019). Active listening involves responding to the speaker in a way that validates their feelings and experiences (Family Caregiver Alliance, 2012). This could involve verbal responses, such as acknowledging the speaker's feelings, or non-verbal responses, such as nodding or maintaining eye contact (Adelman et al., 2014).

Empathetic responses can provide emotional comfort to care recipients (Schulz & Sherwood, 2008). They can feel seen and heard, which can alleviate feelings of loneliness, isolation, or distress. This can contribute to the care recipient's psychological well-being and enhance their relationship with the caregiver (Reinhard et al., 2019).

Furthermore, expressing empathy can help caregivers to build a stronger emotional bond with care recipients (Kramer, 2017). This bond can enrich the caregiving experience, making it more meaningful and fulfilling for both parties (Quinn et al., 2019).

However, empathy should not lead to over-identification with the care recipient's feelings, which can lead to caregiver burnout. Caregivers should strive for a balance, maintaining an empathetic connection while also preserving their emotional boundaries (Reinhard et al., 2019).

Active Listening Challenges

Active listening can be challenging, especially in emotionally charged situations or when caregivers are under stress (Adelman et al., 2014). It requires mental and emotional effort, patience, and self-awareness (Schulz & Sherwood, 2008).

One common challenge is dealing with one's own reactions and emotions while listening (Reinhard et al., 2019). Caregivers might feel anxious, upset, or defensive when care recipients express certain feelings or views. These reactions can interfere with active listening and hinder effective communication (Kramer, 2017).

Another challenge is managing distractions (Quinn et al., 2019). These could be external distractions, such as noise or interruptions, or internal distractions, such as preoccupations or worries. Distractions can divert attention away from the speaker and disrupt the listening process (Family Caregiver Alliance, 2012).

Despite these challenges, active listening is a skill that can be developed and improved over time (Reinhard et al., 2019). Caregivers can cultivate this skill through practice, self-reflection, and training. They can also seek support from professional resources or peer support groups to overcome these challenges (Quinn et al., 2019).

The Impact of Active Listening

The impact of active listening in the caregiver-care recipient relationship can be profound (Kramer, 2017). It can enhance understanding, build trust, and foster an emotional bond between caregivers and care recipients (Reinhard et al., 2019). This can lead to numerous positive outcomes, both for the care recipient and the caregiver (Quinn et al., 2019).

Active listening can improve the cooperation of care recipients (Family Caregiver Alliance, 2012). When they feel heard and understood, they are likely to be more receptive to caregivers' suggestions and advice. This can make caregiving tasks easier and more effective, leading to improved health outcomes for the care recipient (Adelman et al., 2014).

In addition, active listening can enhance the emotional well-being of care recipients (Schulz & Sherwood, 2008). Feeling understood and listened to can alleviate feelings of isolation and loneliness, common issues faced by many care recipients. It can also provide emotional comfort and support, contributing to their overall psychological health (Reinhard et al., 2019).

Active listening can also have positive effects on the caregiver (Kramer, 2017). It can lead to increased caregiver satisfaction, as understanding and connecting with the care recipient can make the caregiving experience more rewarding (Quinn et al., 2019). It can also reduce caregiver stress and burnout, as effective communication can prevent misunderstandings and conflicts (Family Caregiver Alliance, 2012).

Furthermore, active listening can enhance the overall quality of the caregiving relationship (Reinhard et al., 2019). It can foster a mutual sense of respect and understanding, creating a more harmonious and satisfying relationship for both the caregiver and the care recipient (Schulz & Sherwood, 2008).

Active listening is a powerful tool in caregiving (Kramer, 2017). By improving understanding, building trust, expressing empathy, and overcoming challenges, active listening can enhance the caregiving experience and outcomes for both caregivers and care recipients (Quinn et al., 2019).

Empathy

Empathy as a Pillar

Empathy is a foundational pillar in the caregiver-care recipient relationship (Reinhard et al., 2019). Often described as the ability to 'walk in someone else's shoes,' empathy enables caregivers to deeply understand and share the feelings of those they care for (Kramer, 2017). This ability to perceive and connect with the emotional state of the care recipient is a fundamental aspect of caregiving that goes beyond merely providing physical care (Family Caregiver Alliance, 2012).

In the context of caregiving, empathy is about recognizing and validating the unique lived experience of the care recipient (Quinn et al., 2019). Whether they are dealing with physical pain, emotional distress, or the anxiety that often accompanies illness and aging, care recipients have a rich inner life that caregivers need to acknowledge and address (Adelman et al., 2014). By doing so, caregivers can provide personalized and compassionate care that truly meets the care recipient's needs (Schulz & Sherwood, 2008).

Empathy also helps create a nurturing and supportive environment, which is crucial for the overall well-being of the care recipient (Reinhard et al.,

2019). When caregivers approach their roles with empathy, they create an atmosphere of understanding and acceptance. This environment can help alleviate feelings of fear or isolation that care recipients may experience and promote their emotional and psychological well-being (Kramer, 2017).

Empathy strengthens the bond between the caregiver and the care recipient (Quinn et al., 2019). This emotional connection can be a source of comfort and reassurance for care recipients, who often rely heavily on their caregivers for emotional support. For caregivers, this bond can provide a sense of purpose and fulfillment, making their role more rewarding (Family Caregiver Alliance, 2012).

Empathy can enhance communication between caregivers and care recipients (Reinhard et al., 2019). By empathizing with the care recipient, caregivers can better understand their perspectives and needs. This understanding can facilitate more effective communication, leading to improved care and a more harmonious caregiving relationship (Adelman et al., 2014).

Empathy in Action

Empathy in action goes beyond just understanding; it involves demonstrating this understanding in tangible ways (Kramer, 2017). For caregivers, this means actively expressing empathy through their actions and behaviors. This can take many forms, from using comforting words and providing a listening ear, to offering physical comfort and providing patient, compassionate care (Reinhard et al., 2019).

Demonstrating empathy often involves active listening (Quinn et al., 2019). This means not only hearing what the care recipient is saying but also paying attention to non-verbal cues and emotions (Family Caregiver Alliance, 2012). By doing this, caregivers can understand the underlying feelings and concerns of care recipients, which can guide them in providing appropriate care and support (Adelman et al., 2014).

Physical comfort is another important aspect of empathy in action (Schulz & Sherwood, 2008). This could involve providing a comforting touch or helping with physical tasks in a gentle and understanding manner. Physical comfort can help alleviate discomfort or distress and convey a sense of caring and understanding (Reinhard et al., 2019).

Furthermore, empathy in action can involve validating the care recipient's feelings and experiences (Kramer, 2017). Validation is a powerful tool that can help care recipients feel seen and understood. By acknowledging and accepting the care recipient's feelings, caregivers can provide emotional support and foster a stronger connection (Quinn et al., 2019).

Expressing empathy can also involve advocacy (Reinhard et al., 2019). Caregivers, by understanding the care recipient's experiences and needs, can function as advocates for their rights and wishes. This can entail speaking up for the care recipient in healthcare settings or ensuring that their preferences are respected and honored (Family Caregiver Alliance, 2012).

The Power of Empathy

Empathy has transformative power in the caregiver-care recipient relationship (Kramer, 2017). It goes beyond the mere provision of physical care to encompass emotional companionship, making the caregiving experience more meaningful for both parties involved (Reinhard et al., 2019). Empathy enables caregivers to provide care that is attuned to the care recipient's emotional needs, which can lead to improved cooperation, greater satisfaction, and a better quality of life for care recipients (Quinn et al., 2019).

When caregivers approach their roles with empathy, they foster a more positive caregiving experience (Family Caregiver Alliance, 2012). Empathy can transform caregiving from a task-oriented role into a relationship-based role. This shift in perspective can enhance the caregiver-care recipient relationship, making it more rewarding and less burdensome (Adelman et al., 2014).

Empathy can also promote cooperation between caregivers and care recipients (Schulz & Sherwood, 2008). When care recipients feel understood and valued, they are more likely to cooperate with the care plan and communicate openly about their needs and concerns. This can lead to more effective care and a better overall caregiving experience (Reinhard et al., 2019).

Furthermore, empathy can enhance the satisfaction and well-being of care recipients (Kramer, 2017). Feeling understood and cared for can have a profound impact on care recipients' mental and emotional health. It can alleviate feelings of fear or isolation, boost their self-esteem, and promote their overall well-being (Quinn et al., 2019).

Empathy can improve the quality of life for care recipients (Reinhard et al., 2019). By addressing their emotional needs and promoting their psychological well-being, caregivers can contribute to a better quality of life for those they care for. This can lead to improved physical health, more positive emotions, and a greater sense of peace and fulfillment (Family Caregiver Alliance, 2012).

Challenges and Overcoming Them

While empathy is a powerful tool in caregiving, maintaining it can be challenging, especially when caregivers are dealing with their own stressors (Adelman et al., 2014). The emotional labor involved in caregiving can sometimes lead to empathy fatigue, where caregivers find it hard to empathize due to their own emotional exhaustion. However, there are strategies that caregivers can employ to overcome these challenges (Reinhard et al., 2019).

One strategy is to practice self-care (Schulz & Sherwood, 2008). This involves acknowledging one's own emotions and taking steps to address emotional and physical fatigue. By taking care of their own well-being, caregivers can ensure that they have the emotional capacity to empathize with care recipients (Kramer, 2017).

Another strategy is to remember the shared human experience (Quinn et al., 2019). Caregiving can be a profoundly humbling experience that reminds us of our shared vulnerability and humanity. By focusing on this shared experience, caregivers can cultivate a sense of empathy even when faced with challenging situations (Family Caregiver Alliance, 2012).

Mindfulness is another powerful tool for maintaining empathy (Reinhard et al., 2019). Mindfulness involves staying present and attentive to the current moment. By practicing mindfulness, caregivers can stay emotionally connected to the care recipient, which can help them respond more empathetically to the care recipient's needs (Adelman et al., 2014).

Seeking support from others can also help overcome challenges associated with empathy (Schulz & Sherwood, 2008). This could involve reaching out to support groups, therapists, or other caregivers. By sharing experiences and learning from others, caregivers can gain new perspectives and strategies for maintaining empathy (Kramer, 2017).

Education and training can help caregivers develop and sustain empathy (Reinhard et al., 2019). This could involve learning about the care recipient's condition, understanding the typical emotional responses associated with it, and developing strategies for responding empathetically (Quinn et al., 2019).

The Far-reaching Impact of Empathy

The impact of empathy extends far beyond the immediate caregiver-care recipient relationship. It can influence the overall caregiving environment, making it more supportive and less stressful (Kramer, 2017). It can also enhance the caregiver's sense of satisfaction and fulfillment, improve the care recipient's psychological well-being, and even influence broader societal attitudes towards caregiving (Reinhard et al., 2019).

Empathy can create a more supportive caregiving environment (Quinn et al., 2019). When caregivers approach their roles with empathy, they foster an atmosphere of understanding and acceptance. This can reduce stress and conflict, enhance cooperation, and promote a more positive caregiving experience for all involved (Family Caregiver Alliance, 2012).

Empathy can also lead to greater satisfaction and fulfillment for caregivers (Adelman et al., 2014). By connecting deeply with care recipients, caregivers can find greater meaning and purpose in their roles. This can make caregiving more rewarding and mitigate some of the challenges associated with it (Schulz & Sherwood, 2008).

Effective Communication

The Role of Communication

Communication serves as the cornerstone of the caregiver-care-recipient relationship. It is not just about relaying information, but also about understanding and meeting the needs, preferences, and experiences of the person receiving care (Kramer, 2017). As a caregiver, your ability to communicate effectively can directly influence the quality of care and the overall well-being of the care recipient (Reinhard et al., 2019).

In this context, communication goes beyond just verbal exchanges. It encompasses nonverbal cues, emotional subtleties, and even the ability to listen actively (Family Caregiver Alliance, 2012). The caregiver needs to maintain an open, honest, and consistent line of communication to comprehend the needs and wishes of the care recipient fully (Quinn et al., 2019).

At its core, communication helps to establish trust (Adelman et al., 2014). As caregivers share and receive information, they build a rapport with the care recipient. This trust can be a crucial element in allowing the person receiving care to feel comfortable expressing their desires, fears, and expectations (Schulz & Sherwood, 2008).

Furthermore, effective communication can facilitate decision-making in the care process (Reinhard et al., 2019). By understanding the care recipient's physical and emotional state, caregivers can make informed decisions about treatments, routines, and other aspects of care. In turn, this can lead to improved health outcomes and overall quality of life for the person receiving care (Family Caregiver Alliance, 2012).

Communication can serve to alleviate feelings of stress, anxiety, or fear that may arise in a caregiving situation (Kramer, 2017). By discussing these feelings openly, caregivers and care recipients can work together to find strategies to cope and address any issues that may arise (Quinn et al., 2019).

Principles of Effective Communication

Effective communication in the caregiver-care-recipient relationship is rooted in several key principles. The first of these is clarity and conciseness. Caregivers need to express their thoughts and information in a way that is easy to understand (Reinhard et al., 2019). This means avoiding jargon or overly complex explanations and focusing on delivering clear, to-the-point messages (Family Caregiver Alliance, 2012).

Equally important is the tone of communication (Kramer, 2017). Respectful, gentle communication can help to build trust and rapport. Using a positive, empathetic tone can also help to reduce any anxiety or fear that the care recipient might be feeling. It is essential to remember that the way something is said can often be as impactful as what is being said (Quinn et al., 2019).

Nonverbal communication is another crucial aspect of effective communication (Adelman et al., 2014). This includes eye contact, facial expressions, gestures, and body language. These nonverbal cues can often convey more than words alone. For instance, maintaining eye contact can signal attentiveness and respect, while a relaxed posture can help to create a calm and comfortable environment (Schulz & Sherwood, 2008).

Active listening is yet another vital principle (Reinhard et al., 2019). This means not just hearing the words that the care recipient is saying, but also understanding and empathizing with their feelings and experiences. Active listening involves giving your full attention, asking clarifying questions, and providing feedback to ensure that you have fully understood the message (Family Caregiver Alliance, 2012).

It is important to remember that communication is a two-way process (Kramer, 2017). This means engaging the care recipient in the conversation, asking for their input, and valuing their feedback. This can help to ensure that their needs and preferences are being met and that they feel involved and valued in the caregiving process (Quinn et al., 2019).

Nonverbal Communication

Nonverbal communication can sometimes speak louder than words in the caregiver-care recipient relationship (Reinhard et al., 2019). This can include everything from eye contact and facial expressions to gestures and body language. These nonverbal cues can serve to reinforce and enhance verbal communication, as well as convey emotions and attitudes (Kramer, 2017).

Eye contact, for instance, can signal attentiveness and respect. It can help to establish a connection and show the care recipient that you are fully present and engaged in the conversation (Quinn et al., 2019). However, it is important to be mindful of cultural differences and personal preferences, as direct eye contact may not always be comfortable or appropriate (Family Caregiver Alliance, 2012).

Facial expressions can also convey a wide range of emotions (Adelman et al., 2014). A smile can indicate warmth and friendliness, while a furrowed brow might express concern or confusion. By being mindful of your facial expressions, you can help to ensure that your nonverbal cues align with your words (Schulz & Sherwood, 2008).

Body language and gestures can also play a significant role in communication (Reinhard et al., 2019). For example, a relaxed posture can signal comfort and ease, while leaning in can show interest and engagement. Touch can also be a powerful form of nonverbal communication, whether it is a reassuring pat on the back or a gentle hand on the arm. However, always respect personal boundaries and cultural norms when using touch (Kramer, 2017).

It is important to pay attention to the nonverbal cues of the care recipient (Quinn et al., 2019). Their facial expressions, body language, and gestures can provide valuable insights into their feelings and needs. By observing and interpreting these cues, you can better understand and respond to their experiences (Family Caregiver Alliance, 2012).

Communication Challenges and Solutions

Despite its importance, effective communication can sometimes be challenging, especially when dealing with difficult topics or when the care recipient has cognitive or communication impairments. However, there are several strategies that caregivers can use to overcome these challenges (Reinhard et al., 2019).

Using simple, clear language can help to ensure that the message is understood (Kramer, 2017). This is especially important when communicating with care recipients who have cognitive impairments. Avoid jargon and complex language, and break down information into small, manageable parts. Repeat key points if necessary and check for understanding (Quinn et al., 2019).

Visual aids can also be a valuable tool in enhancing communication (Family Caregiver Alliance, 2012). This could involve using pictures, diagrams, or physical objects to illustrate a point or explain a concept. Visual aids can be particularly useful for individuals who have difficulty understanding or processing verbal information (Adelman et al., 2014).

Patience is crucial when overcoming communication challenges (Schulz & Sherwood, 2008). Allow the care recipient plenty of time to process information and respond. Avoid rushing them or interrupting, as this can cause stress and confusion. Instead, maintain a calm, patient demeanor, even if the conversation is slow or difficult (Reinhard et al., 2019).

Empathetic listening can also help to alleviate communication challenges (Kramer, 2017). This involves not just hearing the words that the care recipient is saying, but also understanding and validating their feelings. By showing empathy, caregivers can help to build a trusting, respectful relationship, which can facilitate more effective communication (Quinn et al., 2019).

Practice and feedback can help to improve communication skills (Family Caregiver Alliance, 2012). Regularly engaging in conversation can help caregivers to become more comfortable and proficient in their communication. Additionally, seeking feedback from the care recipient can provide valuable insights into their communication preferences and needs, and can help the caregiver to adapt and improve their communication approach (Reinhard et al., 2019).

Impact of Effective Communication

The impact of effective communication on the caregiver-care recipient relationship cannot be overstated. Firstly, it can enhance the understanding and trust between caregivers and care recipients (Kramer, 2017). By communicating openly and honestly, caregivers can gain a deeper understanding of the care recipient's needs, preferences, and experiences. This can lead to more personalized and effective care (Quinn et al., 2019).

Effective communication can also improve cooperation in the caregiving process (Family Caregiver Alliance, 2012). When caregivers and care recipients have a clear understanding of each other's expectations, they are more likely to work together effectively. This can make the caregiving process smoother and more efficient and can lead to improved satisfaction for both parties (Adelman et al., 2014).

Moreover, effective communication can enhance the emotional connection between caregivers and care recipients (Reinhard et al., 2019). By sharing experiences, expressing emotions, and validating each other's feelings, they can build a strong emotional bond. This can contribute to a supportive, harmonious caregiving environment, which can have a positive impact on the care recipient's emotional well-being (Schulz & Sherwood, 2008).

In addition, effective communication can also have a positive impact on the caregiver's well-being (Kramer, 2017). It can help to prevent misunderstandings and conflicts, which can reduce stress and improve job satisfaction. Furthermore, it can provide caregivers with the reassurance that they are meeting the care recipient's needs and contributing positively to their well-being (Quinn et al., 2019).

Research has shown that effective communication can lead to better health outcomes for care recipients (Family Caregiver Alliance, 2012). It can facilitate informed decision-making, improve adherence to care plans, and promote proactive health behaviors. Overall, effective communication is a powerful tool that can enhance the quality of care and improve the lives of both caregivers and care recipients (Reinhard et al., 2019).

Self-Care

The Importance of Self-Care

Self-care, at its core, is a preventive health strategy involving actions and behaviors that improve, maintain, or restore health (Reinhard et al., 2019). For caregivers, it is an essential yet often overlooked aspect of effective caregiving. In the relentless pursuit of providing the best care for their loved ones, caregivers often de-prioritize their own needs (Family Caregiver Alliance, 2012). However, neglecting self-care can lead to burnout, negatively affecting their ability to provide care and support (Adelman et al., 2014).

Self-care involves taking care of one's physical, emotional, and mental well-being (Schulz & Sherwood, 2008). It is about recognizing one's own needs and taking steps to meet them (Kramer, 2017). It is about treating oneself as kindly and attentively as one would a loved one. For caregivers, self-care is not a luxury but a necessity. It is about ensuring that they are physically, emotionally, and mentally in the best position to provide care (Quinn et al., 2019).

Moreover, self-care for caregivers is not a one-time event. It is a continuous process that requires regular practice (Reinhard et al., 2019). It involves constantly reassessing one's needs and adjusting self-care practices accordingly. It means recognizing signs of stress and fatigue and taking necessary steps to alleviate them. In other words, self-care is not about being selfish; it is about being self-aware and proactive (Family Caregiver Alliance, 2012).

Self-care also involves making hard decisions, such as setting boundaries and learning to say no. This might be difficult for caregivers who often feel a sense of duty and obligation towards their loved ones. However, setting boundaries is crucial to ensuring that caregivers do not overextend themselves, leading to improved care for their loved ones (Adelman et al., 2014).

Self-care is a critical component of caregiving (Schulz & Sherwood, 2008). By prioritizing their own well-being, caregivers can ensure that they are in the best physical and emotional state to provide care. This, in turn, leads to better care for their loved ones and a more fulfilling caregiving experience (Kramer, 2017).

Practices for Self-Care

Self-care practices vary widely as they are often tailored to an individual's needs, preferences, and lifestyle (Reinhard et al., 2019). However, there are some common practices that have been found to be particularly beneficial for caregivers. These include maintaining a healthy diet, getting sufficient sleep, exercising regularly, and taking time out to relax and unwind (Family Caregiver Alliance, 2012).

Eating a balanced diet is vital for maintaining good health and energy levels (Adelman et al., 2014). It is easy for caregivers to neglect their nutrition due to the demands of caregiving. However, consuming nutrient-rich foods can provide the energy needed for caregiving tasks and help combat stress (Schulz & Sherwood, 2008).

Sleep is another critical aspect of self-care. Lack of sleep can lead to fatigue, decreased concentration, and heightened emotional reactions, all of which can affect a caregiver's ability to provide care (Reinhard et al., 2019). Caregivers should aim for 7-9 hours of sleep per night to ensure they are well-rested and prepared for their caregiving duties (Kramer, 2017).

Exercise is a powerful stress reliever and mood booster (Quinn et al., 2019). Regular physical activity can boost energy levels, improve mood, promote better sleep, and improve overall health. Caregivers can incorporate exercise into their routine by taking short walks, doing yoga, or even dancing (Family Caregiver Alliance, 2012).

Taking time to relax and unwind is crucial (Reinhard et al., 2019). This can be as simple as reading a book, meditating, or pursuing a hobby. It is about making time for activities that bring joy and relaxation, which can provide a much-needed break from the demands of caregiving (Adelman et al., 2014).

Self-Care and its Challenges

Despite its importance, self-care can often be challenging for caregivers (Schulz & Sherwood, 2008). Many factors can hinder caregivers from practicing self-care, including time constraints, emotional stress, and lack of social support. However, two of the most common barriers are feelings of guilt and being overwhelmed by the demands of caregiving (Reinhard et al., 2019).

Feeling guilty for focusing on their own needs is a common issue among caregivers (Kramer, 2017). They often feel that every moment and every resource should be devoted to the person they are caring for. This guilt can prevent them from taking the necessary time and space for self-care (Quinn et al., 2019).

Being overwhelmed by the demands of caregiving is another common challenge (Family Caregiver Alliance, 2012). Caregiving can be physically exhausting and emotionally draining. This, combined with other responsibilities, can leave caregivers feeling like they have no time for themselves (Adelman et al., 2014).

It is crucial for caregivers to understand that taking care of themselves is not a selfish act but a necessary step to ensure they can provide the best care possible (Reinhard et al., 2019). It is about maintaining their well-being so they can be there for their loved ones in the best possible way (Schulz & Sherwood, 2008).

Overcoming Barriers to Self-Care

There are several strategies caregivers can use to overcome barriers to self-care. First, it is important to identify personal obstacles, such as feelings of guilt or the inability to delegate tasks (Reinhard et al., 2019). Once these obstacles are identified, caregivers can find ways to address them (Kramer, 2017).

Setting boundaries is one effective way to overcome feelings of guilt (Quinn et al., 2019). By setting and maintaining boundaries, caregivers can ensure they have the time and energy for self-care. This might involve setting specific times for self-care activities or limiting the hours spent on caregiving tasks (Family Caregiver Alliance, 2012).

Seeking help from others can alleviate feelings of being overwhelmed (Adelman et al., 2014). This might involve delegating tasks to other family members, hiring a professional caregiver, or utilizing respite care services. Caregivers need to understand that they do not have to do everything themselves. Asking for help is not a sign of weakness; it is a step towards preserving their well-being (Schulz & Sherwood, 2008).

Adjusting expectations is another key strategy (Reinhard et al., 2019). Many caregivers expect themselves to fulfill their roles perfectly, which can lead to stress and burnout. It is essential to understand that it's okay not to be perfect. Caregivers are human and have their limits. By adjusting their expectations, they can alleviate unnecessary stress and create space for self-care (Kramer, 2017).

It is also essential for caregivers to challenge any misconceptions about self-care (Quinn et al., 2019). Many caregivers may believe they need to do everything themselves or that their needs are not important. Recognizing and challenging these misconceptions can pave the way for improved self-care practices (Family Caregiver Alliance, 2012).

The Impact of Self-Care

The impact of self-care on the caregiver-care recipient relationship can be significant (Reinhard et al., 2019). When caregivers take care of their own needs, they are better equipped to handle the stresses of caregiving. This can lead to a more positive caregiving experience for both parties (Kramer, 2017).

By practicing self-care, caregivers can maintain their physical and emotional health, improving their capacity to provide care (Quinn et al., 2019). This can lead to better quality of care and improved health outcomes for the care recipient (Family Caregiver Alliance, 2012). Moreover, when caregivers are less stressed and healthier, they are more patient and understanding, thereby improving their relationship with the care recipient (Adelman et al., 2014).

When care recipients see their caregivers taking steps to ensure their own well-being, it can also lead to a more balanced relationship (Schulz & Sherwood, 2008). It can reduce feelings of guilt or burden on the part of the care recipient as they see that their caregivers are also taking care of themselves (Reinhard et al., 2019).

Furthermore, self-care can set a positive example for care recipients. Care recipients may be more likely to prioritize their own self-care when they see their caregivers doing the same. This can lead to improved health and well-being for both parties (Kramer, 2017).

Self-care can have a profound impact on the caregiver-care recipient relationship (Quinn et al., 2019). It can lead to improved care, a more balanced relationship, and better health and well-being for both the caregiver and the care recipient (Family Caregiver Alliance, 2012).

Enhancing the Caregiver-Care Recipient Relationship

Enhancing the caregiver-care recipient relationship is a multifaceted process. It involves active listening, empathy, effective communication, and of course, self-care (Reinhard et al., 2019). These strategies not only improve the quality of care provided but also nurture a strong emotional connection between the caregiver and the care recipient (Kramer, 2017).

Active listening involves truly hearing and understanding what the care recipient is saying (Quinn et al., 2019). It's about being present and focused, showing empathy, and responding in a way that makes the care recipient feel heard and understood. Active listening can foster trust and respect, strengthening the caregiver-care recipient relationship (Family Caregiver Alliance, 2012).

Empathy is the ability to understand and share the feelings of another (Adelman et al., 2014). For caregivers, empathy involves understanding the challenges and emotions that the care recipient is experiencing. This can help caregivers provide more compassionate and personalized care (Schulz & Sherwood, 2008).

Effective communication is also crucial (Reinhard et al., 2019). This involves expressing thoughts and feelings clearly and honestly, and addressing any issues or concerns promptly. Effective communication can prevent misunderstandings and conflicts, leading to a more harmonious caregiver-care recipient relationship (Kramer, 2017).

Self-care, as discussed earlier, is also key (Quinn et al., 2019). By taking care of their own needs, caregivers can ensure they are in the best physical and emotional state to provide care (Family Caregiver Alliance, 2012). This can lead to better care for the care recipient and a more positive caregiving experience (Adelman et al., 2014).

Enhancing the caregiver-care recipient relationship involves a combination of active listening, empathy, effective communication, and self-care (Reinhard et al., 2019). Despite the challenges, with commitment, understanding, and the right strategies, caregivers can foster and strengthen this invaluable emotional connection (Schulz & Sherwood, 2008).

6.5: Empowering Caregivers in the Care Management Program-Transforming the Caregiving Landscape

Caregivers form the backbone of any care management program. They are the unsung heroes, tirelessly working behind the scenes, providing care and support for individuals with chronic conditions, disabilities, or cognitive impairments (Reinhard et al., 2019). Yet, despite their pivotal role, caregivers often find themselves in challenging situations, lacking the necessary education, resources, and recognition to excel in their roles (Family Caregiver Alliance, 2012). This deficit not only affects the quality of care provided but also the caregivers' own well-being (Adelman et al., 2014).

Therefore, it is imperative to empower caregivers, creating an environment where they have the support, knowledge, and resources they need to thrive (Schulz & Sherwood, 2008). This involves a comprehensive approach, focusing on three key areas: education, resources, and recognition. By addressing these areas, we can transform the caregiving landscape, ensuring caregivers are well-equipped, well-resourced, and well-respected for the vital role they play (Kramer, 2017).

Here, we delve deeper into these areas, exploring how they can be effectively addressed to empower caregivers and enhance the overall effectiveness of the care management program. The focus is on providing practical solutions and strategies that can be implemented to achieve these objectives (Quinn et al., 2019). This includes looking at current practices, identifying gaps, and proposing innovative approaches to fill these gaps (Reinhard et al., 2019).

This is not just about improving the caregiving profession. It's about transforming lives, improving healthcare, and creating a society where caregivers are valued, respected, and recognized for their vital contributions (Family Caregiver Alliance, 2012). It's about building a future where caregivers have the support they need to provide the best possible care for those who rely on them (Adelman et al., 2014).

Education: Equipping Caregivers with Knowledge and Skills

Caregivers face a myriad of challenges in their daily roles. These range from managing complex medical regimens, coordinating care among multiple providers, and dealing with the emotional and financial burden of caregiving (Reinhard et al., 2019). However, with the right education and training, caregivers can be better equipped to handle these challenges and provide effective care (Family Caregiver Alliance, 2012).

Comprehensive training programs are essential in providing caregivers with the knowledge and skills they require (Adelman et al., 2014). These programs should cover a wide range of topics, such as medication management, communication skills, stress management, and financial planning. By covering these topics, caregivers can develop a broad set of skills that will enable them to excel in their roles (Schulz & Sherwood, 2008).

The mode of delivery of these training programs is equally important. In today's digital age, online platforms can be utilized to deliver training in a flexible and accessible manner (Kramer, 2017). For instance, webinars and online courses allow caregivers to learn at their own pace and convenience, thereby accommodating their often busy schedules (Quinn et al., 2019).

The provision of educational resources is a key component of caregiver education (Reinhard et al., 2019). This can include guides, articles, and toolkits on various caregiving topics. These resources serve as a reference point for caregivers, providing them with the information they need to understand and manage various aspects of caregiving (Family Caregiver Alliance, 2012).

Ongoing education is crucial. Caregiving is a dynamic field, with new developments and research continually emerging (Adelman et al., 2014). Therefore, it is important to ensure that caregivers have access to up-to-date information and are continually learning and developing their skills (Schulz & Sherwood, 2008).

Education should also focus on self-care. Caregivers often neglect their own well-being while caring for others (Reinhard et al., 2019). Therefore, training programs should include topics on stress management, self-care, and mental health to ensure caregivers are also taking care of their own well-being (Kramer, 2017).

Resources, be it assistive devices, respite care services, or support groups, provide caregivers with the practical support they need to carry out their roles effectively (Adelman et al., 2014). They provide relief, support, and practical solutions to the challenges caregivers face, thereby enhancing the quality of care provided (Schulz & Sherwood, 2008).

Recognition, on the other hand, validates caregivers' contributions and honors their hard work and dedication (Reinhard et al., 2019). It boosts their morale, gives them a sense of purpose, and motivates them to continue their invaluable work (Kramer, 2017). Moreover, it raises awareness about the importance of caregiving, thereby fostering a society that values, respects, and supports caregivers (Quinn et al., 2019).

Empowering caregivers is not just about improving their skills, providing resources, or giving recognition (Family Caregiver Alliance, 2012). It's about transforming the caregiving landscape, creating an environment where caregivers are well-equipped, well-resourced, and well-respected. It's about building a future where caregiving is seen not just as a task, but a profession worthy of respect and recognition (Adelman et al., 2014). It's about creating a care management program where caregivers and care recipients alike can thrive. By prioritizing the empowerment of caregivers, we can make this future a reality (Reinhard et al., 2019).

Resources: Providing Tools for Success

The provision of resources is another crucial aspect of empowering caregivers. These resources can come in various forms, including assistive devices, respite care services, and support groups, and play a critical role in supporting caregivers in their roles (Reinhard et al., 2019).

Assistive devices can significantly ease the caregiving process. These can range from mobility aids to medication management systems, and can greatly enhance the quality of care provided, while also reducing the physical strain on caregivers (Family Caregiver Alliance, 2012).

Respite care services provide caregivers with much-needed breaks from their responsibilities (Adelman et al., 2014). These services allow caregivers to rest and rejuvenate, ensuring they can continue to provide high-quality care (Schulz & Sherwood, 2008). Respite care can be provided in various ways, including in-home care, adult daycare programs, or short-term nursing home stays (Reinhard et al., 2019).

Support groups provide a platform for caregivers to share their experiences, challenges, and successes with others in similar situations (Kramer, 2017). These groups can provide emotional support, practical advice, and a sense of community, which can be greatly beneficial for caregivers who often feel isolated in their roles (Quinn et al., 2019).

Online resources can provide caregivers with a wealth of information and support (Family Caregiver Alliance, 2012). This can range from online guides and toolkits to forums and chat groups. These resources can provide caregivers with the information they need to navigate the caregiving process, as well as a platform to connect with others and share experiences (Adelman et al., 2014).

Helplines can provide immediate support and advice to caregivers (Reinhard et al., 2019). These can be particularly beneficial in emergency situations or when caregivers are faced with difficult decisions. Helplines should be staffed by trained professionals who can provide accurate information, advice, and emotional support to caregivers in need (Schulz & Sherwood, 2008).

Recognition: Honoring the Unsung Heroes

While education and resources are crucial, recognition of caregivers' efforts and contributions is equally important (Kramer, 2017). Caregiving, despite its immense value, often remains an unseen and unacknowledged task. Recognizing and honoring caregivers is, therefore, a vital step towards empowering them and enhancing the caregiving landscape (Reinhard et al., 2019).

Awards and recognition programs can be a great way to acknowledge the efforts of caregivers (Quinn et al., 2019). These programs can provide formal recognition of caregivers' hard work and dedication, boosting their morale and encouraging them to continue their valuable work (Family Caregiver Alliance, 2012).

Public acknowledgment and appreciation can also go a long way in recognizing caregivers (Adelman et al., 2014). This can be done through public campaigns, media coverage, and events aimed at raising awareness about the importance of caregivers and their contributions (Reinhard et al., 2019).

Involving caregivers in care planning and decision-making can serve as a form of recognition (Schulz & Sherwood, 2008). This inclusion not only acknowledges their expertise and knowledge about the care recipient but also validates their role as a key player in the care management process (Kramer, 2017).

Providing a platform for caregivers to share their experiences and stories can be another form of recognition (Reinhard et al., 2019). This can be done through platforms such as blogs, podcasts, or public forums. By sharing their stories, caregivers can raise awareness about their roles, challenges, and achievements, thereby gaining recognition and respect from the wider community (Quinn et al., 2019).

Finally, support from employers can be a significant form of recognition for working caregivers (Family Caregiver Alliance, 2012). This can be in the form of flexible work arrangements, financial assistance, or employee assistance programs. By recognizing and supporting their employees' caregiving roles, employers can contribute to the empowerment of caregivers (Adelman et al., 2014).

Empowering Caregivers: Transforming the Caregiving Landscape

Empowering caregivers through education, resources, and recognition is a transformative approach that can significantly enhance the caregiving landscape (Reinhard et al., 2019). With the right knowledge and skills, access to necessary resources, and due recognition, caregivers can truly excel in their roles, thereby enhancing the overall effectiveness of the care management program (Kramer, 2017).

Education equips caregivers with the knowledge and skills they need to navigate the complex world of caregiving (Quinn et al., 2019). It provides them with the tools to manage medical regimens, coordinate care, and cope with the emotional and financial burdens of caregiving. Furthermore, it empowers them to take care of their own health and well-being, which is crucial for their longevity and effectiveness in the caregiving role (Family Caregiver Alliance, 2012).

Resources, be it assistive devices, respite care services, or support groups, provide caregivers with the practical support they need to carry out their roles effectively (Adelman et al., 2014). They provide relief, support, and practical solutions to the challenges caregivers face, thereby enhancing the quality of care provided (Schulz & Sherwood, 2008).

Recognition, on the other hand, validates caregivers' contributions and honors their hard work and dedication (Reinhard et al., 2019). It boosts their morale, gives them a sense of purpose, and motivates them to continue their invaluable work (Kramer, 2017). Moreover, it raises awareness about the importance of caregiving, thereby fostering a society that values, respects, and supports caregivers (Quinn et al., 2019).

Empowering caregivers is not just about improving their skills, providing resources, or giving recognition (Family Caregiver Alliance, 2012). It's about transforming the caregiving landscape, creating an environment where caregivers are well-equipped, well-resourced, and well-respected.

It's about building a future where caregiving is seen not just as a task, but a profession worthy of respect and recognition (Adelman et al., 2014). It's about creating a care management program where caregivers and care recipients alike can thrive. By prioritizing the empowerment of caregivers, we can make this future a reality (Reinhard et al., 2019).

Chapter 7: Connecting Caregivers to Community Resources and Financial Assistance

7.1: Identifying Community Resources for Caregivers

Caring for a loved one can be a rewarding yet challenging experience, fraught with emotional, physical, and financial demands (Reinhard et al., 2019). Amidst the noble endeavor of providing comfort and care, caregivers often overlook their own needs, leading to stress, fatigue, and burnout (Family Caregiver Alliance, 2012). Indeed, caregiving is not a solitary pursuit, and it is often said that it takes a village to care for a loved one (Adelman et al., 2014). This is where community resources come into play, acting as a lifeline for caregivers, offering support, education, and respite (Schulz & Sherwood, 2008).

Community resources are diverse and plentiful, each aimed at addressing a specific aspect of caregiving (Kramer, 2017). However, for many caregivers, the sheer volume of available resources can be overwhelming, making it difficult to identify which ones are most suitable for their needs (Quinn et al., 2019). Therefore, understanding how to navigate these resources effectively is crucial (Reinhard et al., 2019).

The first step in this journey is to conduct a self-assessment, identifying the caregiver's unique needs, values, and preferences (Family Caregiver Alliance, 2012). This critical exercise forms the cornerstone of the resource identification process, as it helps caregivers pinpoint the kinds of assistance they require (Adelman et al., 2014).

The nature of the care recipient's condition, the caregiver's level of comfort and experience, financial situation, physical and emotional health, and their social support network all play a role in shaping the caregiver's needs (Reinhard et al., 2019). Understanding these factors can help caregivers target the most appropriate resources, minimizing time and energy spent on unsuitable options (Schulz & Sherwood, 2008).

After identifying their needs, caregivers can delve into the myriad of community resources available (Kramer, 2017). These resources often fall into several categories, including support groups, respite care services, educational programs, and additional community resources such as information and referral services, care management services, volunteer services, and financial assistance programs (Quinn et al., 2019).

Support Groups: A Sanctuary for Shared Experiences

Engaging in a support group can be a transformative experience for caregivers, providing a safe harbor where they can share their experiences, feelings, and concerns with others in similar situations (Reinhard et al., 2019). Support groups can offer a sense of solidarity and understanding that is often lacking in the caregivers' immediate social circles (Family Caregiver Alliance, 2012).

These groups serve as a forum for caregivers to exchange practical advice and emotional support, helping to lighten the burden of caregiving (Adelman et al., 2014). The shared experiences within the group can offer valuable insights and solutions to common caregiving challenges, enhancing the caregivers' problem-solving abilities (Schulz & Sherwood, 2008).

Support groups also play a pivotal role in mitigating the feelings of isolation and loneliness often associated with caregiving (Kramer, 2017). By fostering a sense of community, these groups can help caregivers feel understood and valued, reducing stress and improving their overall well-being (Quinn et al., 2019).

Many support groups have a specific focus, such as caring for a loved one with Alzheimer's disease or being a young caregiver (Reinhard et al., 2019). This specificity allows caregivers to connect with others who truly understand their unique challenges and experiences (Family Caregiver Alliance, 2012).

Support groups can be found through various community-based organizations, healthcare institutions, and online platforms, allowing caregivers to access support wherever they are (Adelman et al., 2014).

Respite Care Services: An Oasis of Relief

Respite care services provide a lifeline for caregivers, offering temporary relief from their caregiving duties (Reinhard et al., 2019). These services can be a critical component of maintaining the caregiver's physical and emotional health, reducing stress, and preventing burnout (Schulz & Sherwood, 2008).

Respite care can be delivered in various forms, including in-home care, adult day care, and short-term residential care (Kramer, 2017). This flexibility allows caregivers to choose an option that best fits their needs and the needs of the care recipient (Quinn et al., 2019).

By providing a temporary break, respite care enables caregivers to attend to their personal needs, pursue hobbies, and engage in social activities, improving their quality of life (Family Caregiver Alliance, 2012). It also gives caregivers an opportunity to recharge, allowing them to return to their caregiving duties with renewed energy and focus (Adelman et al., 2014).

Respite care also benefits the care recipient by providing a change of scenery, stimulating social interactions, and maintaining their regular routine, particularly in organized settings like adult day care centers (Reinhard et al., 2019).

Respite care services can be found through various community organizations and local Area Agencies on Aging, which are specifically tasked with supporting older adults and their caregivers (Schulz & Sherwood, 2008).

Educational Programs: Empowering Caregivers through Knowledge

Education is a powerful tool for caregivers, equipping them with the necessary knowledge and skills to provide effective care (Reinhard et al., 2019). Educational programs can help caregivers understand the care recipient's condition, learn how to manage symptoms, and communicate effectively with healthcare professionals (Family Caregiver Alliance, 2012).

These programs can take various forms, including workshops, webinars, and online courses (Adelman et al., 2014). They cover a wide range of topics, from understanding specific diseases to learning practical caregiving skills such as safe patient handling and medication management (Schulz & Sherwood, 2008).

Educational programs can also enhance the caregiver's problem-solving abilities, helping them to navigate complex situations and make informed decisions (Kramer, 2017). This increased competence can lead to improved care outcomes for the care recipient and reduce the caregiver's stress level (Quinn et al., 2019).

In addition to disease-related topics, many educational programs also focus on the caregiver's self-care, emphasizing the importance of maintaining their physical and emotional health (Reinhard et al., 2019). These programs teach caregivers strategies to manage stress, balance their responsibilities, and seek support when needed (Family Caregiver Alliance, 2012).

Educational programs can be accessed through various community organizations, healthcare institutions, and online platforms. Many universities also offer caregiver education as part of their continuing education or community outreach initiatives (Adelman et al., 2014).

Additional Community Resources: A Wealth of Support at Your Fingertips

Beyond support groups, respite care services, and educational programs, there are many other community resources available to caregivers (Reinhard et al., 2019). These resources can help caregivers handle a variety of challenges, from navigating the healthcare system to managing the financial aspects of caregiving (Schulz & Sherwood, 2008).

Information and Referral Services provide caregivers with tailored guidance to navigate the complex healthcare and social service systems (Kramer, 2017). These services can help caregivers understand their options, connect with the right services, and access the resources they need quickly and efficiently (Quinn et al., 2019).

Care Management Services assist caregivers in developing a comprehensive care plan for their loved one (Family Caregiver Alliance, 2012). These services can help coordinate care, manage medications, and monitor the care recipient's progress, reducing the caregiver's workload and ensuring the care recipient receives the best possible care (Adelman et al., 2014).

Volunteer Services provide additional support to caregivers, offering help with a variety of tasks (Reinhard et al., 2019). Volunteers can provide companionship for the care recipient, assist with transportation to medical appointments, help with household tasks, and more. These services can significantly reduce the caregiver's responsibilities, allowing them more time to rest and recharge (Schulz & Sherwood, 2008).

Financial Assistance Programs can help offset the costs of caregiving (Kramer, 2017). These programs can help cover medical expenses, home modifications, respite care, and other costs associated with caregiving. Financial assistance can alleviate the financial strain often associated with caregiving, allowing caregivers to focus more on providing care and less on financial worries (Quinn et al., 2019).

These additional community resources can be accessed through various community organizations, local government agencies, and online platforms. Many healthcare institutions also provide guidance to help caregivers connect with these resources (Family Caregiver Alliance, 2012).

Community resources provide invaluable support to caregivers, helping them navigate their caregiving journey with confidence and competence (Reinhard et al., 2019). By assessing their needs and preferences, caregivers can identify the resources most relevant to their situation and maximize the benefits they receive (Adelman et al., 2014).

Whether it's joining a support group, utilizing respite care services, participating in educational programs, or accessing additional community resources, caregivers have a wealth of options to help them provide the best possible care for their loved ones while also taking care of themselves (Schulz & Sherwood, 2008).

It is indeed true that in caregiving, it takes a village, and community resources form the backbone of this supportive village (Kramer, 2017).

7.2: Navigating the Community Resource Landscape

Caregiving, often seen as a labor of love, is an immensely challenging role that requires a significant amount of support and resources (Reinhard et al., 2019). People across the globe, from all walks of life, step into this role out of necessity, love, or both. They care for their loved ones, be it parents, spouses, children, or other family members, often while managing their own responsibilities. The task of caregiving can be quite overwhelming, especially when the caregiver must navigate the complex landscape of community resources to find the support needed (Family Caregiver Alliance, 2012).

The importance of effectively navigating the community resource landscape cannot be overstated. It is a lifeline to many caregivers, enabling them to access critical support services, from medical care to emotional support, from financial assistance to respite care. Yet, the process of identifying and accessing these resources can be daunting, even for the most committed and resourceful caregivers (Adelman et al., 2014).

The role of caregivers is recognized and valued at the societal level, and numerous public and private sector initiatives aim to support them. One such initiative is the National Strategy to Support Family Caregivers, a comprehensive plan that offers practical steps that state, communities, and the private sector can implement. By recognizing the critical role that caregivers play in society, this plan emphasizes the importance of providing them with the necessary support and resources (Schulz & Sherwood, 2008).

However, knowing about the existence of these resources and being able to access them are two different things. The process of finding and securing the right resources can be a significant challenge for caregivers. The community resource landscape is vast and complex, and caregivers may often feel lost or overwhelmed (Kramer, 2017).

To address this, strategies and tools are available to help caregivers navigate this landscape. By leveraging these resources, caregivers can better navigate the community resource landscape, access the support they need, and ensure their loved ones receive the care they deserve (Quinn et al., 2019).

Acquiring Knowledge and Skills

Central to navigating the community resource landscape is the acquisition of knowledge and skills. This involves understanding what resources are available, how to access them, and how they can assist in caregiving roles (Reinhard et al., 2019). To this end, the internet can be an invaluable tool, providing a wealth of information at the click of a button.

Several online platforms offer comprehensive resources for caregivers. They offer a wide array of information, from understanding the basics of caregiving to managing the more complex aspects of the role. These platforms often include resources on specific conditions and how to care for individuals with these conditions, as well as general tips and advice on caregiving (Family Caregiver Alliance, 2012).

Support groups are another valuable resource available online. They offer a platform for caregivers to share their experiences, seek advice, and gain support from others in similar situations. These groups can provide emotional support, practical advice, and a sense of community, helping to alleviate some of the stress and isolation often associated with caregiving (Adelman et al., 2014).

Online training programs are another crucial resource for caregivers. These programs provide caregivers with the necessary skills and knowledge to provide care effectively. They cover a range of topics, from managing medication to understanding legal issues (Schulz & Sherwood, 2008).

Moreover, many of these resources are free or low-cost, making them accessible to caregivers from diverse economic backgrounds. By taking advantage of these resources, caregivers can equip themselves with the knowledge and skills necessary to navigate the community resource landscape effectively (Kramer, 2017).

Connecting with Community-based Organizations

Community-based organizations (CBOs) are another critical resource for caregivers. They provide a range of services that can alleviate some of the burdens associated with caregiving. From providing transportation for medical appointments to delivering meals to offering in-home care, CBOs play an essential role in supporting caregivers (Reinhard et al., 2019).

Area Agencies on Aging (AAAs) are a type of CBO that caregivers can connect with. These agencies provide information on available resources and referrals to appropriate services. They also offer case management services, which can be particularly helpful in coordinating care for individuals with complex health needs (Family Caregiver Alliance, 2012).

Many CBOs also offer caregiver support groups. These groups provide an opportunity for caregivers to connect with others facing similar challenges. They offer a platform for sharing experiences, providing emotional support, and gaining practical advice (Adelman et al., 2014).

In addition to providing services directly, CBOs can also serve as a bridge to other resources. They can provide referrals to other organizations or services that can provide additional support. This can be particularly helpful for caregivers who are unsure where to turn for help (Schulz & Sherwood, 2008).

By connecting with CBOs, caregivers can access a range of services and support to help them in their caregiving journey (Kramer, 2017).

Accessing Support Through Healthcare Providers

Healthcare providers can also be a valuable resource for caregivers. Many providers offer caregiver support services, which can include counseling, education, and other resources. These services can be a lifeline for caregivers, providing them with the support they need to care for their loved ones effectively (Reinhard et al., 2019).

Caregivers can speak with their healthcare provider to learn more about these services. They can provide information on what services are available, how to access them, and how they can assist in caregiving roles (Family Caregiver Alliance, 2012). This can be particularly helpful in addressing the unique challenges and needs that each caregiver may face.

Healthcare providers can also help caregivers coordinate care for their loved ones. This can involve assisting with scheduling appointments, managing medication, and coordinating with other healthcare providers. By playing a role in care coordination, healthcare providers can help to alleviate some of the burdens associated with caregiving (Adelman et al., 2014).

Moreover, healthcare providers can provide caregivers with education on their loved one's condition. This can include information on how to manage symptoms, what to expect as the condition progresses, and how to provide effective care. This education can empower caregivers, providing them with the knowledge they need to care for their loved ones effectively (Schulz & Sherwood, 2008).

Healthcare providers can also provide emotional support for caregivers. The stress and emotional toll of caregiving can be significant, and having a trusted healthcare provider to speak with can be incredibly beneficial. Healthcare providers can provide support, validate caregivers' feelings, and provide strategies for coping with the challenges of caregiving (Kramer, 2017).

Role of Public Health Leaders

Public health leaders play a crucial role in promoting and supporting caregiving. Through their macro-level approach, they can help to identify community resources, uncover inequities, and develop plans that ensure all caregivers have access to the services and support they need (Reinhard et al., 2019).

Public health leaders can employ proven strategies to support caregivers. These strategies can include developing and implementing policies that support caregivers, promoting caregiver health and well-being, and fostering a community environment that values and supports caregiving (Family Caregiver Alliance, 2012).

In addition, public health leaders can work to identify community assets that can support caregivers. These assets can include local organizations, services, and programs that can provide support and resources to caregivers. By identifying these assets, public health leaders can help to ensure that caregivers have access to the resources they need (Adelman et al., 2014).

Public health leaders can also work to uncover inequities in access to caregiver support and services. By identifying these inequities, they can work to address them, ensuring that all caregivers, regardless of their background or circumstances, have access to the support they need (Schulz & Sherwood, 2008).

Finally, public health leaders can develop plans that apply the best available evidence to support caregivers. Through research and evidence-based practices, they can develop strategies and interventions that effectively support caregivers and improve outcomes for care recipients (Kramer, 2017).

The task of navigating the community resource landscape is indeed challenging, but with the right tools and strategies, caregivers can access the necessary support and services. By acquiring knowledge and skills, connecting with community-based organizations, and accessing support through healthcare providers, caregivers can overcome the barriers to accessing resources.

The role that public health leaders play in promoting and supporting caregiving is also crucial. All these combined efforts ensure that the vital contributions of caregivers are recognized, and they are provided with the necessary support and resources. In a society that values the well-being of all its members, nothing could be more important (Quinn et al., 2019).

7.3: Financial Assistance Programs for Caregivers

Financial Assistance Programs for Caregivers: An In-Depth Look

As the population ages, the role of caregiving becomes increasingly vital. Each day, more Americans are finding themselves in the role of caregiver to their elderly loved ones. This role, while often rewarding, can also be overwhelming, both emotionally and financially. The responsibility of caregiving can sometimes require caregivers to cut back on their working hours or even quit their jobs in order to provide full-time care. This not only results in lost income but also impacts their potential retirement savings (Reinhard et al., 2019).

Understanding these challenges, a variety of financial assistance programs have been established to support caregivers in their critical role. These programs, ranging from federal initiatives to state and local programs, aim to alleviate the financial burden associated with caregiving. They offer a variety of services, from direct financial support to respite care and counseling (Family Caregiver Alliance, 2012).

This article delves deeper into the various financial assistance programs available to caregivers. We will explore their services, eligibility criteria, and the impact they have on easing the financial strain of caregiving. The intention is to provide caregivers with a comprehensive overview of the resources at their disposal (Adelman et al., 2014).

Financial assistance for caregivers is not a one-size-fits-all solution. Each program has its unique focus and caters to specific needs. Therefore, it's important for caregivers to be aware of the wide range of options available and to find the resources that best fit their circumstances (Schulz & Sherwood, 2008).

The role of caregiving is complex and multifaceted. It demands a comprehensive approach that goes beyond financial assistance. This includes emotional support, training, and education, among other things.

In the following sections, we will explore these aspects in detail (Kramer, 2017).

National Family Caregiver Support Program (NFCSP)

The National Family Caregiver Support Program (NFCSP) is a significant federally-funded initiative aimed at assisting caregivers. It provides grants to states and territories, which are then used to fund a variety of services that assist family and informal caregivers in caring for older adults in their homes for as long as possible (Reinhard et al., 2019).

The NFCSP offers five categories of services. These include providing information to caregivers about available services, helping caregivers access these services, individual counseling and support groups, respite care, and supplemental services. Each of these services is designed to support caregivers in their roles and alleviate some of the pressures they face (Family Caregiver Alliance, 2012).

In terms of information provision, the NFCSP ensures that caregivers are well-informed about the resources available to them. This is an essential service as many caregivers may not be aware of the assistance they can access. Through this service, caregivers can gain a comprehensive understanding of what help is at hand (Adelman et al., 2014).

To assist caregivers in accessing these services, the NFCSP provides support in navigating the various programs and understanding the eligibility requirements. This can be a daunting task for many caregivers, and having assistance in this process is invaluable (Schulz & Sherwood, 2008).

Providing individual counseling and support groups is another critical service offered by the NFCSP. Caregiving can be emotionally taxing, and having access to counseling and support groups can make a significant difference in managing the emotional stress (Kramer, 2017).

Respite Care and Supplemental Services

Respite care, another service provided by the NFCSP, offers temporary relief to caregivers. This allows them to take a break from their caregiving duties while knowing their loved ones are in safe hands. The respite care service is critical in preventing caregiver burnout and ensuring they have time to recharge (Reinhard et al., 2019).

Supplemental services, on the other hand, provide additional support that complements the care provided by caregivers. This can include home modifications, assistive technologies, and other services that make caregiving tasks easier and enhance the care recipient's quality of life (Family Caregiver Alliance, 2012).

The NFCSP has had a significant impact on the lives of caregivers. Hundreds of thousands of caregivers have benefited from this program, gaining access to assistance, counseling and training, and respite care. This has resulted in reduced caregiver depression, anxiety, and stress, enabling caregivers to provide care for longer periods (Adelman et al., 2014).

Department of Veterans Affairs (VA) Caregiver Support Program

The Department of Veterans Affairs (VA) Caregiver Support Program is another example of a federal program providing financial assistance to caregivers. This program is specifically designed to support caregivers of eligible veterans, providing a monthly stipend, travel expenses, and access to health care insurance if they meet the program's eligibility criteria (Schulz & Sherwood, 2008).

The VA Caregiver Support Program's monthly stipend is a direct form of financial assistance to caregivers. The amount varies depending on the level of care required by the veteran and the local cost of living. This stipend can go a long way in offsetting the financial burden of caregiving (Kramer, 2017).

The program also covers travel expenses associated with the veteran's medical appointments. This is especially helpful for caregivers who live in rural areas or far from VA medical facilities. It not only saves the caregiver money but also ensures that the veteran can access necessary medical care (Reinhard et al., 2019).

Access to health care insurance is another significant benefit of the VA Caregiver Support Program. Many caregivers may not have health insurance of their own, especially if they have had to leave their jobs to provide full-time care. This program ensures that caregivers are covered and can access the medical care they need (Family Caregiver Alliance, 2012).

In addition to these financial assistance measures, the VA Caregiver Support Program offers various other support services. These include counseling, training, and education. These resources can equip caregivers with the skills and knowledge needed to provide the best possible care for their veteran loved ones (Adelman et al., 2014).

The VA Caregiver Support Program recognizes the unique challenges faced by caregivers of veterans. It strives to offer comprehensive support that goes beyond financial assistance. By providing a combination of financial support, training, and emotional support, the program helps caregivers navigate their challenging role (Schulz & Sherwood, 2008).

State and Local Government Programs

Beyond federal programs, financial assistance for caregivers can also be sought from state and local government programs. These programs can vary widely from one location to another, so caregivers should familiarize themselves with the options available in their specific area (Kramer, 2017).

Some states offer cash assistance to low-income families who care for elderly relatives at home. This direct financial assistance can help alleviate some of the financial stress associated with caregiving. It can help cover the cost of care-related expenses, such as medical supplies, home modifications, or assistive technology (Reinhard et al., 2019).

In addition to cash assistance, some state programs provide other forms of support. This can include respite care, counseling, and access to support groups. These services can bolster the caregiver's emotional well-being and help them navigate the challenges of their role (Family Caregiver Alliance, 2012).

Medicaid, a joint federal and state program that helps with medical costs for some people with limited income and resources, may also provide financial assistance to caregivers. This could be particularly beneficial for caregivers who provide care to Medicaid-eligible individuals. One such program under Medicaid is the Home and Community-Based Services (HCBS) waivers program, which can help cover the cost of services in a home or community setting (Adelman et al., 2014).

State and local government programs can play a crucial role in supporting caregivers. It's important for caregivers to research and understand the options available in their area and to apply for the programs for which they qualify (Schulz & Sherwood, 2008).

Non-Profit Organizations

Aside from government programs, various non-profit organizations offer financial assistance and support to caregivers. These organizations often focus on specific diseases or conditions and offer a range of services to caregivers (Kramer, 2017).

The Alzheimer's Association, for example, provides a variety of programs and services to caregivers of individuals with Alzheimer's disease and related dementias. These services include support groups, education and training, and a 24/7 helpline. These resources can be incredibly beneficial for caregivers navigating the complexities of caring for a loved one with dementia (Reinhard et al., 2019).

Support groups offered by non-profit organizations provide a safe space for caregivers to share their experiences and learn from others in similar situations. They can also provide emotional support and a sense of community, which can be vital for caregivers' well-being (Family Caregiver Alliance, 2012).

Education and training programs equip caregivers with the necessary knowledge and skills to effectively care for their loved ones. These programs can cover a variety of topics, from understanding the disease or condition to practical caregiving skills and strategies to manage stress and prevent burnout (Adelman et al., 2014).

Non-profit organizations' helplines serve as a lifeline for caregivers, providing immediate support and guidance. They can provide information, referral to resources, and emotional support at times when caregivers need it the most (Schulz & Sherwood, 2008).

Non-profit organizations play a crucial role in the caregiving landscape. By providing targeted support and resources, they can help caregivers navigate their roles more effectively and improve the quality of care provided to their loved ones (Kramer, 2017).

Caregiving is a complex and demanding role, often requiring significant financial resources. While the task can seem daunting, numerous financial assistance programs are available to support caregivers. From federal programs like the NFCSP and the VA Caregiver Support Program, to state and local programs, and non-profit organizations, caregivers have a variety of resources at their disposal (Reinhard et al., 2019).

However, the role of caregiving extends beyond financial considerations. It is a multi-faceted role that requires emotional support, training, and education. Thankfully, many of these financial assistance programs understand this complexity and offer support that goes beyond financial aid (Family Caregiver Alliance, 2012).

By arming themselves with knowledge about these programs and services, caregivers can better navigate their challenging roles. They can find the support they need to provide the best possible care to their loved ones, while also ensuring their own well-being. Through these efforts, we can work together to create a comprehensive system of caregiver support that truly acknowledges and appreciates the invaluable role caregivers play in our society (Adelman et al., 2014).

7.4: Eligibility Criteria and Application Processes

Financial Assistance for Caregivers: Eligibility Criteria and Application Processes

As a caregiver or member of a care support team, you play a crucial role in maintaining the health and well-being of those you care for. However, the financial aspects of caregiving can often be daunting and complex. Securing financial assistance can be a lifesaver in managing the costs associated with caregiving, but the process of understanding eligibility criteria and navigating through application processes can be overwhelming. This guide aims to provide a comprehensive exploration of the foundations of financial assistance programs, offering detailed insights into the intricacies of eligibility considerations and application procedures. It will also highlight resources available to support caregivers and care support teams in their journey towards securing much-needed financial aid.

Understanding Eligibility Criteria

The Fundamentals of Eligibility Criteria

Financial assistance programs often have specific eligibility criteria that applicants need to meet. These can include income thresholds, insurance coverage, and family size, among others. Understanding these criteria is the first step towards determining whether you or your loved one qualifies for the assistance program (Reinhard et al., 2019).

While federal law does not specify the criteria hospitals should use to determine eligibility, nonprofit hospitals under the Affordable Care Act are required to display and publicize their financial assistance policies (Family Caregiver Alliance, 2012). It is important to thoroughly research the eligibility criteria for each program, as they can vary greatly.

Criteria may include income limits, asset limits, citizenship status, age, disability status, and more (Adelman et al., 2014). Meeting all required criteria is essential, so take time to fully understand what is expected for each program.

Consider consulting with a financial advisor, social worker or other professional who can help interpret complex eligibility guidelines (Schulz & Sherwood, 2008). Maintaining detailed records of income, expenses and other documentation can also help facilitate the process of determining eligibility.

Diversity of Eligibility Criteria

Eligibility criteria can vary widely by state and even by program. Not all patients who are eligible receive the financial assistance they qualify for. This could be due to a lack of awareness or understanding of the programs available (Kramer, 2017). Additionally, there may be differences in eligibility based on demographic factors like gender, which can affect how financial assistance claims are granted (Reinhard et al., 2019).

Eligibility criteria can differ greatly depending on the type of program, with federal, state, local government and non-profit programs often having distinct requirements (Family Caregiver Alliance, 2012). Within a single program, there may be different eligibility standards for different services offered. For instance, respite care eligibility may differ from eligibility for cash assistance (Adelman et al., 2014).

It is important to look at each service individually to determine if you meet the specific criteria. Consulting with a social services coordinator or patient advocate can help navigate these complexities (Schulz & Sherwood, 2008).

Researching Eligibility Criteria

To determine eligibility for financial assistance programs, it is essential to research each specific program thoroughly (Reinhard et al., 2019). There are numerous resources available that allow individuals to compare eligibility for various state and federal benefit programs. These comprehensive databases can be a great starting point in understanding the different criteria for each program (Family Caregiver Alliance, 2012).

When beginning your research, start by making a list of your caregiving needs and desired services. This will help narrow down the programs to investigate further (Adelman et al., 2014).

Be sure to leverage both online and local resources in your research process. Online databases allow efficient comparison across programs, while local non-profits can provide insights into region-specific options (Schulz & Sherwood, 2008).

Consider tracking eligibility criteria in a spreadsheet for easy side-by-side comparisons. This will allow you to efficiently determine which programs are the best fit based on their eligibility standards.

Local Non-profit Organizations and Community Assistance

Support doesn't only come from federal or state programs. Local non-profit organizations and community assistance programs may also provide financial assistance and support (Kramer, 2017). These organizations often have a deep understanding of the local community's needs and may have more flexibility in their criteria and processes (Reinhard et al., 2019).

Local non-profits and community assistance programs can be an excellent source of support due to their regional focus and community-centered approach. They understand the unique needs and challenges facing caregivers in their area (Family Caregiver Alliance, 2012). Connecting with these local organizations can provide personalized guidance in identifying financial assistance options, determining eligibility, and navigating the application process.

Many local non-profits also offer additional resources beyond financial aid, such as support groups, respite care, adult day programs and more (Adelman et al., 2014). Building relationships with these organizations can lead to comprehensive, community-based support.

Understanding Gender Imbalances

There is evidence of gender imbalances in assistance claims, with some groups potentially being more advantaged than others (Reinhard et al.,

2019). It's important to be aware of these disparities and advocate for fair and equitable assistance for all those who are eligible (Family Caregiver Alliance, 2012). Research has revealed disparities in financial assistance claims and awards based on gender and other demographic factors.

This imbalance may stem from explicit or implicit bias in eligibility criteria or application review processes (Adelman et al., 2014). As a caregiver, it is important to be aware of these potential barriers and inequities. Consider reaching out to advocacy groups working to promote equity in caregiving assistance programs (Schulz & Sherwood, 2008).

Where imbalances exist, push for policy and process reforms that create fair access and equal treatment for all applicants. Financial assistance programs should aid all eligible caregivers in need, regardless of any demographic factors.

The Importance of Organization

Once you understand the eligibility criteria, the next step is to navigate the application process. This can be an intricate process that requires attention to detail, organization, and adherence to specific guidelines (Kramer, 2017). Being mindful of any deadlines associated with the application process is essential, as missing a deadline can result in disqualification (Reinhard et al., 2019).

The application process for financial assistance programs can be complex, requiring extensive documentation, forms, and specific application procedures. Therefore, having an organized system is key to successful navigation (Family Caregiver Alliance, 2012). Consider creating a file folder or binder dedicated to each program application. This can store all necessary documents, notes, forms and additional information in one centralized place (Adelman et al., 2014).

Setting reminders for deadlines and tracking application progress in a calendar can also help maintain organization. chaos in the application process will only lead to mistakes, delays and added stress.

Understanding Required Documentation

Many financial assistance programs require extensive documentation. These can include pay stubs, tax returns, and medical bills (Reinhard et al., 2019). It is crucial to keep all documentation organized and readily accessible. Having a systematic approach to gathering and maintaining these documents can significantly smoothen the application process (Family Caregiver Alliance, 2012).

Documentation requirements can differ across programs but often include materials proving identity, income, expenses, and health costs (Adelman et al., 2014). Take time early in the process to understand exactly which documents are required so you can collect them efficiently. Consult with tax preparation experts to obtain necessary past returns.

Talk to your Human Resources department about acquiring pay stubs and employment verification. Keep all documents in a centralized location where they can be easily accessed when it is time to complete the application (Schulz & Sherwood, 2008).

Digital copies can be useful for easy online upload. Let your documents work for you by having them readily available.

Time Management in the Application Process

The application process can be time-consuming, and careful time management is crucial (Kramer, 2017). Allocating specific time to work on the application, keeping track of deadlines, and breaking down the process into manageable steps can help prevent last-minute rushes and ensure a more thorough and accurate application (Reinhard et al., 2019).

The application process can feel overwhelming if not managed proactively. After researching target programs, develop a timeline mapping out key deadlines and the steps needed to complete the applications successfully (Family Caregiver Alliance, 2012). Block out designated timeslots for working on applications each week. Break required tasks into smaller, digestible chunks that can be tackled one by one. Checking items off your to-do list provides motivation to keep pushing forward (Adelman et al., 2014).

Remain diligent meeting target dates on your timeline to prevent a stressful last-minute scramble. With proactive time management, you can approach each application as a manageable series of smaller steps.

Researching Application Procedures

Each financial assistance program may have its own unique application procedures (Reinhard et al., 2019). Thoroughly researching these procedures can prevent errors and omissions that could potentially delay or jeopardize the application (Family Caregiver Alliance, 2012). This research can involve reading through all available information on the program's website, contacting the program directly for clarification, or seeking advice from others who have previously applied (Adelman et al., 2014).

Application requirements can vary greatly across programs, so it is essential to research the specific procedures for each individual program. Start by carefully reviewing all application instructions and protocols on the program website and printed materials. Make note of each required step, collecting any necessary forms and documentation (Schulz & Sherwood, 2008). If any area is unclear, don't hesitate to contact the program administrators directly via phone or email for clarification.

Additionally, consider connecting with others who have undergone the same application process and can provide guidance based on their experiences. Leave no stone unturned to ensure you thoroughly understand the program's unique application process.

Utilizing Available Resources

There are resources available to assist with the application process (Kramer, 2017). These can include guides and tutorials available on the program's website, helplines, and community resources. Taking advantage of these resources can provide valuable guidance and support throughout the application process (Reinhard et al., 2019). Do not hesitate to leverage available resources to assist in navigating the complex application process.

Programs often provide useful tools right on their websites, such as application checklists, instructional guides, and FAQs. Take time to review these carefully (Family Caregiver Alliance, 2012). Community assistance programs may offer help completing applications or provide access to computers and printers. Helplines can also answer questions if any part of the process is unclear (Adelman et al., 2014).

Seek help from financial counselors, social workers or nurses who can provide expertise. Using available resources demonstrates self-advocacy and empowers you to successfully complete each application (Schulz & Sherwood, 2008).

The Eldercare Locator

The Eldercare Locator is a service provided by the U.S. Administration on Aging (Kramer, 2017). It offers a comprehensive database of local resources and services for older adults and their caregivers. This can be a valuable resource in finding local financial assistance programs and support services (Reinhard et al., 2019).

The Eldercare Locator phone line and website connect caregivers to local resources meeting their needs. By answering a few questions about your specific situation, they can provide referrals to relevant services and programs in your community (Family Caregiver Alliance, 2012).

Contact them to get connected with local financial assistance programs, help with applications and eligibility, or additional resources like respite care services, home care, transportation, and more. Their specialists can direct you efficiently, saving time in your search for support (Adelman et al., 2014).

Local Non-profit Organizations and Community Assistance

Local non-profit organizations and community assistance programs can provide invaluable support (Reinhard et al., 2019). They may offer assistance with navigating the application process, organizing documentation, and understanding eligibility criteria. These organizations often have a deep understanding of the local community's needs and can provide personalized guidance and support (Family Caregiver Alliance, 2012).

Seek out local non-profits like religious organizations, community clinics, and aging offices that serve your community. These groups often have staff members well-versed in local resources who can help identify financial assistance programs you may qualify for (Adelman et al., 2014). They can then provide hands-on help completing the applications correctly and efficiently based on their experience supporting other local families.

These non-profits may even offer assistance compiling all required documentation. By connecting with them early in the process, you can access experienced support throughout your financial aid journey (Schulz & Sherwood, 2008).

Online Resources

There are numerous online resources available to assist caregivers in finding financial assistance (Kramer, 2017). These can include comprehensive databases that allow comparison of various state and federal benefit programs, guides and tutorials to assist in the application process, and forums where caregivers can share experiences and advice (Reinhard et al., 2019). Online resources are invaluable in researching financial assistance options and navigating the application process.

Utilize databases like BenefitsCheckUp.org to search and compare potential programs (Family Caregiver Alliance, 2012). Program websites themselves also house step-by-step application instructions and toolkits outlining required documents. Connect with other caregivers through forums and social media groups to gain insights based on real-world experiences (Adelman et al., 2014). Compile your findings into an organized file or notebook for easy reference throughout the process. With myriad online resources at your fingertips, you can access the support you need efficiently.

Seeking Professional Advice

In some cases, it may be beneficial to seek professional advice. Financial advisors, social workers, or legal professionals specializing in eldercare can provide expert guidance on navigating financial assistance programs (Reinhard et al., 2019). They can help interpret the complex language of program guidelines, ensure all required documentation is in order, and provide advice on maximizing potential benefits (Family Caregiver Alliance, 2012).

If you feel overwhelmed navigating eligibility guidelines and application requirements, consider seeking help from professionals with expertise in this area. Financial advisors can review your personal finances and identify programs that are the best fit (Adelman et al., 2014). Social workers have specialized knowledge on programs and eligibility criteria and can advise you throughout the process.

Legal professionals can interpret confusing policies and ensure you comply with all regulations accurately (Schulz & Sherwood, 2008). With professional assistance, you can ensure applications are airtight and maximize your chances of being approved.

Support Groups and Peer Networks

Support can also come from other caregivers who have already navigated the process (Kramer, 2017). Support groups and peer networks can be a source of practical advice, emotional support, and shared experiences. They can offer insights into the application process that may not be available through official channels (Reinhard et al., 2019).

Connecting with support groups and peers can provide invaluable guidance based on others' firsthand experiences navigating financial assistance applications. Fellow caregivers who have just gone through the process can provide tips to streamline the process and avoid common pitfalls (Family Caregiver Alliance, 2012).

Joining a support group also provides the opportunity to share your own frustrations and victories along the way with others who can relate. You can gain emotional support while also learning practical strategies to increase your chance of success (Adelman et al., 2014).

7.5: Advocacy and Support for Caregivers

Across the United States, there are millions of dedicated individuals tirelessly caring for loved ones with chronic illnesses, disabilities, and age-related issues. They are the unsung heroes of the nation's healthcare system, providing essential care and support, often without recognition or adequate resources (Reinhard et al., 2019). Despite their integral role, caregivers often face significant challenges and barriers, ranging from financial strain and physical exhaustion to emotional distress (Family Caregiver Alliance, 2012).

Caregiving is not a solitary task. It is a collective responsibility, one that requires societal acknowledgment, support, and resources to enable caregivers to provide high-quality care (Adelman et al., 2014). For this reason, advocacy and support for caregivers have emerged as crucial aspects of the broader healthcare discourse.

Advocacy efforts aim to amplify the voices of caregivers, ensuring their needs are considered in policy-making and resource allocation (Schulz & Sherwood, 2008). Support, on the other hand, offers caregivers the tangible resources and emotional reinforcement they need to continue their caregiving journey (Kramer, 2017).

The advocacy and support movement for caregivers draws its strength from community solidarity. By building communities of caregivers, we not only reduce feelings of isolation and burnout but also empower caregivers to advocate for their needs (Reinhard et al., 2019). The essence of these communities is mutual support and understanding, creating a safe space for caregivers to share their experiences, challenges, and triumphs (Family Caregiver Alliance, 2012).

Here, we delve into the importance of advocacy for caregivers, the necessity of support structures, and the crucial role of building community and solidarity among caregivers (Adelman et al., 2014). This exploration aims to shed light on the multifaceted nature of caregiving and the need for a concerted societal effort to support those who bear the burden of care (Schulz & Sherwood, 2008).

Understanding the Need for Advocacy

Caregiving is often a private, hidden role, going unrecognized by society at large. This invisibility can lead to a lack of understanding about the demands and struggles that caregivers face on a daily basis (Kramer, 2017). Advocacy plays a vital role in bringing these issues to light, forcing society and policymakers to confront and address them. It becomes the voice for the voiceless, highlighting the challenges caregivers face and demanding action (Reinhard et al., 2019).

Advocacy also serves to raise awareness about the critical role caregivers play in the health and welfare system. Caregivers contribute significantly to the health and well-being of individuals in need, often taking on substantial responsibilities without compensation or support (Family Caregiver Alliance, 2012).

Despite this, they are often overlooked in policy-making processes. Advocacy seeks to rectify this, ensuring that the role and contributions of caregivers are acknowledged and appropriately valued (Adelman et al., 2014).

In addition, advocacy is crucial in pushing for systemic change. Many of the challenges caregivers face are rooted in societal attitudes and structures. Advocacy works to reshape these attitudes and structures, pushing for policies and legislation that recognize and support caregivers (Schulz & Sherwood, 2008).

This can involve advocating for caregiver rights, lobbying for more funding for caregiver support programs, and pushing for changes in workplace policies to accommodate caregivers.

The Role of Advocacy Organizations

Advocacy organizations are the driving force behind efforts to improve the conditions and recognition of caregivers. They work tirelessly to raise awareness about the issues caregivers face, lobby for policy changes, and provide resources and support for caregivers (Kramer, 2017). They operate at various levels, from local to state and federal, to ensure that the voices of caregivers are heard and their needs addressed (Reinhard et al., 2019).

At the local and state level, advocacy organizations often work to influence laws and policies that directly affect caregivers in their communities. This might involve working with local government officials to improve access to respite care or lobbying state legislators to increase funding for caregiver support services (Family Caregiver Alliance, 2012). These organizations understand the unique needs and challenges of caregivers in their communities and are best positioned to advocate for them (Adelman et al., 2014).

At the federal level, advocacy organizations aim to influence national policy and legislation. They often focus on larger systemic changes, such as advocating for the recognition of caregivers in the healthcare system or pushing for national caregiver support programs (Schulz & Sherwood, 2008). They use research, data, and personal stories to highlight the importance of caregivers and the need for comprehensive support systems.

Advocacy in Action

A significant achievement of advocacy efforts in recent years is the establishment of offices and departments dedicated to caregiver health and well-being at the federal level. These offices are tasked with improving caregiver support systems and resources, acknowledging the vital role caregivers play in the healthcare system (Kramer, 2017).

For example, in the United States, the Administration for Community Living (ACL) has a dedicated office for caregiver support which works to improve and expand services for the nation's family caregivers. This office was established as a result of advocacy efforts, highlighting the power of advocacy to effect change (Reinhard et al., 2019).

Similarly, the Department of Veterans Affairs has established the Caregiver Support Program, which provides resources and support for caregivers of veterans. This program was established in response to advocacy efforts highlighting the unique challenges faced by caregivers of veterans (Family Caregiver Alliance, 2012).

These are just a few examples of how advocacy can lead to real, tangible changes that benefit caregivers. Through continued advocacy efforts, it is hoped that more such changes will be achieved in the future (Adelman et al., 2014).

The Impact of Advocacy

The impact of advocacy on caregivers and the broader health and social care system cannot be overstated. Advocacy has brought about significant changes in policy and legislation that have improved the recognition and support of caregivers (Schulz & Sherwood, 2008). These changes have resulted in increased resources for caregivers, better services, and improved rights and protections.

Advocacy has also led to a greater recognition of the role and value of caregivers in the health and social care system (Kramer, 2017). This recognition has helped to validate the experiences and contributions of caregivers, leading to increased self-esteem and reduced feelings of isolation among caregivers.

Finally, advocacy has helped to shift societal attitudes towards caregiving. It has brought the struggles and contributions of caregivers into the public eye, fostering a greater understanding and appreciation for their role. This shift in attitudes is crucial in creating a society that values and supports caregivers (Reinhard et al., 2019).

The Future of Advocacy

The future of advocacy for caregivers looks promising. There is a growing recognition of the importance of caregivers and the challenges they face, both within the healthcare system and in society at large (Family Caregiver Alliance, 2012). This recognition is leading to increased support for advocacy efforts and a greater willingness among policymakers to take action (Adelman et al., 2014).

As more people become caregivers, the need for advocacy is only going to increase. The aging population and the increasing prevalence of chronic diseases mean that more people will require care in the future. Advocacy will be crucial in ensuring that these caregivers are recognized and supported (Schulz & Sherwood, 2008).

Moreover, as the caregiving landscape continues to evolve, new challenges and issues are likely to emerge. Advocacy will need to adapt to these changes and continue to push for policies and support systems that meet the needs of all caregivers. With the continued dedication and hard work of advocacy organizations, the future of advocacy for caregivers looks bright (Kramer, 2017).

The Role of Support

Support for caregivers is essential for managing the multifaceted demands of caregiving and enhancing caregivers' ability to provide high-quality care over the long-term (Reinhard et al., 2019). Caregiving often involves substantial physical labor, which can lead to injuries and exhaustion.

Emotionally, witnessing the decline of loved ones and managing one's own grief and anxiety can be deeply draining. Financially, caregiving may require reduced work hours or expenditures on medical equipment, straining caregivers' resources. Without adequate physical, emotional, and financial support, caregiver burnout is a significant risk.

Comprehensive support addresses these challenges through respite care for rest, counseling for emotional needs, and financial assistance programs (Adelman et al., 2014). Assistive equipment and training on safe lifting techniques can also help reduce physical strain.

Support groups provide community and peer validation, reminding caregivers they are not alone. With ongoing support across domains, caregivers can find balance and avoid burnout while continuing to provide attentive care driven by love, not obligation.

Their enhanced health and well-being translates directly into higher quality care for loved ones. Investing in caregiver support is investing in the overall healthcare system.

Understanding the Need for Support

Caregiving, while fulfilling, can sometimes be overwhelming - physically, emotionally, and financially. The responsibilities of caring for a loved one can take a toll on a caregiver's personal life, leading to stress and burnout (Reinhard et al., 2019).

The physical demands of caregiving, such as assisting with mobility, personal care, and medical procedures, can lead to physical fatigue.

The emotional demands, such as managing the emotional distress of the person they're caring for, witnessing their physical or mental decline, and dealing with the emotional impact of their condition, can lead to emotional exhaustion (Family Caregiver Alliance, 2012).

Financially, caregiving can be demanding as well. Caregivers often need to make sacrifices, such as cutting down on work hours, giving up jobs, or spending personal savings to cover care-related costs (Adelman et al., 2014). In many cases, they may have to pay for medical supplies, home modifications, professional care services, and other related expenses out of their own pockets.

Support for caregivers thus becomes crucial. It helps them navigate these challenges, ensuring they can continue to provide care without compromising their own well-being. The right support can alleviate their stress, prevent burnout, and help them balance their caregiving responsibilities with their personal needs and other commitments (Schulz & Sherwood, 2008).

Forms of Support

Support for caregivers can take many forms. One of the most essential forms of support is counseling or psychological support. Caregiving can stir up a wide range of emotions, from fear and anxiety to anger and grief. Professional counseling can help caregivers manage these emotions, build resilience, and maintain their mental health (Kramer, 2017).

Respite care is another critical form of support. It provides temporary relief to caregivers, giving them a chance to rest, recharge, and take care of their own needs. Whether it's for a few hours a week or a longer period, respite care can significantly reduce caregiver stress and prevent burnout (Reinhard et al., 2019).

Education and training are also important. Caregivers often need to learn new skills to provide care, from administering medication to using medical equipment. Training programs can help caregivers gain these skills, increasing their confidence and competence in their caregiving role (Family Caregiver Alliance, 2012).

Finally, peer support groups offer emotional support and a sense of community. These groups provide a safe space where caregivers can share their experiences, offer advice, and provide comfort to each other. They remind caregivers that they are not alone and that their experiences and feelings are valid and understood (Adelman et al., 2014).

The Role of Support Organizations

Support organizations have a crucial role in providing these forms of support to caregivers. They offer a wide range of resources tailored to caregivers' needs. These organizations may offer counseling services, respite care programs, training courses, and peer support groups (Schulz & Sherwood, 2008).

Webinars and online resources can provide information and education on a wide range of caregiving topics, from managing specific health conditions to navigating healthcare systems. Helplines and online forums can offer immediate advice and support, helping caregivers deal with emergencies or crises.

These organizations also advocate for caregivers' rights, working towards policy changes that can provide better support for caregivers. They raise awareness about the challenges caregivers face and the contributions they make, helping society recognize and value their role (Kramer, 2017).

Building Community and Solidarity

Caregiving can often feel lonely and isolating. Caregivers may feel like no one else understands what they're going through. Creating a sense of community and solidarity among caregivers can help alleviate these feelings. It provides caregivers with a sense of belonging and understanding, knowing that there are others who share their experiences (Reinhard et al., 2019).

Building a community also provides a platform for caregivers to share information, tips, and advice. It allows them to learn from each other's experiences, finding solutions to common challenges and gaining new insights into their role (Family Caregiver Alliance, 2012).

Communities also provide emotional support. They offer a safe space where caregivers can express their feelings without judgment, find comfort in others' empathy, and draw strength from their shared experiences. This emotional support can be a powerful tool in managing stress and preventing burnout (Adelman et al., 2014).

Moreover, communities can empower caregivers to advocate for their rights. Together, they can raise their voices, influence policy changes, and work towards better support and resources for caregivers. This collective action can lead to significant improvements in caregivers' lives (Schulz & Sherwood, 2008).

The Role of Community Networks

Community networks play a crucial role in fostering these communities. These networks can be local, regional, or national, connecting caregivers across different areas. They use various platforms, such as social media, online forums, and face-to-face meetings, to facilitate communication and collaboration among caregivers.

These networks provide a space for caregivers to share their stories, exchange tips and advice, and support each other. They organize events and activities that bring caregivers together, fostering a sense of community and camaraderie (Kramer, 2017).

Community networks also advocate for caregivers. They represent caregivers' voices in policy discussions, campaigning for better support and resources. They raise public awareness about the challenges caregivers face and the contributions they make, helping to change public attitudes and policies towards caregiving (Reinhard et al., 2019).

Through these roles, community networks are making a significant difference in caregivers' lives. They are reducing the isolation and stress often associated with caregiving, promoting self-care and resilience among caregivers, and empowering them to advocate for their needs (Family Caregiver Alliance, 2012).

The Impact of Community and Solidarity

Building community and solidarity among caregivers can have a profound impact. It can reduce feelings of isolation and loneliness, providing caregivers with a sense of belonging and understanding. It can provide emotional support, helping caregivers manage stress and maintain their mental health. It can also provide practical support, as caregivers can share advice and tips, learn from each other's experiences, and collaborate to solve common challenges (Adelman et al., 2014).

Moreover, community and solidarity can empower caregivers. It can give them a collective voice, enabling them to advocate for policy changes and better support. It can also boost their confidence and self-efficacy, as they see others facing similar challenges and successfully navigating their caregiving roles (Schulz & Sherwood, 2008).

In these ways, community and solidarity can significantly improve caregivers' well-being and quality of life. It can also enhance the quality of care they provide, as they gain knowledge, skills, and emotional resilience from their community. Ultimately, this can lead to better outcomes for both caregivers and those they care for (Kramer, 2017).

Advancing Technology for Caregivers

With the continued advancements in technology, there is great potential to further ease the burdens of caregivers. Mobile apps can offer reminders for medication, virtual consultations with healthcare professionals, and online communities for peer support. Wearable devices can monitor health metrics of the cared-for person, and telehealth services can reduce the need for frequent hospital visits (Reinhard et al., 2019).

Machine learning can also be leveraged to provide personalized insights and recommendations for caregivers. For instance, predictive analytics could be used to anticipate health crises before they happen, allowing for early intervention and potentially reducing the need for emergency care (Family Caregiver Alliance, 2012).

Policy Changes and Legislation

In parallel with technology advancements, policy changes and legislation can also make a significant difference in the lives of caregivers. Advocacy organizations can work to influence policies that provide greater financial support for caregivers, recognize their contributions to society, and ensure their rights are protected (Adelman et al., 2014).

Policies could be implemented that provide tax credits for caregivers, mandate workplace policies that offer flexibility for caregiver duties, and ensure access to affordable respite care. Legislation could also protect caregivers from discrimination, and ensure they have the same rights and protections as other workers (Schulz & Sherwood, 2008).

Public Awareness and Education

Public awareness and education are also critical. The more society understands about the role and importance of caregivers, the more support they will receive. This could be facilitated through public awareness campaigns, educational programs in schools, and media coverage (Kramer, 2017).

Education can also play a role in preparing future generations for caregiving roles. For instance, incorporating caregiving education into school curriculums could help young people understand the importance of caregiving, develop empathy for caregivers and those in need of care, and equip them with basic caregiving skills (Reinhard et al., 2019).

Collaborative Efforts

The journey ahead is not one that caregivers or advocacy organizations should walk alone. Collaboration amongst healthcare providers, tech companies, policymakers, and the public can create a more supportive environment for caregivers (Family Caregiver Alliance, 2012).

Healthcare providers can play a role by recognizing and respecting the role of caregivers, and by involving them in decision-making processes. Tech companies can contribute by continuing to innovate and develop solutions that make caregiving tasks easier. Policymakers can help by implementing supportive policies and legislation. The public can contribute by showing understanding, respect and support for caregivers in their communities (Adelman et al., 2014).

With the continued dedication and hard work of advocacy organizations, and with the support of healthcare providers, tech companies, policymakers, and the public, the future of advocacy for caregivers indeed looks bright. By continuing to provide resources, services, and advocacy, these organizations can ensure that caregivers receive the recognition and support they deserve. And as society continues to value and appreciate caregivers, the quality of life for both caregivers and those they care for will continue to rise (Schulz & Sherwood, 2008).

The Future of Community and Solidarity

The future of community and solidarity among caregivers looks promising. As more caregivers connect and share their experiences, the collective voice of caregivers is becoming stronger. This increased strength is empowering caregivers to advocate for their needs and is changing societal attitudes towards caregiving (Kramer, 2017).

The positive outcomes for caregivers, as a result of the support and community they receive, can create a ripple effect extending far beyond the individual. When caregivers are better equipped to handle their roles, it doesn't just benefit them personally; it also benefits the people they are caring for, their families, and society at large (Reinhard et al., 2019).

Benefits to the Care Recipient

When a caregiver receives adequate support, it can directly impact the quality of care they provide. Caregivers who have access to resources, education, and respite are more likely to be patient, understanding, and effective in their roles. They're better equipped to manage the physical needs of their loved ones, from administering medication correctly to providing physical assistance. They're also more able to provide emotional support, creating an environment that's comforting and enriching for the person they're caring for (Family Caregiver Alliance, 2012).

Benefits to Family

The impact also extends to the caregiver's family. By helping caregivers manage the stress and demands of their role, support and community can reduce tension within the family. It can also make it easier for families to navigate the challenges of caregiving together, fostering better communication and understanding among family members (Adelman et al., 2014).

Moreover, when children in the family see the caregiver receiving support, it can model healthy coping mechanisms and the importance of community. This can have long-term benefits for children, teaching them valuable lessons about compassion, resilience, and the importance of seeking and offering support (Schulz & Sherwood, 2008).

Benefits to Society

On a larger scale, supporting caregivers can have significant societal benefits. Caregivers play a crucial role in healthcare systems, often filling gaps in formal healthcare services. By providing care at home, they reduce the burden on healthcare facilities and save healthcare costs. When caregivers are well-supported, they can continue to play this role effectively, contributing to more sustainable and efficient healthcare systems (Kramer, 2017).

In addition, when caregivers receive the support they need, they're more likely to stay healthy, both physically and emotionally. This reduces the risk of caregivers needing healthcare services themselves due to stress-related health issues, further conserving valuable healthcare resources (Reinhard et al., 2019).

By advocating for policy changes that better support caregivers, communities can drive societal change. They can help create a society that values and supports caregiving, recognizing it as a vital contribution to the health and welfare of its members (Family Caregiver Alliance, 2012).

The support that caregivers receive, and the community and solidarity they experience, can have profound impacts. These impacts extend from the individual caregiver to the person they're caring for, their family, and society as a whole. By providing caregivers with the resources, respite, education, and community they need, we can not only improve their quality of life but also enhance the quality of care they provide, foster healthier family dynamics, and contribute to a more efficient and compassionate society (Adelman et al., 2014).

Chapter 8: Recognizing and Addressing Caregiver Burnout

8.1: Understanding Caregiver Burnout- Causes, Signs, and Consequences

The act of caring for a loved one is a profound expression of compassion and altruism. However, it's not without its challenges. Caregivers often find themselves in a constant balancing act, juggling their own needs with those of the people they care for. This constant pressure, paired with the emotional toll of watching a loved one in pain or distress, can lead to a state of chronic stress known as caregiver burnout (Reinhard et al., 2019). This condition, while common, is not inevitable and can be mitigated with the right strategies and resources.

Caregiver burnout is a state of physical, emotional, and mental exhaustion that stems from the unrelenting stress of caregiving. It's more than just feeling tired or stressed out after a long day. It's a persistent state of fatigue and overwhelm that pervades all aspects of a caregiver's life, from their job to their relationships, impacting their overall well-being (Family Caregiver Alliance, 2012).

It's important to understand that caregiver burnout isn't the same as clinical depression, though the two can coexist. Caregiver burnout is a direct result of the caregiver's role and responsibilities, and it can lead to depression if not addressed. In addition, caregiver burnout may also contribute to various physical health problems, such as chronic fatigue, insomnia, and obesity (Adelman et al., 2014).

The causes of caregiver burnout are multifaceted and complex, influenced by a range of factors that include the caregiver's personality and coping mechanisms, the demands and nature of the caregiving role, the health and behavior of the person being cared for, and the social and emotional support available to the caregiver (Schulz & Sherwood, 2008). The manifestation of caregiver burnout can be quite varied, ranging from physical symptoms to emotional and behavioral changes.

Understanding the causes, signs, and consequences of caregiver burnout, as well as strategies to cope with and prevent it, is crucial to supporting the well-being of caregivers and ensuring the best possible care for those they look after. This comprehensive guide will delve into each of these aspects in detail (Kramer, 2017).

Defining Caregiver Burnout

Caregiver burnout is a state of physical, emotional, and mental exhaustion that can occur when caregivers do not get the help they need or if they try to do more than they are able, either physically or financially. Caregivers who are burned out may experience fatigue, stress, anxiety, and depression (Reinhard et al., 2019).

Physical Exhaustion: Physical exhaustion is one of the most immediate and noticeable symptoms of caregiver burnout. It's more than just feeling tired after a long day of work. It's a deep-seated fatigue that doesn't go away with rest or sleep. This can be due to the physical demands of caregiving, such as lifting or assisting the person they are caring for, or it could be the result of chronic stress and anxiety taking a toll on the body (Family Caregiver Alliance, 2012).

Emotional Exhaustion: Emotional exhaustion in caregiver burnout can manifest as feelings of sadness, irritability, or numbness. Caregivers may feel emotionally drained and unable to cope with their emotions, leading to feelings of detachment and disinterest in activities they once enjoyed. This is often the result of the constant emotional stress and pressure that come with caregiving, particularly when caring for a loved one with a serious or terminal illness (Adelman et al., 2014).

Mental Exhaustion: Mental exhaustion from caregiver burnout can affect a person's ability to think clearly, make decisions, and focus on tasks. Caregivers may find themselves forgetting things, having trouble concentrating, or making mistakes they wouldn't normally make. This can be due to the constant need to stay alert and attentive to the needs of the person they are caring for, as well as the ongoing stress and worry associated with their role (Schulz & Sherwood, 2008).

Caregiver burnout is not just a state of being tired; it's a state of being depleted. It involves a decline in physical, emotional, and mental resources that significantly impacts a caregiver's life. However, it's important to remember that caregiver burnout is not the same as clinical depression. While it may lead to depression if not addressed, it's a distinct condition with its own causes, symptoms, and treatments (Kramer, 2017).

Causes of Caregiver Burnout

Caregiver burnout stems from a complex interplay of personal, caregiving-related, and external factors (Reinhard et al., 2019).

Personal Factors: Personality traits like neuroticism, difficulty coping with stress, and low resilience increase inherent vulnerability. Past experiences with adversity or trauma can diminish coping abilities long-term. Concurrent physical health problems like chronic pain or obesity reduce capacity to handle caregiving duties.

Pre-existing mental health conditions such as anxiety and depression raise risk. Overall self-care habits around diet, exercise, sleep, and medical care impact resilience reserves. Cultural factors influence perceptions of caregiving burden as well.

Conducting a holistic assessment of all these personal elements provides deeper insights into an individual's risk profile. Targeted interventions can then build coping skills and manage identified vulnerabilities (Family Caregiver Alliance, 2012).

Caregiving-Related Factors: Specific details of the caregiving role also contribute significantly to burnout potential. Caring for individuals with complex medical needs, functional impairments, or dementia poses unique challenges requiring specialized knowledge and skills. Higher levels of dependency for personal care and supervision demand more time and energy. Difficult behaviors like aggression or wandering increase caregiver stress.

The relationship history and dynamic between caregiver and care receiver affects the emotional burden as well. Duration of caregiving over months or years steadily compounds the toll. Understanding the multifaceted nature of an individual's caregiving duties reveals situational risk factors amenable to support (Adelman et al., 2014).

External Factors: Environmental elements outside the caregiver's influence additionally affect burnout likelihood. Social support from family, friends, and community provides stress buffers. Availability of respite care and support groups facilitates coping. Concurrent major responsibilities like full-time work and childrearing exacerbate strain. Financial costs coupled with lost wages increase economic pressures.

Navigating complex healthcare and insurance systems becomes frustrating. Legal considerations add further complications. Assessing these external variables illuminates avenues for systemic interventions at the organizational and societal levels to improve caregiver experiences and prevent burnout (Schulz & Sherwood, 2008).

Evaluating how all these risk factors intersect provides valuable insights into an individual caregiver's unique stress profile. This multi-domain assessment enables targeted, personalized interventions to build resilience, manage vulnerabilities, and modify situational factors to proactively prevent caregiver burnout (Kramer, 2017).

Signs of Caregiver Burnout

Early recognition of the diverse signs of caregiver burnout across physical, emotional, and behavioral realms makes timely intervention possible (Reinhard et al., 2019).

Physical Symptoms: Persistent exhaustion, fatigue, low energy, and sleep disturbances demonstrate the physiological effects of chronic stress. Headaches, gastrointestinal problems, appetite changes, and weight fluctuations may emerge. Increased illnesses and infections can result from a weakened immune system. Chronic generalized pain and soreness may arise from the physical demands of caregiving. Conducting regular personal inventory of these physical complaints helps identify subtle changes that signal emerging issues (Family Caregiver Alliance, 2012).

Emotional Symptoms: Heightened anxiety, sadness, anger, guilt, resentment, and loneliness point to the psychological impacts of caregiver stress. Feeling constantly overwhelmed, trapped, hopeless, or emotionally detached from the care receiver are important indicators.

Loss of meaning, purpose, and satisfaction with life arise as well. Tracking negative thought and mood patterns over time through journaling is an effective way to aid early detection of these emotional signs (Adelman et al., 2014).

Behavioral Symptoms: Withdrawal from usual activities and important social relationships demonstrates the insidious effects of isolation. Neglect of personal self-care like healthy eating, exercising, and medical care shows disregard for individual needs.

Turning to unhealthy coping mechanisms like excess drinking provides a warning signal. Monitoring any lifestyle changes in social engagement, self-care, and risky behaviors is key for recognizing subtle behavioral indicators of burnout (Schulz & Sherwood, 2008).

Carefully evaluating emerging issues across physical, emotional, and behavioral realms on an ongoing basis provides the most effective means of early detection, making timely interventions possible (Kramer, 2017). Stopping burnout in its tracks is critical for supporting caregiver health and well-being over the long term.

Consequences of Caregiver Burnout

If left unaddressed, caregiver burnout can lead to a range of serious consequences for both the caregiver and the person they're caring for.

Understanding these potential outcomes can highlight the importance of addressing caregiver burnout early and effectively (Reinhard et al., 2019).

Poor Physical Health: Chronic stress and neglect of personal health can lead to a range of health problems, including chronic fatigue, insomnia, obesity, and weakened immune function. Long-term, this can increase the risk of serious health conditions, such as heart disease, diabetes, and other chronic conditions (Family Caregiver Alliance, 2012).

Poor Mental Health: Caregiver burnout can also lead to mental health problems, such as depression and anxiety. Chronic stress can exacerbate existing mental health conditions and can lead to the development of new ones. This can have a profound impact on a caregiver's quality of life and their ability to perform their caregiving duties effectively (Adelman et al., 2014).

Lower Quality of Care: Caregiver burnout can affect the quality of care that caregivers are able to provide. Exhaustion, irritability, and decreased patience can lead to rushed or inadequate care. In severe cases, it can even lead to neglect or abuse (Schulz & Sherwood, 2008).

Caregiver Turnover: Burnout is a common reason for caregivers leaving their roles, leading to high turnover rates in caregiving professions. For family caregivers, it can mean having to find alternative care arrangements for their loved ones (Kramer, 2017).

Impact on the Care Recipient: The consequences of caregiver burnout also extend to the person being cared for. They may receive lower-quality care, experience more frequent changes in caregivers, and suffer from the emotional impact of their caregiver's stress and exhaustion (Reinhard et al., 2019).

The consequences of caregiver burnout highlight the importance of recognizing and addressing this issue. Caregivers need support and resources to manage their stress and prevent burnout. With the right help and strategies, caregivers can continue to provide care for their loved ones without compromising their own health and well-being. It's important for caregivers to remember that they're not alone, and that help is available (Family Caregiver Alliance, 2012). It's not a sign of weakness to seek help, but a strength to recognize when it's needed and to take steps to ensure the best possible care for themselves and their loved ones.

Mitigating Caregiver Burnout

While caregiver burnout can be overwhelming, it's not inevitable. There are strategies and resources available to help caregivers manage their stress and prevent burnout (Adelman et al., 2014).

Seeking Support: One of the most effective ways to mitigate caregiver burnout is to seek support. This can come from friends and family, support groups, therapists, or healthcare professionals. Support can provide a valuable outlet for stress and can also provide practical advice and resources for managing caregiving responsibilities (Schulz & Sherwood, 2008). Online forums and local community groups can also offer an opportunity to connect with other caregivers, share experiences, and learn from each other.

Respite Care: Respite care is a service that provides temporary relief for caregivers. This can range from a few hours of in-home care to a few weeks of care in a residential facility. Respite care allows caregivers to take a break, rest, and recharge, which can significantly reduce the risk of burnout (Kramer, 2017).

Self-Care: Caregivers often neglect their own needs in order to focus on the person they're caring for. However, taking care of one's own physical and mental health is crucial to preventing burnout. This includes maintaining a healthy diet, getting regular exercise, ensuring adequate sleep, and seeking medical attention when needed. It also involves taking time for personal interests and hobbies, and maintaining social connections (Reinhard et al., 2019).

Setting Boundaries: It's important for caregivers to set and maintain boundaries in their caregiving role. This includes setting realistic expectations about what they can and cannot do, saying no when necessary, and delegating tasks to others when possible. It also involves taking regular breaks and ensuring time for rest and relaxation (Family Caregiver Alliance, 2012).

Education and Training: Knowledge is power, and this is particularly true for caregivers. Understanding the nature of the person's condition, knowing what to expect, and learning how to manage various caregiving tasks can reduce stress and increase confidence. Many organizations offer training programs and resources for caregivers (Adelman et al., 2014).

Professional Help: In some cases, professional help may be needed to manage the symptoms of caregiver burnout. This can include therapy or counseling, medication, or other treatments. Mental health professionals can provide strategies for managing stress, addressing feelings of guilt or overwhelm, and improving overall well-being (Schulz & Sherwood, 2008).

Caregiver burnout is a serious issue that can have profound consequences for caregivers and those they care for. However, with the right support, resources, and strategies, caregivers can manage their stress and maintain their well-being while continuing to provide care for their loved ones. It's important for caregivers to remember that they're not alone, and that help is available. It's not a sign of weakness to seek help, but a strength to recognize when it's needed and to take steps to ensure the best possible care for themselves and their loved ones (Kramer, 2017).

8.2: Identifying Community Resources for Burnout Support

Caring for a loved one can be immensely rewarding, but it can also be physically, emotionally, and mentally draining. Caregivers constantly find themselves fulfilling the needs of others, often putting their own needs aside. This self-sacrificing approach can lead to burnout if they fail to take care of themselves (Reinhard et al., 2019).

Burnout is a state of chronic physical and emotional exhaustion. It can lead to feelings of anxiety, depression, and detachment, affecting both physical and mental health (Family Caregiver Alliance, 2012). Recognizing the signs of caregiver stress and burnout is the first step towards prevention. Some of these signs include excessive fatigue, loss of interest in activities once enjoyed, neglecting personal needs, and feeling overwhelmed and trapped (Adelman et al., 2014).

Finding the right support is crucial in preventing and managing caregiver burnout. Various community resources offer much-needed respite and support for caregivers battling burnout. These resources can provide emotional support, practical assistance, and financial support (Schulz & Sherwood, 2008). By identifying and utilizing these resources, caregivers can find relief, strength, and the ability to continue their caregiving journey.

Emotional support is invaluable for caregivers experiencing burnout. Caregivers should understand that it is perfectly normal to feel overwhelmed and seek help. They should not isolate themselves or bear the burden alone. Support groups are a wonderful resource for caregivers as they offer a safe space to share experiences, seek advice, and find solace in the shared experiences of others (Kramer, 2017).

Support Groups

Support groups provide a platform for caregivers to share their experiences, express their feelings, and seek advice. These groups can be a lifeline for caregivers, helping them feel less isolated and understood. They offer an environment where caregivers can express their fears, frustrations, and hopes without judgment (Reinhard et al., 2019).

Support groups can be found in most communities and online. They usually consist of people who are going through similar experiences, making them a valuable source of practical advice and emotional support. These groups often host meetings where caregivers can share their experiences, learn from others, and gain valuable insights into managing their circumstances (Family Caregiver Alliance, 2012).

Apart from emotional support, support groups often provide educational resources. These resources can help caregivers understand the physical and mental health issues their loved ones might be facing, giving them a better understanding of their caregiving role. This knowledge can empower caregivers, helping them make informed decisions about their loved ones' care (Adelman et al., 2014).

Online support groups are also a valuable resource for caregivers. They offer the same benefits as traditional support groups, with the added convenience of accessibility. Online support groups are available 24/7, allowing caregivers to seek support at their convenience. They can be particularly beneficial for caregivers who may not have the time or ability to attend in-person meetings (Schulz & Sherwood, 2008).

In conclusion, support groups are a valuable resource for caregivers facing burnout. They provide emotional support, practical advice, and educational resources that can help caregivers in their journey. By participating in support groups, caregivers can feel less isolated and more empowered in their caregiving roles (Kramer, 2017).

Practical Assistance

Practical assistance plays a pivotal role in preventing and managing caregiver burnout. Caregivers often find themselves overwhelmed with various responsibilities that can include medical care, personal care, and household chores. Finding resources that can offer practical assistance can greatly alleviate these burdens (Reinhard et al., 2019).

One such resource is respite care services. Respite care allows caregivers to take a break from their caregiving responsibilities, providing temporary relief. These services can range from a few hours of in-home care to a few weeks of care provided in a specialized facility. This break can provide caregivers with much-needed time to rest, recharge, and attend to their personal needs (Family Caregiver Alliance, 2012).

In-home care services are another valuable resource for caregivers. These services can provide assistance with various tasks such as meal preparation, personal care, medication management, and housekeeping. This help can lighten the caregiver's load, reducing stress and freeing up time for self-care (Adelman et al., 2014).

Adult day care centers can also provide practical assistance. These centers offer care and companionship for older adults during the day, allowing caregivers to work or take a break. They usually provide meals, social activities, and some health-related services, ensuring that the care recipients are well taken care of (Schulz & Sherwood, 2008).

Transportation services can also be a valuable resource for caregivers. Many communities offer transportation services for older adults, helping them get to medical appointments, grocery stores, and social activities. This service can reduce the caregiver's workload, providing more time for self-care (Kramer, 2017).

In conclusion, practical assistance can greatly alleviate the burdens faced by caregivers. Resources such as respite care, in-home care, adult day care centers, and transportation services can provide caregivers with much-needed support, reducing stress and burnout.

Financial Support

Caregiving can often lead to financial stress, adding to the challenges faced by caregivers. However, financial support is available to help ease this burden. By exploring and utilizing these resources, caregivers can focus more on providing care and less on financial worries (Reinhard et al., 2019).

Medicaid, for instance, provides financial assistance to eligible individuals. It can cover the cost of medical care, prescription drugs, in-home care, and other services. Caregivers should check the eligibility criteria in their state to see if they or their loved ones qualify for this assistance (Family Caregiver Alliance, 2012).

The Department of Veterans Affairs also provides financial assistance to eligible veterans and their caregivers. This assistance can cover the cost of a range of services, including medical care, equipment, home modifications, and respite care. Again, it's essential to check the eligibility criteria specific to their situation (Adelman et al., 2014).

Nonprofit organizations and charities often provide financial assistance to caregivers. These organizations can offer grants to cover the cost of medical equipment, home modifications, respite care, and other services. They may also provide resources such as free meals, transportation services, and support groups (Schulz & Sherwood, 2008).

Finally, tax credits and deductions can also provide financial relief for caregivers. Caregivers may be eligible for tax credits for dependent care, medical expenses, and other related costs. It's advisable to consult with a tax professional to understand what credits and deductions may be available (Kramer, 2017).

Financial support can help alleviate the financial stress faced by caregivers. Resources such as Medicaid, veteran benefits, nonprofit organizations, and tax credits can provide significant relief. By exploring and utilizing these resources, caregivers can focus more on their caregiving responsibilities and less on financial worries.

8.3: Encouraging Self-Care Practices for Caregivers

Being a caregiver is a demanding and often unappreciated role. It requires unyielding commitment, patience, and emotional strength. However, in the process of continually caring for others, caregivers often neglect their own needs, which can lead to burnout and decreased effectiveness in the caregiving role.

While the selfless nature of caregiving is admirable, it can also become a trap. The constant focus on others often means that caregivers do not make time for their own physical, emotional, and mental well-being. This neglect can lead to a variety of negative health outcomes, including chronic stress, burnout, depression, and physical ailments.

The concept of self-care, often overlooked in our fast-paced society, is of paramount importance in the caregiving role. Self-care refers to actions and attitudes which contribute to the maintenance of well-being and personal health and promote human development. In the context of caregiving, self-care is essential not only for the caregiver's own health but also for the quality of care they provide.

In essence, self-care is not a luxury but a necessity for caregivers. By taking care of themselves, caregivers can maintain their physical and mental health, enhance their resilience, and continue to provide effective support to those they care for. This article explores the importance of self-care for caregivers, provides practical strategies for self-care, and discusses how to cultivate an awareness and mindset shift to prioritize self-care.

Benefits of Self-Care

The benefits of self-care are manifold, particularly for caregivers who are often under immense pressure. When caregivers take time to look after their own needs, they are better equipped to support those they care for. Furthermore, self-care can help to prevent the onset of caregiver burnout, a state of physical, emotional, and mental exhaustion that can negatively impact the quality of care provided.

Research has shown that regular self-care practices can significantly improve both physical and mental health. This is because these practices can help to reduce stress, boost mood, and improve sleep quality, all of which are crucial for maintaining good health. Moreover, these practices can also enhance emotional resilience, enabling caregivers to better cope with the challenges of their role.

Moreover, self-care can also lead to improved relationships with those being cared for. When caregivers are well-rested and free from excessive stress, they are likely to be more patient, empathetic, and understanding. This can lead to a more positive environment and improved communication between the caregiver and the person being cared for.

Self-care practices can empower caregivers by giving them a sense of control over their lives. Often, the demands of caregiving can make caregivers feel as if they are losing control. By establishing regular self-care routines, caregivers can regain a sense of control and improve their self-esteem.

Finally, self-care practices can also provide caregivers with a much-needed break from their responsibilities. This opportunity to relax and rejuvenate can help to prevent burnout and maintain the long-term sustainability of the caregiving role.

Practical Strategies for Self-Care

When it comes to self-care, one size does not fit all. The strategies that work for one person may not work for another. Therefore, it is important for caregivers to find self-care practices that fit their preferences, resources, and lifestyles. The following are some practical strategies that caregivers can consider incorporating into their daily routines.

Caregivers should ensure they are dedicating some time each day to activities they find enjoyable and relaxing. This "me time" is crucial for mental well-being and can be spent on anything from reading a book, listening to music, taking a nature walk, or pursuing a hobby. This personal time can serve as a respite from caregiving duties and help rejuvenate the mind and body.

Mindfulness practices such as meditation, deep breathing exercises, and yoga can be incredibly beneficial for caregivers. These activities can help lower stress levels, improve focus and attention, and foster a sense of inner peace. They can also help caregivers to stay present and engaged in their role, rather than becoming overwhelmed by future worries or past regrets.

A healthy diet plays a crucial role in maintaining physical health and energy levels. Caregivers should aim for balanced meals including plenty of fruits, vegetables, whole grains, lean proteins, and healthy fats. It's also important to stay hydrated and to limit the intake of processed foods, caffeine, and alcohol, which can all negatively impact energy levels and mood.

Getting sufficient, quality sleep is non-negotiable for caregivers. Sleep is essential for physical recovery, mental clarity, and emotional stability. Caregivers should aim to establish regular sleep schedules, create a restful sleeping environment, and develop relaxing bedtime routines to promote better sleep.

Building and maintaining social connections can provide caregivers with emotional support and reduce feelings of isolation. This could involve staying in touch with friends and family, joining caregiver support groups, or seeking counseling or therapy. Social connections can provide a safe space for caregivers to express their feelings, share experiences, and seek advice.

Cultivating Awareness and Mindset Shift

The importance of self-care is well established, yet many caregivers struggle to prioritize it. This is often due to a perceived lack of time, feelings of guilt, or a lack of awareness about the importance of self-care. Therefore, cultivating a mindset shift and increasing awareness about the importance of self-care are critical steps in encouraging caregivers to prioritize their own well-being.

Reframing self-care as an act of compassion, rather than a selfish act, is a crucial mindset shift. Caregivers need to understand that looking after their own needs is not only beneficial for them but also for the people they are caring for. When caregivers are healthy, relaxed, and content, they are better positioned to provide high-quality care.

Caregivers should learn to recognize the signs of stress and burnout. These can include feelings of being overwhelmed, constant fatigue, irritability, trouble sleeping, and loss of interest in previously enjoyed activities. Recognizing these signs early can allow caregivers to take proactive steps to manage their stress and prevent burnout.

Seeking help when needed is another important aspect of self-care. Many caregivers feel they need to do everything themselves and hesitate to ask for help. However, reaching out for help when needed is not a sign of weakness but a strength. It can alleviate the caregiving burden and provide caregivers the time and space they need for self-care.

Utilizing available resources can be highly beneficial for caregivers. There are numerous resources available, such as educational workshops, support groups, online forums, and self-care apps. These resources can provide caregivers with valuable information, practical strategies, and emotional support to help them manage their caregiving responsibilities while also looking after their own well-being.

Practicing self-compassion is an essential part of self-care. Caregivers often place high expectations on themselves and feel guilty if they can't meet them. However, it's important for caregivers to understand that it's okay to have limitations and to not be perfect. By being kind to themselves, caregivers can better handle the stresses of their role and maintain their emotional well-being.

Self-care is an essential component of effective caregiving. It involves taking care of one's physical, emotional, and mental health through various practices such as regular relaxation, healthy eating, sufficient sleep, and maintaining social connections. By reframing self-care as an act of compassion, recognizing signs of stress, seeking help when needed, utilizing available resources, and practicing self-compassion, caregivers can better manage their responsibilities and provide the highest level of care to their loved ones. It's time for caregivers to realize that taking care of themselves is not a luxury, but a necessity, and to prioritize their well-being alongside the well-being of those they care for.

8.4: Early Intervention for Burnout Prevention- Recognizing the Importance of Caregiver Well-being

Caregiving is a role that demands immense dedication, compassion, and patience. It is a selfless act of providing assistance to individuals who are unable to perform daily tasks due to various reasons such as age, illness, or disability (Reinhard et al., 2019). A caregiver's role can be physically demanding and emotionally draining, often leading to a high level of stress.

The intense demands of caregiving, coupled with the emotional toll of seeing a loved one in distress, can often lead to burnout. Burnout in caregivers is characterized by emotional exhaustion, depersonalization, and a sense of reduced personal accomplishment, leading to a decline in their overall well-being (Family Caregiver Alliance, 2012). The ripple effect of caregiver burnout can extend to the quality of care provided, adversely impacting the care recipient's health and well-being.

Preventing caregiver burnout is therefore not only critical for the caregiver's health but also for the effective care of the recipient (Adelman et al., 2014). One key strategy to prevent burnout is early intervention, which involves recognizing the early signs of burnout and taking proactive measures to address them.

Early intervention is a recognition of the importance of caregiver well-being, acknowledging that caregivers, like everyone else, have their limits and need support to continue their caregiving role effectively (Schulz & Sherwood, 2008). It is a proactive approach that promotes the caregiver's physical, emotional, and cognitive health, thereby enhancing their capacity to provide care.

Here, we delve deeper into the concept of early intervention for caregiver burnout prevention. We will look at how to recognize the early signs of burnout, proactive measures for prevention, and the role of care support teams (Kramer, 2017).

Recognizing Early Signs of Burnout

Burnout among caregivers is a gradual process that often goes unnoticed until it becomes severe. The early signs of burnout may manifest physically, emotionally, and cognitively, and recognizing these signs is the first step towards early intervention (Reinhard et al., 2019).

Physically, caregivers may experience chronic fatigue, frequent headaches, and disturbed sleep patterns. These symptoms can be subtle at the beginning, with caregivers often attributing them to the normal stresses of caregiving. However, if these symptoms persist and intensify over time, they could be indicative of impending burnout (Family Caregiver Alliance, 2012).

Emotionally, caregivers may experience feelings of sadness, irritability, and anxiety. They may find themselves becoming increasingly short-tempered or prone to emotional outbursts. They may also feel a sense of dread or reluctance in performing their caregiving duties, or a feeling of being overwhelmed by their responsibilities (Adelman et al., 2014).

Cognitively, burnout can affect a caregiver's ability to concentrate, remember details, and make decisions. They may find themselves making more mistakes than usual, forgetting important tasks, or having difficulty focusing on their duties. Negative self-talk, such as feelings of inadequacy or failure, can also be a sign of burnout (Schulz & Sherwood, 2008).

Recognizing these signs requires a sense of self-awareness and honesty from caregivers. They need to listen to their bodies, acknowledge their feelings, and be mindful of changes in their behavior or attitude towards caregiving. Recognizing these signs is the first step towards seeking help and preventing full-blown burnout (Kramer, 2017).

Proactive Measures for Prevention

Preventing caregiver burnout requires a proactive approach. Caregivers need to prioritize their own well-being alongside their caregiving responsibilities. This can be achieved through various strategies, including self-care, setting boundaries, seeking professional assistance, and practicing stress management techniques (Reinhard et al., 2019).

Self-care is an integral part of burnout prevention. It involves taking care of one's physical, emotional, and mental health. This can include taking regular breaks from caregiving duties, eating a balanced diet, getting regular exercise, and ensuring adequate sleep. It also involves engaging in activities that bring joy and relaxation, like reading, gardening, painting, or listening to music (Family Caregiver Alliance, 2012).

Setting boundaries is another important strategy for preventing burnout. Caregivers need to communicate their limits to the care recipient and other family members, and not hesitate to say no when necessary. This may involve delegating tasks, using respite care services, or seeking help from other family members or friends. It also involves setting realistic expectations of what they can and cannot do, thereby reducing the risk of overburdening themselves (Adelman et al., 2014).

Seeking professional assistance is crucial when early signs of burnout persist despite self-care efforts. Therapists or counselors who specialize in caregiver support can provide tailored guidance and coping strategies. They can help caregivers understand their feelings, work through their challenges, and develop effective stress management techniques (Schulz & Sherwood, 2008).

Practicing stress management techniques can help caregivers manage their stress levels more effectively. Techniques such as deep breathing exercises, progressive muscle relaxation, meditation, and journaling can help reduce stress and promote overall well-being. Additionally, engaging in enjoyable activities can serve as a form of distraction from caregiving duties, providing a much-needed break and a boost in mood (Kramer, 2017).

Care Support Teams

Care support teams play a pivotal role in preventing caregiver burnout. They provide a network of support, both practical and emotional, helping caregivers navigate the complexities and challenges of caregiving (Reinhard et al., 2019).

A care support team can comprise various individuals and organizations. Healthcare professionals, such as doctors and nurses, can provide medical advice and guidance on managing the care recipient's health conditions (Family Caregiver Alliance, 2012). Social workers can assist with navigating social services and resources, such as respite care or financial aid, that can alleviate some of the caregiving responsibilities (Adelman et al., 2014).

Community organizations, such as senior centers or religious organizations, can offer support groups where caregivers can share their experiences and learn from others in similar situations. These groups can provide emotional support and a sense of community, helping caregivers feel less isolated in their journey. They can also provide practical advice and resources that can help in managing caregiving responsibilities (Schulz & Sherwood, 2008).

Volunteer groups can provide practical assistance, such as help with errands or housekeeping tasks, providing respite for caregivers. They can also offer companionship to the care recipient, thereby providing a break for the caregiver and enhancing the care recipient's social engagement (Kramer, 2017).

In addition to the practical and emotional support, care support teams can also provide educational resources to caregivers. These can include workshops, seminars, or online resources that provide information on various aspects of caregiving, such as managing specific health conditions, understanding legal and financial issues, or learning stress management techniques.

Early intervention is crucial in preventing caregiver burnout. Recognizing the early signs of burnout, taking proactive measures for prevention, and leveraging the support of care support teams are key strategies for ensuring caregiver well-being. By prioritizing their own health and well-being, caregivers can continue to provide quality care to their loved ones, ensuring their well-being and enhancing their quality of life..

8.5: Promoting Long-Term Burnout Management

Caregiving is an integral part of our societal fabric, with millions across the globe dedicating their lives to care for others (Reinhard et al., 2019). However, the nature of this work, whether professional or familial, often leads caregivers into a state of exhaustion and chronic stress, widely recognized as caregiver burnout. This burnout is not merely a consequence of long hours or hard work, but it's a complex phenomenon rooted in the physical, emotional, and psychological demands of caregiving (Family Caregiver Alliance, 2012).

Unfortunately, caregiver burnout doesn't only affect the caregiver. It has far-reaching impacts, affecting the quality of care provided, the caregiver's relationships, and their overall quality of life. Burnout can lead to feelings of isolation, depression, and anxiety, and in severe cases, it can result in physical illness (Adelman et al., 2014). Consequently, this impacts the care recipient's well-being, creating a cycle of stress and deteriorating health.

In people-oriented professions like healthcare, education, and social work, burnout is particularly prevalent. These professions require not only physical stamina but also emotional resilience, often in high-stress and emotionally demanding environments. The consequences of burnout in such professions can be severe, with high turnover rates, low morale, and reduced productivity (Schulz & Sherwood, 2008).

Recognizing the importance of caregiver well-being, there is a growing emphasis on long-term burnout management. It's crucial to understand that burnout is not an individual failing but a systemic issue that requires comprehensive, long-term strategies. These strategies must encompass not only immediate relief and short-term coping mechanisms but also a sustainable, long-term approach that addresses the root causes of burnout (Kramer, 2017).

This long-term approach to burnout management must focus on providing ongoing support, addressing mental health through counseling and therapy, providing relief through respite care services, and fostering a holistic approach that encompasses the caregiver's entire ecosystem. This involves not only the caregiver but their family and friends, their community, their employers, and society at large.

Ongoing Support

The need for ongoing support is a key aspect of long-term burnout management. Caregiving, whether in a professional or personal capacity, can be an isolating experience. Caregivers need to feel valued, heard, and supported, and this support must be sustained and consistent (Reinhard et al., 2019).

Employers have a significant role to play in providing this ongoing support. They need to cultivate a supportive work environment where caregivers feel valued and appreciated. This includes recognizing the caregiver's contribution, providing opportunities for growth and development, and ensuring fair compensation. A positive work environment can help reduce stress and prevent burnout (Family Caregiver Alliance, 2012).

One essential aspect of ongoing support is the ability to manage workload effectively. Caregivers often struggle with heavy workloads, leading to chronic stress and burnout. Employers must ensure that workloads are manageable, provide adequate staffing, and offer flexible work arrangements where possible (Adelman et al., 2014).

Another critical aspect of ongoing support is providing opportunities for social connection. Caregivers need a sense of community and connection to prevent feelings of isolation. This could be facilitated through team-building activities, peer support groups, or social events. These connections can provide emotional support and a sense of belonging (Schulz & Sherwood, 2008).

Ongoing support must align with the caregiver's values and goals. Caregivers are more likely to experience burnout if they feel a disconnect between their work and their personal values or goals. Employers can help align work with these values by creating a mission-driven culture and providing opportunities for meaningful work (Kramer, 2017).

Counseling and Therapy

Addressing mental health is a crucial component of long-term burnout management. The emotional and psychological demands of caregiving can lead to serious mental health issues, including depression and anxiety. As such, caregivers must have access to mental health resources, including counseling and therapy services (Reinhard et al., 2019).

Cognitive-behavioral therapy (CBT) is one such resource. CBT is a type of talk therapy that helps individuals identify and change negative thought patterns, leading to more positive feelings and behaviors. For caregivers, CBT can help manage the stress and emotional challenges associated with their role (Family Caregiver Alliance, 2012).

Mindfulness-based stress reduction (MBSR) is another therapy that can benefit caregivers. MBSR teaches individuals to focus on the present moment, helping to reduce stress and improve mental well-being. Caregivers often juggle multiple responsibilities, and MBSR can help them stay grounded and focused (Adelman et al., 2014).

Acceptance and commitment therapy (ACT) is also beneficial for caregivers. ACT helps individuals accept what they cannot change and commit to actions that improve their situation. For caregivers, this might mean accepting the challenges of their role and committing to self-care practices to manage stress (Schulz & Sherwood, 2008).

In addition to these therapies, caregivers may also benefit from support groups. These groups provide a safe space for caregivers to share their experiences, learn from others, and find emotional support. Participating in a support group can help caregivers feel less alone and more understood (Kramer, 2017).

Respite Care Services

Respite care services are another critical component of a comprehensive burnout management plan. The constant demands of caregiving can leave little time or energy for personal care or relaxation, leading to burnout (Reinhard et al., 2019). Respite care services provide temporary relief for caregivers, allowing them some time to rest and recharge.

Respite care can take many forms, including in-home services, adult day care centers, or short-term residential facilities. The type of respite care chosen depends on the needs of the caregiver and the care recipient (Family Caregiver Alliance, 2012). Regardless of the format, the goal is to provide the caregiver with a break from their caregiving duties (Adelman et al., 2014).

Employers can support their caregiving employees by offering respite care benefits. These benefits could include paid time off, flexible work schedules, or even financial assistance for respite care services. This not only supports the caregiver's mental and physical health but can also lead to increased productivity and job satisfaction (Schulz & Sherwood, 2008).

In addition to employer-provided benefits, community resources can also offer respite care services. Many communities have local organizations that provide respite care services, often at a reduced cost or even for free. These organizations can be a valuable resource for caregivers who need a break (Kramer, 2017).

While respite care provides a temporary break, it can have long-lasting benefits. Regularly scheduled respite can help caregivers manage stress, reduce feelings of overwhelm, and prevent burnout. It also gives caregivers the opportunity to engage in self-care activities, which can improve their overall well-being.

Holistic Approach

A holistic approach to burnout management acknowledges that burnout is not only about managing workload or stress. It involves considering the caregiver's entire ecosystem, including their physical health, mental health, social connections, and environmental factors (Reinhard et al., 2019).

Physical health is a crucial aspect of this holistic approach. Caregivers need to maintain their physical health to manage the demands of their role and prevent burnout. Regular exercise, a balanced diet, and adequate sleep are all essential for physical health and well-being (Family Caregiver Alliance, 2012).

Mental health is another critical component. As mentioned earlier, caregivers should have access to mental health resources, including counseling and therapy services. These services can help manage the emotional and psychological challenges associated with caregiving (Adelman et al., 2014).

Social connections are also vital for preventing burnout. Caregivers need to feel connected to others and have a support network they can rely on. This could include family and friends, fellow caregivers, or support groups. These connections can provide emotional support, practical assistance, and a sense of belonging (Schulz & Sherwood, 2008).

The environment in which caregivers work also plays a significant role in burnout. A supportive work environment that values caregivers and provides ongoing support can help prevent burnout. On the other hand, a toxic or unsupportive work environment can increase the risk of burnout (Kramer, 2017).

Lastly, societal structures and policies can influence caregiver burnout. Policies that provide financial assistance, flexible work arrangements, and access to respite care can support caregivers and prevent burnout. Society needs to recognize and value the essential work of caregivers and support them through comprehensive policies and programs.

Promoting the long-term management of caregiver burnout is a complex but necessary endeavor. It involves not only addressing immediate stressors but also cultivating a supportive, sustainable environment that addresses the root causes of burnout. This requires a collective effort from employers, communities, and society at large.

CHAPTER 9: Special Populations

Caring for individuals with specialized needs requires immense compassion, patience, insight, and support. Throughout society, diverse populations face distinct physical, developmental, medical, and psychosocial challenges that necessitate tailored care approaches, accommodating environments, and specialized resources. Their caregivers courageously take on responsibilities spanning medical care, emotional support, advocacy, education, and assistance with daily living activities.

However, these caregivers often face myriad complexities in providing adequate care while attending to their own needs. Understanding the unique caregiving demands faced by special populations is essential to developing targeted solutions that empower both caregivers and care recipients. This knowledge highlights system gaps, informs caregiver education and training, and enables advocacy for enhanced services and policies that foster dignity for all.

Policymakers, healthcare leaders, educators, and communities must collaboratively assess and address the multifaceted needs of special populations and their caregivers. With compassion and proactive problem-solving, we can uplift human potential, enrich quality of life, and build more inclusive communities. This chapter explores caregiving challenges, best practices, and support strategies for thirteen special populations.

Their experiences provide insights that can guide efforts to enhance equitable care access, resources, and caregiver empowerment across all of society..

9.1 Elderly Individuals

As the population ages, a growing number of elderly individuals require specialized care and assistance. The elderly are defined as those aged 65 years or older. This group faces declining health and functional status as part of the normal aging process, which is often compounded by complex chronic medical conditions (Reinhard et al., 2019).

Assistive care enables the elderly to maintain independence, safety, and quality of life. Both professional and familial caregivers provide invaluable medical, emotional, and daily living support. However, elderly caregiving also poses unique challenges that must be addressed through tailored approaches, environments, resources, and policies (Family Caregiver Alliance, 2012).

With global demographic shifts leading to larger aging populations, supporting elderly individuals and their caregivers is becoming an urgent priority worldwide.

Challenges

Elderly caregiving involves managing age-related cognitive and physical decline amidst complex co-occurring conditions. Prevalent issues like dementia, mobility impairments, incontinence, and chronic diseases require extensive medical knowledge and hands-on care (Adelman et al., 2014). Caregivers must vigilantly address risks like falls, self-neglect, or medication nonadherence through environmental precautions, while also planning appropriate living transitions over time.

Providing personal care with activities like bathing, dressing, feeding, or toileting can be physically taxing yet essential for those with dependency in daily living skills. Behavioral issues like aggression, wandering, sundowning, or resistance to care also arise frequently due to psychiatric and neurological conditions like Alzheimer's disease or other dementias.

These behaviors require specialized communication approaches and sensitivity. Caregivers additionally face profound role shifts as adult children transition into caring for aging parents. This reversal can spur complicated grief over the loss of previous family roles. Balancing intensive elderly caregiving with other demanding family obligations or professional responsibilities leads to social isolation, exhaustion, guilt, and career sacrifice.

Maintaining elders' social connections, cognitive stimulation, and quality of life poses an additional challenge given mobility limitations and cognitive changes. In navigating these multifaceted medical, emotional, and practical issues, elderly caregivers require extensive training, tailored resources, community support, and policies that enable their vital labor of care.

Approaches

To address these complex challenges, elderly caregivers need specialized education and training, planned respite, counseling, home modifications, care coordination services, and community resources (Schulz & Sherwood, 2008). They must learn proper techniques to provide hygiene assistance, medication management, mobility aids, and other personal care safely and effectively.

Caregivers also need training on compassionate, evidence-based approaches to address behavioral issues like wandering, aggression, or sundowning that maintain dignity. Home modifications, adaptive equipment, adult day services, and in-home respite enhance safety and provide needed breaks from continually demanding responsibilities. Support groups, counseling, and education on anticipatory grief and evolving family roles help caregivers process profound emotional adjustments.

Geriatric case managers and social workers can assist with healthcare system navigation, legal considerations, and major care transition decisions as elders' needs change. Promoting continued community inclusion through specialized social programming and transportation services also maintains quality of life for homebound elders.

A holistic, person-centered approach empowering both elderly individuals and their dedicated caregivers is essential to enabling this population to age with dignity.

Resource Considerations

Key resources for supporting elderly populations and their caregivers include:

Adult day programs for social engagement, activity, and caregiver respite (Kramer, 2017) - Adult day programs provide supervised activities and social engagement for elderly individuals during the day, allowing caregivers respite. Centers are found through local aging agencies. Programs provide cognitive stimulation and socialization for isolated seniors and much needed breaks for caregivers at risk for burnout.

Support groups to process emotional, social, and anticipatory grief issues with peers (Reinhard et al., 2019) - Support groups create a judgement-free space to share experiences and find solace with other caregivers. Local social service agencies or religious institutions often host groups. Participating provides validation and coping strategies to help caregivers navigate complex emotional terrain.

Geriatric care managers to coordinate care services and guide care transitions (Family Caregiver Alliance, 2012) - Geriatric care managers are professionals who can assess needs, create care plans, coordinate services, and guide major transitions. They are hired privately or accessed through home care agencies. Their expertise saves caregivers time and provides reassurance during difficult decisions.

Home health aides for personal care assistance with daily living activities (Adelman et al., 2014) - Home health aides assist with personal care in the home, providing bathing, dressing, and hygiene help. Home care agencies arrange services. Aides reduce caregiver demands and allow seniors to age in place safely.

Social workers to navigate care systems, legal considerations, and major transition planning (Schulz & Sherwood, 2008) - Social workers help access services, understand healthcare rights, complete paperwork, and plan major transitions. Hospitals, government aging agencies, and nonprofits employ them. Their assistance secures resources and clarifies complicated bureaucracy.

Home safety evaluations and environmental modifications by occupational therapists (Kramer, 2017) - Occupational therapists assess home safety risks and recommend modifications like grab bars. Caregivers can request evaluations through doctors or home care agencies. Implementing suggestions reduces fall risks and improves independence.

Validation therapy training for caregivers managing behavioral issues with compassion (Reinhard et al., 2019) - Validation therapy provides strategies for interpreting and responding to problematic behaviors with empathy. Local aging agencies may offer training. Techniques enhance communication, reduce caregiver stress, and uphold dignity.

Individual and family counseling for grief support and evolving roles (Family Caregiver Alliance, 2012) - Counseling helps process anticipatory loss, role changes, and complicated grief. Community mental health centers or private practices provide services. Therapy improves coping skills during challenging transitions.

Specialized elderly recreation programs tailored to abilities (Adelman et al., 2014) - Specialized programs adapt activities to limitations to promote engagement. Local parks or senior centers offer opportunities. Staying active provides meaning and enrich connection.

Palliative and hospice care programs for end-of-life planning and pain management (Schulz & Sherwood, 2008) - Palliative and hospice programs manage pain, provide counsel, and ease difficult decisions at end of life. Hospitals and home health agencies have programs. They provide comfort and guidance as life closes.

The elderly represent a population with distinct care needs amid age-related cognitive and functional decline, chronic illnesses, evolving roles, and psychosocial issues. Specialized assistance enables dignity, safety, and continued quality of life for this group. However, elderly caregivers face medical, emotional, financial, and practical challenges themselves.

Compassionate, holistic caregiver support through tailored training, planned respite, counseling, system navigation, emotional validation, and facilitating community inclusion is essential to empowering this vulnerable population. With global aging demographics, implementing proactive solutions to assist both caregivers and elderly care recipients is an imperative priority..

9.2 Individuals with Disabilities

Individuals with disabilities encompass those with congenital or acquired physical, developmental, intellectual, and chronic health challenges requiring ongoing assistance (Reinhard et al., 2019). These disabilities create challenges with mobility, self-care, communication, cognition, education, socialization, accessing healthcare, and participating in community life (Family Caregiver Alliance, 2012).

Caregivers provide critical hands-on support with medical care, therapies, daily living activities, developmental interventions, advocacy, system navigation, and community inclusion. However, significant societal barriers remain, including inaccessible built environments, stigma, inadequate coordination of services, and unaffordable access to resources.

Improving accommodations, support services, accessibility, affordable healthcare, and acceptance of disabilities is imperative yet often overlooked by social systems and policies. Caregivers take on these battles while also managing overwhelming individual responsibilities. Their vital work enables dignity, quality of life, and human potential for this population.

Challenges

Disability caregiving poses medically, emotionally, practically, and socially complex responsibilities. Extensive training is required for specialized medical tasks like tube feeding, catheter care, tracheostomy maintenance, wound dressing, orthotic management, and handling behaviors stemming from conditions like autism or PTSD (Adelman et al., 2014).

Coordinating extremely fragmented healthcare, educational, vocational, transportation, and disability services poses major obstacles to securing benefits, quality care, and resources (Schulz & Sherwood, 2008). Funding gaps create significant barriers to obtaining adequate in-home care, respite, specialized equipment, assistive technologies, therapies, and community participation supports.

Caregiving also requires extensively adapting living environments for accessibility and safety, facilitating inclusion in schools and community programs to prevent isolation, and tirelessly advocating for accommodation and acceptance.

Coping with grief over loss of envisioned futures, dependence, judgment from others, and children's future uncertainties requires tremendous emotional strength and support. Upholding human dignity and maximizing quality of life remain paramount.

Approaches

Supporting individuals with disabilities and their devoted caregivers requires both individual and systemic change. Improved accessibility, social inclusion, affordable access to coordinated quality services, and public awareness is imperative (Reinhard et al., 2019). Enhanced accessibility standards, accommodations in schools and workplaces, inclusive recreation programs, specialized therapies, and disability representation in media and community life can help reduce stigma over time.

For caregivers, tailored training, planned respite, bereavement counseling, peer support groups, expert case management, and determined legal advocacy are invaluable but inadequately accessible (Family Caregiver Alliance, 2012).

Policy changes enabling equitable caregiver compensation, workplace flexibility, consistent funding for services, and improved coordination of care could provide much-needed stability amid fragmentation. Most importantly, upholding autonomy, independence, and self-determination for those with disabilities must remain the focus (Adelman et al., 2014).

With compassion and determined advocacy, we can empower those with disabilities to maximize life quality and human potential.

Resource Considerations

Key resources for disability caregivers include:

Respite care services through home care agencies or community programs for temporary relief (Schulz & Sherwood, 2008). Respite provides caregivers periodic breaks from relentless demands. Home care agencies, local disability services, and nonprofits offer respite options. Setting up regular respite routines is key for caregiver health.

Training on specific conditions, required therapies, assistive technology use, and behavioral supports through local disability services agencies (Kramer, 2017). Knowledge allows quality, confident care. Disability organizations provide training on meeting specialized needs. Seeking education empowers caregiver skills.

Specialized recreational and social programs tailored to abilities through parks and recreation departments, therapeutic providers, and nonprofits (Reinhard et al., 2019). These facilitate community inclusion and acceptance. Caregivers can research local accessible programs for engagement opportunities that build social connections.

Parent networking and support groups through disability advocacy organizations and social media for sharing experiences (Family Caregiver Alliance, 2012). Peer understanding reduces isolation. Groups provide validation and problem-solving strategies from shared experiences. Support aids resilience.

Disability living skills training for independence and coaching on accessing accommodations through independent living centers (Adelman et al., 2014). Skills build autonomy. Independent living centers teach functional life skills for greater independence. Training focuses on person's strengths and goals.

Special education instructional assistants and individualized education program advocates through school districts who help secure appropriate accommodations and inclusion (Schulz & Sherwood, 2008). Education access is imperative. Advocates empower caregivers to obtain suitable educational supports, services, and placement.

Social workers through government and nonprofit agencies to coordinate services and guide system navigation to obtain resources (Kramer, 2017). They assist with bureaucracy. Social workers have expertise in accessing programs and benefits. They save caregivers time and stress.

Home health aides for personal care assistance with activities of daily living through home care agencies (Reinhard et al., 2019). This provides hands-on support. Home health aides help with daily activities like dressing, hygiene, and mobility. Reliable assistance reduces caregiver load.

Occupational therapists for home accessibility evaluations and modifications through hospitals, rehab centers, or private practices (Family Caregiver Alliance, 2012). Home adaptations enable independence. OTs recommend adaptive equipment and home modifications for greater safety and autonomy.

Disability attorneys and legal advocates for benefits appeals and upholding disability rights through nonprofit legal aid services (Adelman et al., 2014). They fight for equity under the law. Legal advocacy secures entitled benefits and upholds disability rights. Attorneys lend expert negotiation skills.

Caregivers for individuals with disabilities perform vital developmental, medical, emotional, and inclusion work. However, they require extensive training, respite, emotional support, care coordination, and systemic improvements in accessibility, affordability, inclusion, and public awareness. With compassionate, person-centered approaches, we can empower those with disabilities to maximize independence, community engagement, and human potential..

9.3 Children with Special Needs

Children with special needs include those with learning disabilities, developmental delays, chronic medical conditions, mental health disorders, and other impairments requiring early, specialized interventions and lifelong support (Reinhard et al., 2019). These children benefit immensely from tailored education, therapies, and care approaches fostering development, self-regulation, and inclusion.

However, securing affordable access to quality coordinated services often poses immense obstacles for families. Caregivers provide critical developmental, medical, educational, and emotional support amid funding limitations, system fragmentation, public misconceptions, and complex care burdens.

Still, with compassionate, empowering approaches, proper support systems, and societal change over time, these children can defy expectations and reach their highest potential (Family Caregiver Alliance, 2012).

Challenges

Caring for children with special needs requires learning highly specialized medical procedures, managing challenging behaviors, coordinating frequently fragmented healthcare and educational services, facilitating social inclusion, handling judgment or misunderstandings from others, and planning for major lifelong transitional stages including long-term living arrangements and guardianship considerations (Adelman et al., 2014).

Caregivers often struggle immensely to secure affordable access to high-quality care including in-home nursing, respite, specialized equipment, therapies, appropriate school services, healthcare, and future living support amid inadequate funding and fragmented systems (Schulz & Sherwood, 2008). Special needs families frequently face denial of entitled benefits, subpar educational placements, public stigma, grief over loss of envisioned futures, and relentless worry over children's lifespan independence and quality of life.

Prioritizing caregiver mental health support and self-care is imperative, yet difficult to achieve without sufficient affordable respite and systemic improvements. Still, little progress will occur without dedicated caregivers bravely navigating these obstacles.

Approaches

Truly supporting children with special needs and their devoted families requires seismic systemic change coupled with individual empowerment. Vastly improving affordability, accessibility, inclusion, care coordination, and public awareness constitute the most pressing needs (Kramer, 2017).

Major policy reforms securing equitable, consistent funding and expert care management guidance would help alleviate currently unmanageable fragmentation.

Enhanced educator sensitivity training, accommodations, recreational inclusion, public awareness campaigns, and anti-bullying efforts can help foster acceptance and empower families over time. Accessible respite programs, specialized caregiver mental health support, tailored medical training, unrelenting legal advocacy for school services, and proactive transition planning also greatly empower families to better manage this lifelong journey.

Most importantly, upholding children's dignity, choices, interests, abilities, and self-determination must remain central across all care and decision-making (Reinhard et al., 2019).

Resource Considerations

Key resources to aid children with special needs and their dedicated caregivers include:

Respite care through home nursing agencies, adult day programs, or specialized community respite facilities to temporarily relieve unrelenting demands (Family Caregiver Alliance, 2012). Respite provides caregivers much-needed breaks from constant demands. Home care agencies, community respite programs, and nonprofits offer options. Planned respite prevents burnout.

Parent support groups, disability networks and online communities for sharing experiences and resources (Adelman et al., 2014). Connecting with other special needs parents provides vital empathy and advice for navigating common challenges. Groups are available through nonprofits, social media, and hospitals. Shared experiences combat isolation.

Special education instructional assistants and individualized education program advocates to secure appropriate accommodations and inclusion (Schulz & Sherwood, 2008). These advocates empower caregivers to obtain suitable educational supports, services, and placement to equalize opportunity. Every child deserves appropriate education.

Social workers to assist with care coordination, system navigation, legal considerations, and emotional support through an overwhelming lifelong journey (Kramer, 2017). Social workers have expertise connecting families to resources and providing counseling during difficulties. Their assistance smooths out fragmented systems.

Disability therapy providers like applied behavior analysis companies providing specialized modalities tailored to the child's needs (Reinhard et al., 2019). Research-based therapies delivered consistently foster developmental progress. Vetted providers are key to quality care.

Assistive technology professionals to assess equipment that can improve communication, mobility, and independence (Family Caregiver Alliance, 2012). Customized technologies enable functional abilities and greater autonomy. Training empowers optimal use.

Specialized pediatricians with expertise in the child's diagnoses who provide quality medical care (Adelman et al., 2014). Their condition knowledge guides proactive treatment planning for the best outcomes. Finding the right provider match is crucial.

Financial planning assistance regarding long-term disability-related costs and future security (Schulz & Sherwood, 2008). Planning for adulthood costs brings peace of mind. Qualified special needs financial planners deliver this specialized service.

Legal advocates upholding special education and disability rights (Kramer, 2017). When districts deny entitled services, lawsuits enforce accommodations. Nonprofit disability law centers provide legal aid.

Sibling support groups addressing special needs family dynamics, experiences, and concerns (Reinhard et al., 2019). Siblings have unique journeys often unacknowledged. Groups validate challenges and foster empathy.

Caring for children with special needs requires immense dedication yet systemic barriers impede affordable, quality care access. However, with improved support services, caregiver empowerment programs, public awareness, and inclusion efforts, these children can defy expectations. Their future possibilities remain boundless. Progress takes collective compassion and action.

9.4 Mental Health Patients

Introduction

Individuals with mental illness face unique obstacles in securing ongoing treatment and stability amid stigma and systemic barriers (Reinhard et al., 2019). Mental illnesses like depression, anxiety, bipolar disorder, schizophrenia, OCD, and PTSD create symptoms impeding emotional, cognitive, social, and functional capacities.

Caregivers play pivotal roles bolstering recovery through compassionate support, promoting stability, ensuring treatment access, managing crises, and understanding needs associated with specific diagnoses (Family Caregiver Alliance, 2012).

However, significant societal change is still required to empower those with mental illness to thrive through improved affordability, reduced stigma, tailored support systems, and optimized community integration. This care partnership facilitated by understanding, empathy, and properly aligned services provides a powerful antidote to suffering—yet its potential remains constrained without collective compassionate action.

Challenges

Mental health caregiving poses multifaceted challenges including providing consistent emotional support during crises, encouraging treatment adherence, managing risks, maintaining realistic expectations through gradual recovery, securing affordable coordinated care, increasing social connection, assisting with daily functioning, and planning for future care needs (Schulz & Sherwood, 2008).

Judgment from others, disjointed systems, risks during crises, housing/job instability, and caregiver stress all threaten progress. Stigma remains a major obstacle to inclusion and willingness to seek help.

However, recovery is possible with proper treatment, stability, empowered caregiver support, and societal change. This requires further expanding access, affordability, coordination, and quality within mental healthcare.

Resource Considerations

Key resources for supporting mental illness populations and their caregivers include:

Warm lines for non-crisis emotional support (Reinhard et al., 2019). Warm lines provide compassionate listening and validation during stressful times when not in crisis. Many mental health agencies offer this service. Talking reduces isolation.

Peer support groups to reduce isolation (Family Caregiver Alliance, 2012). Sharing stories and advice with others facing similar struggles combats loneliness. Groups exist through nonprofits and sometimes clinics. Mutual understanding is powerful.

Clubhouses for socialization and skill development (Adelman et al., 2014). Clubhouses build community and abilities for better functioning through classes, recreation, and work programs. They take referrals from providers. Membership creates belonging.

ACT and FACT teams providing multi-disciplinary community-based care (Schulz & Sherwood, 2008). These mobile crisis teams deliver individualized, holistic support directly to those in need. Clinics and social service agencies have teams. On-site care increases stability.

Individual and family counseling to process challenges (Kramer, 2017). Talk therapy helps develop skills for managing symptoms, communication, and caregiver stresses. Clinics, community centers, and private practices offer counseling. Healing requires expression.

Psychosocial rehabilitation promoting stability and functioning (Reinhard et al., 2019). Rehab focuses on role functioning through socialization and life skills development. Mental health centers provide programs. Everyday abilities enable independence.

Caregiver education on diagnoses, treatment options, and crisis prevention (Family Caregiver Alliance, 2012). Knowing conditions in depth improves care quality, empathy, and crisis response skills. Advocacy groups and providers offer training. Knowledge is power.

Housing, transportation, and employment assistance programs (Adelman et al., 2014). Support services that increase stability. Government and nonprofit agencies have programs. Stability aids functioning and recovery.

Healthcare proxies and psychiatric advance directives for future planning (Schulz & Sherwood, 2008). Legal documents preserve care preferences and avoid gaps. Lawyers can aid creation. Planning ahead prevents crises.

Mindfulness training for caregiver stress management (Kramer, 2017). Meditation and mindfulness practices reduce anxiety. Classes are available in many communities. Stress management empowers ethical, high-quality care.

With compassion, mental health literacy, strong care partnerships, support systems, and continued societal change to reduce stigma, recovery and community integration is possible. Shared understanding empowers growth.

But true empowerment requires extending mental healthcare beyond clinical settings into communities of care. Through both individual and collective action, we uphold our shared humanity.

9.5 Chronic Illness Patients

Chronic illnesses like cancer, diabetes, COPD, heart disease, and neurological conditions require continual medical management and significant lifestyle adaptations over months or years (Reinhard et al., 2019). Patients face shifting physical and cognitive capacities, unpredictable disease flares, complex evolving decisions about treatment options, and profound grief over functional losses that often accumulate gradually over time (Family Caregiver Alliance, 2012).

Caregivers serve immensely vital roles providing multifaceted medical, physical, emotional, and practical support through all phases of illness (Adelman et al., 2014). This care partnership of understanding, skill, tenacity, and compassion can empower patients to maintain engagement in valued life activities, connect meaningfully with loved ones, and find purpose amid relentless and often progressive illness burdens.

However, widespread barriers to affordable access to coordinated, quality care threaten patient well-being and caregiver health (Schulz & Sherwood, 2008). Still, resilience is possible when care aligns holistically with patient preferences, knowledge builds caregiver competence and confidence, and communities come alongside both patients and caregivers with understanding and support.

Challenges

Caring for individuals with chronic illness involves learning highly complex health management routines across medical, nutrition, exercise, and emotional domains; vigilantly monitoring for subtle symptom changes indicating needs for prompt intervention; providing hands-on assistance with self-care, mobility and medications during acute exacerbations or post-treatment recovery periods; repeatedly navigating frustratingly disconnected healthcare systems to secure affordable access to appropriate quality providers and treatments; weighing agonizing benefit and risk tradeoffs regarding evolving advanced treatment options and clinical trials with uncertain outlooks; proactively planning future care decisions amid unpredictable illness trajectories; ensuring patients maintain engagement in valued community and family activities despite limitations and mobility impairments; offering compassionate emotional and spiritual support through the relentless ups and downs of managing incurable and frequently worsening illness burdens; and helping both patients and other family members cope with grief and fear surrounding disease progression, declining health, and mortality (Kramer, 2017).

The physical and emotional toll of caregiving under such unrelenting strain with inadequate systemic supports threatens caregiver health, while the potential loss of patient autonomy and dignity in the absence of holistic care tailored to individual priorities denies our shared humanity.

Approaches

Truly empowering individuals living with chronic illness and upholding quality of life requires improving accessibility, affordability, coordination, and quality of healthcare while also providing whole-person supports spanning medical, emotional, practical, spiritual, and relational domains (Family Caregiver Alliance, 2012).

High-quality disease education and training equips caregivers with the knowledge to confidently manage intricate treatment regimens and monitor subtle symptom changes over time (Adelman et al., 2014). Integrated palliative care teams play essential roles addressing pain, grief, mortality fears, and holistic sources of distress through all phases of illness.

Home modifications, adaptive equipment, and accessible transportation enable preservation of function and community participation. Peer support groups and counseling provide reassurance amid the isolating challenges of navigating unpredictable declines. Cross-sector care coordination models utilizing nurse case managers, social workers, and community health workers foster care continuity and system navigation (Schulz & Sherwood, 2008).

Most importantly, care guided by patient priorities, dignity, and shared decision-making every step of the way preserves autonomy and purpose when much feels beyond control (Kramer, 2017). With compassion and multidimensional supports, individuals can maintain meaning, relationships, and emotional health amid chronic illness. But slim access to most supportive services keeps this ideal distant. Progress relies on collective action.

Resource Considerations

Key resources for supporting chronic illness patient populations and their caregivers include:

Palliative care for multifaceted comfort and planning (Kramer, 2017). Palliative teams address complex physical, emotional, and spiritual sources of distress starting at diagnosis along with disease education and future planning. Hospitals and home health agencies provide services. Support empowers quality of life.

Home health assistance with medical and daily living tasks (Reinhard et al., 2019). Home health aides assist with hands-on medical care, personal hygiene, mobility, and household activities during flares or post-treatment. Home care agencies arrange services. Support provides needed respite.

Support groups for sharing experiences and emotional support (Family Caregiver Alliance, 2012). Connecting with peers facing similar challenges combats isolation. Groups exist online and through nonprofits. Shared experiences provide reassurance.

Health advocacy assistance to secure quality affordable care (Adelman et al., 2014). Advocates assist with system navigation, paperwork, and appeals to obtain entitled treatment and coverage. Nonprofit agencies offer these services. Advocacy secures access.

Individual counseling for processing grief and life changes (Schulz & Sherwood, 2008). Talk therapy helps develop skills for coping with ongoing loss and adapting to evolving limitations. Community providers offer counseling. Expression aids resilience.

Online patient communities that create connection (Kramer, 2017). Platforms like social media groups and forums connect patients and caregivers facing the same disease. Shared stories combat isolation.

Home modifications and adaptive equipment to preserve safety and function (Reinhard et al., 2019). Ramps, grab bars, lifts help navigate the home while mobility aids enable independence. OTs recommend appropriate aids. Modifications maintain quality of life.

Respite care for temporary relief (Family Caregiver Alliance, 2012). Adult day programs and in-home respite gives caregivers much needed breaks. Nonprofits and home care agencies provide respite. Planned relief prevents fatigue.

Specialty pharmacies that assist with medication access (Adelman et al., 2014). These pharmacies aid with insurance approvals, copay reductions and medication delivery. Social workers help connect to options. Assistance improves adherence.

Social workers to coordinate resources and system navigation (Schulz & Sherwood, 2008). Social workers connect families to supports and help streamline complex systems. Hospitals and government agencies employ them. Their expertise links services.

Through expanded accessibility, support systems, community integration, holistic care delivery, and caregiver empowerment initiatives, we can uphold dignity for those facing chronic illness (Reinhard et al., 2019). Illness may constrain certain capacities.

But the human spirit remains boundless when cared for compassionately. Gaps remain in supporting this courageous population. But progress is possible through both individual understanding and collective societal change to align systems with the values of those they should serve. Where there is care, there is hope.

9.5 Individuals with Autism Spectrum Disorder

Introduction

Caring for individuals with Autism Spectrum Disorder (ASD) poses unique rewards and challenges (Reinhard et al., 2019). ASD is a complex neurodevelopmental disorder characterized by differences in social communication, sensory processing, repetitive behaviors, and cognitive as well as skill profiles (Family Caregiver Alliance, 2012). Caregivers play integral roles implementing specialized therapies, adapting home and school environments to accommodate needs, promoting inclusion in community life, coordinating frequently disconnected services across sectors, planning major life transitions proactively, and relentlessly advocating for awareness and acceptance (Adelman et al., 2014). With compassion, understanding, and properly tailored supports, those with ASD can achieve meaningful emotional connection, independence, dignified treatment, and purpose. However, widespread misconceptions coupled with systemic barriers to affordable quality care impede progress (Schulz & Sherwood, 2008). Fostering a society that celebrates neurodiversity requires collective openness to understand and embrace all minds. Still, committed caregivers pave the way each day through steadfast love and support.

Challenges

Caring for individuals with ASD extensively involves learning and adeptly delivering specialized interventions, accommodating unique sensory needs through visual structure and predictable routines, vigilantly ensuring safety amidst impulsivity risks, ardently securing appropriate educational services and peer supports, gently correcting public misconceptions while modeling acceptance, relentlessly coordinating input across frequently disconnected medical, mental health, educational, vocational, and disability services, struggling to access daily respite given the intensity of 24/7 behavioral and therapeutic demands, proactively planning for adulthood transitions

509

including guardianship considerations, workspace accommodations, and supportive living options, and processing grief over lost dreams for neurotypical experiences while reframing hope (Kramer, 2017).

Judgment from others, prohibitive costs, service access difficulties, and the overwhelming intensity of managing multifaceted developmental, systemic, and public awareness needs evoke deep caregiver stress. Still, neurodiversity itself has value when accepted with compassion. Full life quality is attainable for individuals with ASD through environmental accommodation and social inclusion.

Approaches

Fully supporting individuals with ASD and their devoted caregivers requires seismic systemic improvements coupled with compassionate person-centered care (Kramer, 2017). Vastly expanding affordable access to coordinated evidence-based therapies, trained providers, caregiver respite, tailored transition services, and adaptive technologies is imperative (Reinhard et al., 2019).

Improved neurodiversity training for educators, employers, and healthcare providers can foster inclusion. Awareness campaigns, public education, and social media representation help counter misconceptions over time. Policy and workplace reforms enabling flexible accommodations and preventing discrimination empower participation. For families, access to high-quality respite, behavioral supports, mourning counseling, and caregiver mental health services is invaluable but profoundly lacking (Family Caregiver Alliance, 2012).

Collaborative support teams providing practical assistance with system navigation and legal advocacy can smooth out inequities. Most importantly, all efforts should uphold personhood, dignity, interests, and self-determination for those with ASD (Adelman et al., 2014). Care powered by compassion and voice can empower growth, connection, and purpose.

Progress relies on both individual understanding and collective action towards justice. We all have roles in building societies that embrace and empower neurodiversity.

Resource Considerations

Key resources for supporting ASD populations and their caregivers include:

Applied behavior analysis for skill development (Kramer, 2017). ABA applies techniques based on learning theory to teach socially significant skills. Certified providers deliver intensive ABA therapy. Consistency with interventions fosters developmental gains.

Speech, occupational, and physical therapies to address needs (Reinhard et al., 2019). Therapies improve communication, fine motor abilities, sensory regulation, and mobility. Clinics, schools, and private practices offer therapies. Individualized therapies target specific skill deficits.

Sensory integration therapy and specialized equipment (Family Caregiver Alliance, 2012). This therapy increases ability to process sensory input through activities. OTs provide therapy, while catalogs carry equipment to address sensitivities. Accommodating sensitivities reduces anxiety.

Social skills classes to learn relationship behaviors (Adelman et al., 2014). Classes break down nuances of social interaction through modeling and role play. Community centers and nonprofits offer group or individual training. Social skill development enables connection.

Special education assistance for appropriate accommodations (Schulz & Sherwood, 2008). Advocates empower families to obtain IEP services and appropriate classroom placement. Knowledge of regulations equalizes access.

Parent training on behavioral techniques, safety, and advocacy (Kramer, 2017). Classes through agencies teach caregivers about ASD and specialized interventions. Knowledge informs care approaches.

Respite care through home programs or adult facilities (Reinhard et al., 2019). In-home respite provides temporary relief from care demands. Nonprofits offer respite options. Planned breaks prevent caregiver burnout.

Support groups for sharing advice and experience (Family Caregiver Alliance, 2012). Online and in-person groups connect caregivers facing similar challenges. Shared stories provide validation.

Adult services for continued life skills training (Adelman et al., 2014). Day programs provide ongoing skill training for greater independence. Centers tailor activities to abilities and interests. Services further progress.

Legal help with guardianship and disability rights issues (Schulz & Sherwood, 2008). Laws surrounding guardianship and entitlements are complex. Attorneys provide guidance. Expertise secures rights.

With openness, compassion, community inclusion efforts, equitable access to needs-tailored services and supports, and workplace/societal acceptance of neurodiversity, individuals with ASD can find connection, independence, dignity, and purpose (Reinhard et al., 2019).

But progress relies on collective change starting with awareness. There is neurodiversity in humanity—and humanity in understanding.

9.7 Military Veterans

Introduction

Caring for injured or aging military veterans poses profound rewards and multifaceted challenges (Reinhard et al., 2019). Their caregivers provide extensive medical, emotional, psychosocial, and practical assistance managing service-connected disabilities, integrating back into civilian life, finding meaningful daily activities, and rebuilding purpose following tremendous loss or trauma (Family Caregiver Alliance, 2012).

However, widespread systemic complexities within the veterans' affairs bureaucracies, accompanied by debilitating psychological stresses related to prior warzone exposure and injuries sustained in the line of duty, often evoke immense obstacles for veterans and families (Kramer, 2017). Still, with compassion, camaraderie, counseling, disability adaptation, future planning, and societal understanding of veterans' sacrifices, meaningful healing and purpose are possible despite disability or trauma (Adelman et al., 2014).

These courageous heroes deserve no less in return for their profound commitments defending foundational freedoms. Ensuring high-quality accessible care is a shared moral obligation.

Challenges

Extensive caregiving tasks include thoroughly learning medical management for complex injuries like amputations, traumatic brain injuries, spinal cord trauma, blindness, and PTSD; patiently motivating veterans to persevere with rehabilitation and engagement amid devastating losses; providing reliable transportation to and from extensive medical appointments; tenaciously battling dense bureaucracies to secure entitled benefits and quality care; sensitively managing behavioral symptoms triggered by past trauma and loss; dependably performing necessary household tasks and self-care that veterans can no longer independently manage due to disability; facilitating welcoming social connections amid isolation and civilian cultural divides; offering compassionate counseling for anxieties over potential redeployment or in processing grief regarding changed abilities post-injury; and proactively planning for potential long-term progressive care needs (Schulz & Sherwood, 2008).

Witnessing painful disability adjustments combined with navigating fragmented support systems evokes deep stress for caregivers lacking respite and shared understanding from broader society.

Approaches

Fully empowering injured veterans and their devoted caregivers necessitates seismic societal shifts to uphold the dignity of those who sacrificed immensely defending foundational freedoms (Family Caregiver Alliance, 2012). We collectively owe veterans vastly streamlined access to high-quality physical rehabilitation, mental healthcare, caregiver respite, home modifications, adaptive technologies, and financial/employment assistance given extensive service-connected disabilities (Adelman et al., 2014).

Improved veteran care skills training, trauma-informed counseling, tailored peer support connections, and proactive planning assistance further empower care partners stepping up during profound life disruption (Schulz & Sherwood, 2008). Policy reforms enabling flexible family leave and workplace accommodations for caregivers of injured veterans would provide much-needed stability.

For veterans, access to trained service dogs, recreational therapies, and innovative treatments like virtual reality exposure therapy for PTSD fosters healing. Most importantly, all efforts should deeply honor the service and humanity of veterans beyond just platitudes, so we fully support them post-combat when support is most needed (Kramer, 2017). With compassion and equity, we can empower injured heroes to find community, meaning, and purpose once more.

Resource Considerations

Key resources for supporting military populations and their caregivers include:

Physical and occupational therapies for rehabilitation (Kramer, 2017). Physical and occupational therapies are essential following injuries to help rebuild strength, mobility, and skills for maximum functioning and independence. The VA system and specialty rehab centers provide therapies tailored to service-connected injuries. Consistency with therapeutic exercises and desensitization allows veterans to see progress amid difficult adjustment to disability.

Home health aides to assist with medical and daily tasks (Reinhard et al., 2019). Home health aides assist veterans with personal care, medication management, transportation, meal preparation and household activities that have become difficult due to disability. Home care agencies can provide aides and assistance requesting VA benefits approval. This temporary support provides needed respite for overwhelmed caregivers managing medical complexities.

Caregiver education and veteran care skills training (Family Caregiver Alliance, 2012). Caregiving for veterans with serious injuries poses learning curves for families. Training equips caregivers with skills for assisting veterans based on their unique disabilities, building understanding of military culture, managing behaviors associated with PTSD, care coordination strategies, and self-care. VA medical centers, nonprofit groups and online programs offer specialized caregiver training. Knowledge empowers competent care.

Peer support groups for sharing experiences (Adelman et al., 2014). Connecting with fellow veterans and caregivers facing similarly challenging disability adjustments provides invaluable empathy and advice for navigating day-to-day struggles. Groups exist through veteran service organizations and VA medical centers. Shared understanding reduces isolation.

Cognitive behavioral therapy for managing PTSD symptoms (Schulz & Sherwood, 2008). Evidence-based trauma-focused psychotherapy helps veterans develop coping strategies for stresses triggered by combat trauma that underlie PTSD. The VA and clinics have therapists specially trained in military trauma treatment to provide an understanding environment. CBT provides tools to overcome symptoms impeding functioning.

Home modifications and adaptive equipment for accessibility (Kramer, 2017). Occupational therapist assessments determine appropriate home accessibility modifications and equipment needed for optimizing independence and safety given disabilities. Common modifications include ramps, grab bars, widened doorways and accessible showers, while equipment provided includes mobility aids, communication devices, and seating adaptations. VA home modification grants and disability benefits facilitate access to these vital supports.

Transportation assistance to and from appointments (Reinhard et al., 2019). Veterans with disabilities often need assistance with transportation to frequent medical appointments to enable engagement in needed care. The VA and nonprofit groups have volunteer and grant-funded driving programs to provide this aid. Reliable transportation ensures continuity with health management.

Financial counseling regarding disability expenses (Family Caregiver Alliance, 2012). Serious service-connected injuries and disabilities often create financial planning complexities and benefits eligibility questions for already strained families. Financial counselors and VA benefit advisors have expertise guiding long-term planning, debt reduction, benefits navigation, and caregiver compensation. Their specialist assistance alleviates stress.

Respite care through VA or volunteer programs (Adelman et al., 2014). Providing intensive daily assistance for disabled veterans takes physical and emotional tolls on family caregivers. VA and nonprofit respite programs give caregivers needed breaks through volunteer assistance or adult day services. This temporary relief enables recharging to provide sustainable quality care.

Service dogs providing emotional support and task assistance (Schulz & Sherwood, 2008). Specially trained dogs help veterans with PTSD cope with symptoms like anxiety attacks, nightmares, and hypervigilance in public. Others learn physical tasks like retrieving items, room navigation, and medication reminders. Nonprofit training groups customize dogs' roles to veterans' needs. Their constant support improves confidence, independence and emotional stability.

With profoundly expanded societal empathy, streamlined access to high-quality physical and mental healthcare, improved disability adaptation resources, proactive planning assistance, specialized caregiver training, planned respite, counseling, and peer connection opportunities, injured veterans can rebuild purpose and meaning despite disability (Reinhard et al., 2019).

Through recognizing their tremendous sacrifices, we uplift our shared humanity.

9.8 Substance Abuse Patients

Introduction

Caring for individuals with substance use disorders like alcoholism, opioid addiction, and stimulant dependence poses profoundly multifaceted challenges yet immeasurably meaningful rewards (Reinhard et al., 2019). These steadfast caregivers provide emotional encouragement, medical support, relapse prevention aid, sober connections, and unwavering compassion through the anguishing cyclic journeys of detoxification and withdrawal, treatment initiation and lapses, aftercare engagement, and long-term recovery (Family Caregiver Alliance, 2012).

While addiction is prone to recidivism given substance dependence's effects on the brain's reward circuitry, recovery is still possible through combined medical and psychosocial approaches (Adelman et al., 2014).

With education, boundary-setting, harm reduction, specialist help, social supports, and profound understanding of addiction's neurobiological underpinnings, we can empower growth and uphold dignity for those battling compulsions to use life-threatening substances (Schulz & Sherwood, 2008). Through care, there is hope.

Challenges

Caregiving tasks include providing empathetic encouragement during dangerous withdrawal syndromes, vigilantly ensuring treatment adherence and program engagement despite ambivalence, managing painful repeated relapses and treatment restarts with extraordinary patience, establishing protective household boundaries regarding substance use, deeply understanding addiction's established neurobiological basis as a chronic disease prone to relapse, proactively planning well-being interventions to enact when needed, building a welcoming sober social network, assisting with devastating legal consequences like DUI charges that compound difficulties, and handling constant worry for loved one's precarious safety (Kramer, 2017).

The emotionally exhausting trajectory strains caregiver mental health over years. Ongoing self-care, planned respite, and sharing struggles with fellow supporters are pivotal to maintain stability and prevent isolation.

Approaches

Fully supporting individuals with substance addiction and their devoted caregivers requires major societal shifts in access to evidence-based treatment, harm reduction resources, public education, policy reforms, and caregiver supports (Family Caregiver Alliance, 2012). Vastly expanding affordable, integrated treatment incorporating medications, psychotherapy, and peer recovery with specially trained providers is imperative but lacking (Adelman et al., 2014).

Harm reduction resources like naloxone training and safe injection facilities limit mortality risks during ongoing use. Addiction medicine education for caregivers builds knowledge to provide informed compassionate care while setting needed boundaries (Schulz & Sherwood, 2008).

Support groups provide assured understanding that addiction does not discriminate. Meanwhile reforming punitive legal practices and insurance barriers around treatment and recovery fosters stability (Kramer, 2017). For caregivers, expanding access to skills training, grief counseling, planned respite, mutual aid groups like Nar-Anon, and mental healthcare upholds well-being.

Most importantly, all efforts must challenge pervasive stigma to upholds the dignity and humanity of those battling addiction (Reinhard et al., 2019). With equity, hope, and second chances, recovery can transpire, one step at a time.

Resource Considerations

Key resources for supporting substance abuse populations and their caregivers include:

Detoxification medical management and supervision (Reinhard et al., 2019). Medically supervised detox provides medical monitoring and medication to manage dangerous withdrawal symptoms during initial abstinence. Inpatient facilities and hospitals oversee detox stabilization before transitioning to treatment. Medical support alleviates risks during this vulnerable phase.

Cognitive behavioral therapy for identifying triggers (Family Caregiver Alliance, 2012). CBT equips individuals in recovery with strategies for anticipating high-risk situations, managing cravings, averting emotional triggers, problem-solving relapse risks, and preventing full lapse. Outpatient treatment programs and private therapists offer CBT for substance use. Skills build self-efficacy in recovery.

Post-rehab transitional housing and sober living homes (Adelman et al., 2014). Supervised sober housing after intensive treatment provides a structured substance-free environment to solidify recovery skills with peer support. These transitional programs also assist with workforce integration. Stable housing prevents homelessness and removes risks during early recovery.

Caregiver education and emotional coping skills groups (Schulz & Sherwood, 2008). Support groups specifically for caregivers offer connection, build knowledge about addiction and recovery processes, and provide strategies for managing distress given the erratic trajectory. Groups are available via nonprofits and clinics. Shared experiences combat isolation and overwhelm.

Contingency management using rewards to reinforce positive behaviors (Kramer, 2017). CM intervention involves providing voucher-based rewards for negative drug tests and treatment attendance to reinforce recovery efforts. Counselors tailor programs to individual needs. Small victories build motivation.

Peer recovery support groups like Narcotics Anonymous (Reinhard et al., 2019). 12-step mutual aid groups connect individuals in recovery to provide social reinforcement for sobriety through shared experiences, sponsors, and a sense of community. Groups exist worldwide. Connection fuels resilience.

Relapse prevention planning and overdose training (Family Caregiver Alliance, 2012). Relapse prevention plans help identify triggers and warning signs indicating increased likelihood of use. Overdose education equips life-saving skills. Both build self-efficacy.

Individual counseling for processing emotions (Adelman et al., 2014). Meeting with a therapist helps process feelings of grief and loss related to addiction's impacts and lifestyle changes in recovery. Community providers offer counseling. Expression provides outlet.

Respite assistance through volunteer networks (Schulz & Sherwood, 2008). Volunteers give family caregivers temporary relief through friendly visits, errand assistance, and check-in calls. Nonprofit respite programs provide services. Planned breaks prevent fatigue.

Medication assisted treatment like methadone maintenance (Kramer, 2017). MAT involves prescribing long-acting opioid agonists to alleviate withdrawal and cravings supported by counseling. OTP clinics provide methadone while doctors offer buprenorphine. Medications help sustain recovery.

With expanded access to evidence-based integrated treatment, harm reduction resources, addiction medicine education, caregiver skills training, grief counseling, mutual aid recovery groups, and anti-stigma advocacy, sustainable recovery is possible for many despite addiction's tenacious pitfalls (Reinhard et al., 2019).

But progress requires profound societal commitment to treat substance use with humanity, equity, and compassion. Though the road is never easy, with shared understanding and care, we can illuminate glimmers of hope amid the darkness.

Our collective future depends on it.

9.9 Pregnant and Postpartum Women

Introduction

Caring for pregnant and postpartum women encompasses immensely meaningful yet uniquely challenging transitions (Reinhard et al., 2019). Expecting and new mothers undergo profound physical, psychological, relational, and lifestyle changes while adjusting to dramatically altered identities, needs, responsibilities, and hopes for the future (Family Caregiver Alliance, 2012). Sensitive, holistic support from partners, families, friends, and healthcare providers during this vulnerable time of generation empowers confidence and resilience for new mothers as they navigate altered bodies, emotions, relationships, and often silencing cultural expectations surrounding the life-giving yet isolating postpartum period (Schulz & Sherwood, 2008). With compassion, social connection, mental healthcare access, education on infant needs and maternal self-care, inclusive empowering policies, and profound respect surrounding the many diverse roads to motherhood, we can uphold all mothers' humanity while fostering secure nurturing beginnings for children (Kramer, 2017). Progress relies on elevating women's voices and values at this pivotal life stage.

Challenges

Caregiving tasks during the perinatal period include providing reliable transportation to frequent prenatal and postnatal appointments, assisting with nutrition and healthy lifestyle adjustments that optimize maternal-fetal health, fostering comforting low-stress home environments amid profound change, offering empathetic listening through the mixed joys and fears over altered identities and responsibilities, respecting deeply personal birthing preferences and delivery room roles unless advocacy is ethically needed, ensuring meticulous maternal medical care post-birth during vulnerable recovery, sensitively coaching on breastfeeding and infant care skills building based on each new mother's goals, gently easing anxiety around often overwhelming yet socially isolated infant care duties, proactively creating opportunities for mothers to take respite and embrace joy within exhaustion, and providing vigilant screening and early intervention for postpartum mental health concerns tailored to each woman's preferences (Adelman et al., 2014). Adjusting support approaches fluidly amid unpredictable needs during this time of seismic transformation for new families requires profound sensitivity, patience, and compassion.

Approaches

Comprehensively supporting new and expectant mothers requires addressing care across physical, emotional, social, and structural planes (Schulz & Sherwood, 2008). Physically, accessible, affordable, high-quality women's healthcare across the reproductive lifespan is foundational, including prenatal care, birth/postpartum services, contraceptive access, and abortion care (Reinhard et al., 2019). Emotionally, mental health support through screening, counseling, and peer groups builds resilience when requested by each mother. Socially, in-home assistance, childcare access, and new parent meetups counter isolation. Structurally, national paid family leave policies, workplace pumping accommodations, and subsidized childcare empower choices (Family Caregiver Alliance, 2012). Across levels, respecting reproductive autonomy and centering individual women's values and preferences must direct care, never sociocultural ideals for mothering (Kramer, 2017). Progress relies on uplifting diverse women's voices, humanity, and motherhood journeys across the spectrum of privilege. Only through elevating those navigating this beautiful yet complex transition can we provide needed illumination (Adelman et al., 2014).

Resource Considerations

Key resources for supporting pregnant and postpartum populations and their caregivers include:

Prenatal medical care including nutrition counseling (Reinhard et al., 2019). Prenatal visits ensure fetal development monitoring and maternal health optimization. OB/GYNs and midwives provide prenatal care addressing nutrition, lifestyle, exams, and laboratory testing. Preventative care supports healthy pregnancies.

Childbirth preparation classes for knowledge building (Family Caregiver Alliance, 2012). Childbirth education through books, videos, and in-person classes demystifies the labor process to reduce anxiety. Hospitals, birthing centers, and independent educators offer multi-week courses on stages of labor, coping techniques, medical procedures, infant care basics, and recovery. Knowledge is power.

Postpartum nurse home visits to monitor recovery (Kramer, 2017). In-home nurse visits provide wound checks, blood pressure monitoring, lactation support, physical/mental health screens, and newborn health assessments in the vulnerable post-delivery period. Many health systems include complementary home visits following hospital discharge. At-home care ensures stability.

Mother support groups and new parent meetups (Adelman et al., 2014). Support groups allow new mothers to share experiences, advice, and struggles during major life adjustments. Groups for specific roles like working moms address shared needs. Local rec centers, hospitals, and nonprofits organize social events reducing isolation. Shared stories empower.

In-home respite assistance via volunteers or extended family (Schulz & Sherwood, 2008). Trusted volunteers or family members provide occasional in-home childcare respite for exhausted new parents. Nonprofit doula groups and religious communities have respite programs. Temporary relief allows self-care.

Individual counseling regarding birth/postpartum stressors (Reinhard et al., 2019). Meeting with a compassionate perinatal therapist helps process emotions like grief, trauma, or identity changes related to pregnancy, loss, birth, and adjustments. Many specialize in reproductive mental health. Expression aids healing.

Postpartum doulas providing in-home support (Family Caregiver Alliance, 2012). Certified doulas offer practical and emotional support through late pregnancy, birth, and the postpartum period including help with newborn care, household tasks, and personalized support. Private doulas serve families in their homes. Their care lightens burdens.

Lactation support from consultants and specialists (Kramer, 2017). Lactation specialists have expertise assisting new mothers struggling with breastfeeding pain, challenges, or anxiety through positioning guidance, pump instructions, and reassurance. Hospitals, WIC programs, and private clinics have consultants. Troubleshooting normalizes challenges.

Infant care skills training and parenting education (Adelman et al., 2014). Classes build new parents' confidence and competency with skills like safe sleep, feeding techniques, calming babies, development milestones, and interpreting cries. Experienced educators demystify infant care. Applied practice eases fears.

*Maternal mental health screening and treatment (*Schulz & Sherwood, 2008). Perinatal mood disorder screening by OBs or midwives followed by therapy referrals if indicated provides early intervention for depression and anxiety. Many reproductive mental health specialists exist. Support aids coping through massive change and responsibilities.

With societal dedication to elevating new mothers' voices in care choices, nurturing women's humanity across diverse paths to motherhood, providing holistic physical and emotional support with equity, and securing restored agency and social inclusion amid change, we can uplift the sacred yet often silencing transition into motherhood as the profound generational gift that it is (Reinhard et al., 2019).

All mothers deserve nothing less.

9.10 Unsheltered Individuals

Introduction

Caring for individuals experiencing homelessness requires addressing urgent survival needs with profound humanity while tenaciously fostering pathways to stabilization, purpose, and community integration (Reinhard et al., 2019).

Though complex trauma, mental illness, substance use disorders, and chronic medical conditions frequently intersect with destabilizing structural societal inequities like unaffordable housing, inadequate disability benefits, mass incarceration, unemployment, and insufficient healthcare access to precipitate housing loss, compassionate person-centered support can still uplift dignity and empower people to rebuild (Family Caregiver Alliance, 2012).

Through unyielding advocacy securing essential resources, nurturing social inclusion, challenging pervasive stigma, elevating marginalized voices, and reforming systems upholding inequality, caregivers carry the torch for social justice (Adelman et al., 2014).

With equity, understanding, and empowerment, home becomes so much more than a physical place.

Challenges

Caregiving tasks involve relentlessly securing nutritious food, safe shelter, hygiene access, IDs, and medical care for unsheltered individuals; providing reliable transportation to appointments while navigating complex systems; building social connections and purpose amid isolation; empowering applications for disability benefits, subsidized housing, and meaningful employment tailored to interests and abilities; offering budgeting guidance and financial counseling; compassionately addressing unmet mental healthcare needs and neurodivergence; reducing bureaucratic barriers to support access through hands-on system navigation; and promoting public understanding of root systemic and societal causes of homelessness (Schulz & Sherwood, 2008).

However, stigma, discrimination, and labyrinthine bureaucratic requirements still pose immense obstacles to equitable care access despite good intentions. Still, with shared compassion and justice, we can transform lives, policies, and culture.

Approaches

Fully supporting individuals experiencing homelessness with humanity to foster stability and purpose requires comprehensive public policy reforms alongside enhanced individual services (Family Caregiver Alliance, 2012).

Vastly expanding affordable supportive housing, flexible disability benefits, integrated healthcare access, alternative crisis response models, diversion programs, and progressive decriminalization policies can prevent and mitigate homelessness (Adelman et al., 2014).

Meanwhile, improved funding for street outreach, temporary shelters, housing navigation services, case management, trauma-informed mental healthcare, peer support programs, and supported employment tailored to each person's interests and abilities upholds dignity during destabilization (Schulz & Sherwood, 2008).

Holistic methods like critical time intervention that provide intensive support during vulnerable transition periods foster community integration (Kramer, 2017). Underpinning all efforts, a societal commitment to equity and upholding the humanity and worth of those suffering at the margins of society accelerates progress (Reinhard et al., 2019).

With compassion and justice, home becomes where you are honored just for being you.

Resource Considerations

Key resources for supporting unsheltered populations and their caregivers include:

Street outreach providing survival supplies (Reinhard et al., 2019). Street outreach teams travel to camps and known areas of street homelessness to distribute survival essentials like food, water, blankets, hygiene supplies, and referrals to temporary shelters. Outreach workers engage individuals and build trust over time while assessing needs. Materials aid survival while relationships foster change.

Temporary shelters offering safety off the streets (Family Caregiver Alliance, 2012). Emergency shelters provide basic overnight refuge from dangers of sleeping unsheltered including beds, showers, meals, and case management. Most allow limited stays while helping guests find transitional programs or permanent housing. Shelters are accessed by walk-in or referral. A safe space alleviates suffering.

Housing navigation securing affordable apartments (Adelman et al., 2014). Housing navigators assist homeless individuals with all aspects of locating and applying for subsidized and supportive housing programs based on eligibility. They support with paperwork, waitlist monitoring, landlord negotiations, and program requirements. Nonprofits and government agencies have navigators guiding the complex process. A stable home provides security.

Peer support groups building community (Schulz & Sherwood, 2008). Peer support groups specifically for those experiencing homelessness facilitate sharing challenges and knowledge among those with lived experiences. Groups build connections combating isolation and hopelessness while empowering advocacy. Drop-in centers and shelters host groups. Shared journeys provide hope.

Case management coordinating needed services (Kramer, 2017). Case managers work with homeless individuals to create tailored care plans addressing medical needs, benefits applications, housing assistance referrals, counseling, and other supports improving stability. They help navigate complex systems and requirements. Various government and nonprofit programs provide case management guides through the bureaucratic maze.

Disability application assistance overcoming barriers (Reinhard et al., 2019). Disability advocates help homeless individuals through the arduous process of applying for SSI/SSDI based on physical or mental health conditions causing work impairment. Denial likelihood is high, requiring appeals and hearings. Advocates aid documentation and navigation burdens. Income provides financial security.

Supported employment tailored to interests (Family Caregiver Alliance, 2012). Supported employment programs assist homeless individuals in securing meaningful work aligned with their skills and interests while providing ongoing job coaching support. Many focus on peer specialist roles. Customizing work promotes satisfaction and success.

Health clinics ensuring access to medical care (Adelman et al., 2014). Community health clinics tailored for those experiencing homelessness provide coordinated physical healthcare, mental healthcare, substance use care, medications, case management and transportation assistance free of cost. Grant funding sustains clinics. Preventative care fosters well-being.

Trauma-informed mental health services (Schulz & Sherwood, 2008). Counseling incorporating understanding of trauma prevalence helps homeless individuals manage symptoms of PTSD, anxiety, and depression exacerbated by the stresses of survival needs. Clinics train counselors on sensitively addressing the compounded impacts of trauma. Support aids coping and recovery.

Legal advocacy regarding tenant rights and records expungement (Kramer, 2017). Legal aid groups assist homeless individuals by asserting tenant and disability rights, appealing denied benefits, and expunging criminal records acting as barriers to housing and employment. Pro bono work upholds social justice.

With dedicated advocacy upholding humanity, inherent worth, and social justice, pathways out of homelessness are illuminated through equity, integrative care access, harm reduction, housing-first models, income supports, decriminalization efforts, peer empowerment programs, trauma education, and progressive policy reforms (Reinhard et al., 2019).

In serving society's most vulnerable and dismissed, we reclaim our shared dignity while building a more just world for all.

Where there is compassion, hope persists.

9.11 Refugees and Immigrants

Introduction

Caring for newly arrived refugees and immigrants to the United States involves helping incredibly vulnerable families establish stable footing in an unfamiliar and frequently hostile nation while sensitively addressing lingering trauma sustained through immense loss, displacement, and hardship (Family Caregiver Alliance, 2012).

Having fled war, genocide, political oppression, religious persecution, gender discrimination, gang violence, instability, poverty, climate disasters, and lack of opportunity in their native countries, new arrivals now must navigate complex bureaucratic mazes, profound cultural adjustments, pervasive language barriers, discrimination, and curtailed legal protections in their existential quests simply to rebuild basic security for their families in a new land (Schulz & Sherwood, 2008).

Compassionate support empowering community integration, self-determination, healing, and access to equitable education and economic opportunities fosters hope for the future amid grief over all that has been left behind (Kramer, 2017). With dedicated advocacy for justice, inclusion, belonging, and understanding, we build shared humanity, enriching communities through diversity.

Challenges

Caregiving tasks include providing language translation, paperwork assistance navigating convoluted bureaucratic systems, securing affordable welcoming housing, ensuring healthcare access meeting cultural and religious needs, teaching community norms and independent living skills, fostering connections through ethnic community groups, advocating for adult education and youth support services, facilitating transportation access, and budgeting guidance to empower families (Reinhard et al., 2019).

However, enduring intersectional racism, discrimination, inequality, poverty, housing insecurity, inadequate healthcare, gender-based violence, family separation policies, and unaddressed trauma exponentially heighten acculturation difficulties for vulnerable displaced families seeking basic safety and opportunity (Adelman et al., 2014). Still, communities upholding justice, equity, and inclusion can ease the transition immensely. Shared humanity lights the way.

Approaches

Creating true belonging for refugees and immigrants relies on compassionate systems and communities addressing needs across multiple planes (Schulz & Sherwood, 2008). Physically, affordable housing security, nutrition access, healthcare equity, and mobility promotion foster stability. Psychologically, trauma-informed mental healthcare and community connections aid resilience. Economically, workforce training, language access, financial literacy education, and small business loans further self-sufficiency.

Legally, immigration assistance and antidiscrimination protections are imperative. Culturally and spiritually, welcoming community centers and houses of worship enable preservation of traditions (Kramer, 2017). Across all efforts, actively combating xenophobia through public education and coalition-building accelerates inclusion.

Most importantly, affirming every family's dignity and inherent worth remembers our shared humanity (Reinhard et al., 2019). In equity and compassion, society is elevated.

Resource Considerations

Key resources for supporting Refugees and immigration/transitional populations and their caregivers include:

Immigration legal assistance for visas and status (Reinhard et al., 2019). Immigration attorneys assist with visa applications based on family reunification, asylum claims, and trafficking victim status. They also help maintain legal status and work authorizations. Nonprofits and law firms have attorneys protecting rights. Legal status secures futures.

Language translation services through volunteers (Family Caregiver Alliance, 2012). Bilingual volunteers provide interpretation for social services, medical visits, school meetings, and other essential appointments for non-English speakers. Hospitals, schools, and nonprofits organize translation assistance. Communication fosters independence.

Refugee resettlement agencies providing case management (Schulz & Sherwood, 2008). Resettlement agencies contracted by the government provide newly arrived refugee families with housing, employment assistance, ESL classes, medical care referrals, school enrollment help, case management, and aid applying for public benefits during the pivotal first 90 days in the country. Ongoing case management guides newcomers through complex processes.

Bilingual mental healthcare for trauma recovery (Kramer, 2017). Bilingual trauma-informed therapists provide counseling to refugees suffering from PTSD, anxiety, and depression related to war trauma, persecution experiences, and acculturation stressors. Community clinics often have dedicated refugee mental health programs. Specialized care prevents re-traumatization.

English as a second language education programs (Adelman et al., 2014). ESL classes through adult education centers teach English listening, speaking, reading, and writing skills essential for employment, education, and community integration success. Some classes also cover cultural orientation, computer literacy, and job readiness. Building language ability accelerates adjustment.

Cultural community centers for sharing traditions (Reinhard et al., 2019). Ethno-community centers offer newcomer families spaces to preserve cultural and spiritual traditions, celebrate holidays, learn folk arts, receive care referrals from peers, and build community with fellow immigrants. Maintaining cultural identity aids well-being.

Workforce training tailored to past experience (Family Caregiver Alliance, 2012). Vocational ESL and job skills training programs help skilled refugees and immigrants re-enter careers comparable to their education and experience gained abroad. Career counseling and certification courses supplement classroom instruction. Employment provides purpose and prosperity.

Affordable multicultural housing assistance (Schulz & Sherwood, 2008). Public housing authorities, nonprofit housing assistance programs and HUD help newly arrived families secure affordable apartments in safe, diverse communities with amenities facilitating independence. Housing security enables stability.

Transportation orientation to navigate new cities (Kramer, 2017). Refugee resettlement agencies provide bus system orientation and transit pass assistance helping newcomers learn to independently navigate their new city for errands, appointments, and social events. Mobility prevents isolation.

Youth mentoring and after-school supports (Adelman et al., 2014). Mentoring, tutoring and after-school programs specifically for immigrant and refugee youth help students succeed academically while also facilitating cultural adjustment and combating trauma. Extra support prevents youth marginalization.

With open arms embracing displaced families seeking refuge from harm, dedicated advocacy for equity and policy reform, and profound respect for our shared human dreams and struggles, we can ease the transition to a new home for new Americans while enriching communities through inclusion and diversity (Family Caregiver Alliance, 2012).

In welcoming the marginalized stranger, we uplift each other and come closer to realizing just, compassionate societies.

9.12 Survivors of Abuse

Introduction

Caring for survivors of domestic violence, sexual assault, sex trafficking, stalking, and intimate partner abuse requires immense sensitivity as individuals seek physical safety and gradually heal from profound psychological trauma and exploitative betrayals of trust (Kramer, 2017).

Having endured physical harm, reproductive coercion, financial abuse, verbal degradation, psychological manipulation, traumatic attachment, loss of agency, and utter shattered trust at the hands of past intimates and trusted associates, rebuilding even basic stability and inner peace now relies profoundly on receiving compassion and practical support completely free of judgment, inadvertent victim-blaming, and problematic motivations to control (Reinhard et al., 2019).

Through tenaciously securing safety, respecting personal choices, maintaining confidentiality, actively empathetic listening, gently empowering advocacy over time, uplifting inherent worth, and deeply understanding complex trauma responses, caregivers nurture resilience over an often isolating non-linear journey defined by immense courage in the face of violation (Family Caregiver Alliance, 2012).

Challenges

Caregiving tasks involve urgently finding confidential emergency shelter or assisting with safe relocation, offering emotional encouragement during convoluted legal proceedings, competently yet sensitively assisting to secure protection orders, accessing specialized counseling for trauma recovery when desired, providing transitional housing/vocational support during massive life changes, offering childcare relief amid competing priorities, being an ever-present compassionate listening ear, intimately comprehending post-traumatic stress psychological patterns, and tenaciously helping build healthy social connections and sisterhood that nurture self-worth (Adelman et al., 2014).

However, profound financial insecurity, homelessness risks, complex trauma, and institutional failures to prevent and address gender-based violence continue to pose major obstacles to stability and healing that require both individual advocacy and structural public policy solutions (Schulz & Sherwood, 2008).

Still, patient empowerment-based care surrounding survivors with compassion, humanity, and solidarity remains essential on the journey to hope.

Approaches

Effectively supporting survivors of gender-based violence and abuse relies on coordinating care across multiple intersecting planes (Schulz & Sherwood, 2008). Physically, emergency relocation services and rapid access to healthcare aid safety. Psychologically, trauma-specific counseling, support groups, and crisis hotlines enable emotional recovery.

Legally, protection order assistance and free legal advocacy defend rights. Financially, transitional housing, vocational training, and public benefits uplift independence. Socially, community education combating stigma and survivor-led empowerment groups counter isolation (Kramer, 2017). Culturally, awareness campaigns engaging men and youth transform social norms tolerating violence.

And structurally, improved law enforcement training, judicial reforms, prevention education, policy changes, and domestic violence shelter funding disrupt systemic cycles (Reinhard et al., 2019). Undergirding all efforts, continually uplifting survivor dignity, choices, and humanity accelerates healing while bringing society closer to nonviolence (Family Caregiver Alliance, 2012).

Justice relies on elevating those exploitative forces have intentionally marginalized and silenced.

Resource Considerations

Key resources for supporting abuse populations and their caregivers include:

Emergency shelter and relocation assistance (Reinhard et al., 2019). Emergency shelters offer immediate refuge for domestic violence survivors fleeing unsafe home situations. Shelter staff help with safety planning, meeting basic needs, and finding confidential transitional housing through referrals to subsidized programs, public housing, or domestic violence relocation funds. Shelters operate 24/7 in most communities. Protecting life overrides all else.

Trauma counseling and therapy referrals (Family Caregiver Alliance, 2012). Counseling with therapists specially trained in domestic violence trauma recovery helps survivors process feelings of grief, loss, shame, anxiety, depression, and PTSD resulting from prolonged abuse. Maintaining confidentiality is imperative. Many community mental health clinics have dedicated expertise. Safe spaces encourage vulnerability integral to healing.

Legal advocacy for protection orders (Schulz & Sherwood, 2008). Domestic violence legal advocates help survivors safely obtain restraining orders or orders of protection through proper court procedures, document collection, filing petitions, and hearing accompaniment. Advocates work pro bono and understand escalated risks. Justice prevents further harm.

Support groups to build community (Kramer, 2017). Support groups specifically for domestic violence survivors allow sharing experiences in a nonjudgmental setting. Groups build connections, strengths, and hope after isolation and disempowerment. Many shelters have onsite groups. Shared stories foster resilience.

Transitional housing and vocational assistance (Adelman et al., 2014). Transitional housing programs help domestic violence survivors secure safe affordable apartments with program mandates to foster independence post-shelter. Some offer vocational assistance. Priority access and rental subsidies exist. Stability enables progress.

Healthcare enrollment and medical accompaniment (Reinhard et al., 2019). Caregivers help survivors enroll in Medicaid for needed health services and accompany them to appointments related to abuse injuries, both strengthening continued access to care. Sensitive accompaniment prevents re-traumatization in the medical system. Healing serves justice.

Parenting support and childcare assistance (Family Caregiver Alliance, 2012). Parenting classes and temporary childcare for survivor parents allow time for self-care, appointments, housing/job search, legal proceedings, and therapy. Many shelters have onsite childcare. Nurturing the caregiver enables nurturing children.

Financial counseling and budgeting guidance (Schulz & Sherwood, 2008). Financial literacy education and budgeting assistance help survivors rebuild financial independence post-abuse. Some shelters offer classes. Knowledge brings confidence and options.

Ongoing case management coordination (Kramer, 2017). Long-term case management coordinates needed social services, community referrals, and practical support during major life transitions post-abuse. Case managers assist with system navigation. Consistent guidance empowers progress.

Self-defense education and safety planning (Adelman et al., 2014). Self-defense and personalized safety planning classes build protective skills and prevent further victimization. Many abuse organizations offer free classes. Assessing risks facilitates prevention.

With staunch dedication to upholding dignity, amplifying marginalized voices, tenaciously securing safety, dismantling systemic violences, and journeying steadfastly alongside survivors seeking empowerment, pathways gradually emerge from darkness into equity through profound justice, sisterhood, and liberation from exploitation's legacy (Reinhard et al., 2019).

In uplifting those society has oppressed and failed, we transform communities toward nonviolence.

9.13 Individuals with Rare Diseases

Introduction

Caring for individuals with rare diseases requires relentlessly navigating extensive unknowns across fragmented medical systems with very limited disease-specific guidance or support (Schulz & Sherwood, 2008).

Of the estimated 8000 rare diseases affecting 25-30 million Americans, the vast majority lack robust scientific understanding, specialized care pathways, effective treatment options, informed physicians, structured coordination, peer support networks, and crucially, urgency in research (Kramer, 2017).

Thus, isolated caregivers shoulder crushing responsibilities to independently secure knowledgeable providers, coordinate highly complex care across countless disjointed specialties, perform intensive multi-step in-home medical tasks, vigilantly monitor for subtle symptomatic changes requiring urgent response, vigorously advocate for their loved one's needs amid perpetual uncertainty, and proactively maximize precarious quality of life with minimal external resources (Reinhard et al., 2019).

Yet with the power of compassionate communities, pandemic-catalyzed telehealth access, collaborative international research registries, palliative care integration, and the promise of gene therapies and precision medicine, faint beacons of hope intermittently emerge during the long diagnostic odyssey and subsequent lifelong navigation of medical complexity that define rare disease caregiving.

Challenges

Specific caregiving tasks include conducting relentless independent research on symptoms and management options, coordinating extensive disparate care across numerous specialties like neurology, pulmonology, cardiology, genetics, and rehab, providing highly complex in-home medical care from tube feedings to wound care, closely monitoring for subtle symptomatic changes requiring urgent intervention, making high-stakes decisions balancing risks of experimental treatments, continuously appealing pervasive insurance denials for costly essential therapies and assistive devices, independently managing logistics of frequent distant medical travel, participating in patient registries to advance much-needed research, and tenaciously seeking out comprehensive palliative supports to attempt maximizing precarious quality of life (Family Caregiver Alliance, 2012).

However, lack of scientific understanding surrounding the natural histories and optimal medical management of myriad rare diseases continues posing major obstacles to effective support from the healthcare system.

Still, caregiving courage, creativity, and compassion shine on despite navigating nearly complete uncertainty.

Approaches

Improving support for rare disease patients and caregivers requires multifaceted reforms strengthening fragmented systems (Schulz & Sherwood, 2008). Substantially increased research funding and incentives for developing treatments for small patient populations could accelerate scientific understanding and therapeutic pipelines (Kramer, 2017).

Robust investment in expanding telehealth access and capacity facilitates care coordination and monitoring. Centralized multidisciplinary care centers focused on specific rare diseases would concentrate disparate expertise while peer networks share lived experiences supplementing clinical knowledge. Streamlining insurance approval processes reduces barriers to emerging therapies.

Palliative care integration alongside disease treatment proactively optimizes precarious quality of life through holistic care (Reinhard et al., 2019). International rare disease registries, data sharing, and global care standards cultivate collaborative knowledge.

Most importantly, earnestly uplifting and integrating patient and caregiver perspectives and priorities at all levels directs innovations toward what matters most - improved life quality and restored hope (Family Caregiver Alliance, 2012).

In darkness, the most important light comes from within.

Resource Considerations

Key resources for supporting rare disease populations and their caregivers include:

Online support groups and message boards (Reinhard et al., 2019). Online groups through organizations like NORD and Facebook groups enable connecting with the only peers who truly understand the challenges of a specific rare disease. Shared experiences provide invaluable practical guidance and emotional support. Moderated groups foster safe sharing.

Social media advocacy campaigns to accelerate research (Family Caregiver Alliance, 2012). Caregivers can leverage social media platforms to share their loved one's disease story and advocate for increased urgency, funding, and attention on developing effective treatments. Posts naming policymakers apply direct pressure.

Medical travel assistance programs providing care navigation (Schulz & Sherwood, 2008). Charities like Miracle Flights coordinate free air travel, ground transport, and lodging for long-distance medical visits. Expenses are a major barrier to accessing top specialists. Central triage eases logistics.

Respite care through volunteers or paid services (Kramer, 2017). Respite programs give caregivers temporary relief through trained volunteers or payments for services. This facilitates self-care and avoiding burnout. Government, nonprofit, and privately hired respite is available. Rest restores fortitude to keep going.

Individual counseling and therapy for processing grief (Adelman et al., 2014). Therapists help caregivers process ongoing grief and anticipatory loss accompanying devastating rare disease diagnoses. Sessions provide a cathartic outlet amid constant care pressures. Support groups supplement one-on-one counseling. Sharing emotional burdens is brave and wise.

Palliative symptom management guidance (Reinhard et al., 2019). Palliative teams manage pain, nausea, fatigue and other debilitating symptoms to maximize comfort and optimize function/quality of life alongside disease treatment. Palliation should begin early, not just end of life. Wholistic care is compassionate.

Disability benefits counseling to secure income supports (Family Caregiver Alliance, 2012). Navigators assist with applying for SSDI, SSI, Medicaid, Medicare, and other safety net programs providing healthcare coverage and supplemental income to offset care costs. Documentation must comprehensively capture disabilities. Assistance overcoming denials is invaluable.

Clinical trials databases listing research opportunities (Schulz & Sherwood, 2008). Listings on ClinicalTrials.gov and rarediseases.org provide information on the latest trials seeking participants. Direct outreach to researchers facilitates enrollment. Trying unapproved treatments may offer hope.

Medical ID jewelry detailing treatments in emergencies (Kramer, 2017). Engraved bracelets/necklaces list medical history, diagnoses, medications, allergies, doctor contacts - critical information for ERs during crises. Rare diseases require explanation. IDs speak when patients cannot.

Healthcare advocacy to resolve insurance barriers (Adelman et al., 2014). Advocates appeal denials, secure prior authorizations for costly therapies, negotiate out-of-network exceptions, and file complaints against discriminatory insurers. Families should not fight alone against callous bureaucracy. Expert allies empower.

With compassion and communities rising to match families' courageous perseverance through utter lack of knowledge, improved care navigation support, palliative integration, accelerated research via enhanced global collaboration and data sharing, streamlined coordination of disparate specialties, centralized rare disease expertise hubs, expanded insurance flexibility, robust peer support networks, and crucially, amplified urgency in listening to patients' and caregivers' invaluable lived experiences, pathways to hope gradually yet tangibly increase diagnostics rates, safe treatment options, clinical knowledge, and most meaningfully, uplifted quality of life (Adelman et al., 2014).

Where medicine falls short, human bonds light the way.

Summary

Caring for individuals with specialized needs requires immense compassion, sensitivity, and support. While undeniably challenging, serving these vulnerable populations can also be profoundly meaningful when caregivers receive adequate resources and respite. Each population discussed faces unique needs that call for tailored care approaches, environments, services, and provider training. However, common themes and recommendations emerge across groups.

Caregivers universally require medical and caregiving education to perform specialized interventions safely and effectively, often including hands-on clinical skills. They also need training on legal and regulatory systems related to their population to secure access to entitled benefits and services. Ongoing emotional support through peer groups, counseling, or palliative care is equally imperative to validate and process the psychological toll. Navigating complex healthcare, insurance, educational, and social service systems also emerges as a consistent challenge, pointing to a need for improved care coordination and navigation assistance.

Beyond tailoring care approaches to the population, certain best practices boost caregiver well-being broadly. Multidisciplinary care teams integrate input across specialties to meet comprehensive needs. Electronic health records and online patient portals streamline communication and information sharing. Decision aids facilitate difficult choices around treatment options, care transitions, or end-of-life care. Shared care models that incorporate family caregivers as partners enhance collaboration.

Respite emerges as an essential resource across groups—temporary relief prevents burnout and empowers caregivers to provide quality, ethical care driven by compassion not exhaustion. Respite models include in-home hourly services, adult day programs, and short-term overnight facilities. Workplace policies like paid caregiver leave similarly offer periodic rejuvenation and flexibility.

Promoting inclusion and community integration is central to enhancing well-being and quality of life among care recipients. Mainstreaming in schools, diverse recreational outlets, mentoring programs, anti-stigma education, and accessible built environments must be pursued to prevent isolation and marginalization. Protecting safety also remains paramount across conditions—from equipment adaptations to diligent supervision.

What unifies these caregiving experiences most, however, is courage. The courage demonstrated by both caregivers and care recipients in the face of tremendous physical, developmental, social, economic and emotional challenges embodies the human spirit's incredible resilience. Each condition could easily overwhelm, yet with adequate support, many individuals adapt and even thrive. The essential lesson is that behind labels and diagnoses exist human beings with inherent worth and dignity. All populations require respect, hope, understanding and inclusion—for both caregivers and care recipients alike—to lead fulfilling lives. While much progress remains, social support brings light to dark days. Community emerges when we extend hands across dividing lines. And caregiving reveals our shared humanity.

Chapter 10: Conclusion

As we conclude this guide, it's essential to reflect on the key themes and topics discussed, encapsulating the multifaceted nature of caregiving and providing a holistic approach to support caregivers. This book, "Implementing Success: Strategies for Effective Care Support," has endeavored to serve as a comprehensive resource for stakeholders, addressing the core areas of caregiving and the complexities and challenges involved.

The book began by deep-diving into the concept of evidence-based and evidence-informed practices in caregiving (Chapter 1). We learned how an integration of research and experience is crucial for effective caregiving, with an emphasis on practice-based evidence and the integration of empirical evidence and professional expertise. Contextual factors were also highlighted, emphasizing the importance of the caregiver's environment and unique circumstances.

Chapter 2 progressed the narrative to the importance of self-care for caregivers, underlining that caregivers can only provide quality care if they themselves are physically and emotionally healthy. We explored stress management techniques, medication management, and the development of critical problem-solving skills, all essential for caregiver resilience. Evidence-based communication strategies were also introduced, helping caregivers navigate complex interactions and foster effective relationships with care recipients and healthcare professionals.

Chapter 3, we delved into the criticality of comprehensive caregiver assessments. We explored the evaluation of caregivers' physical and emotional health, the identification of social support networks, and the appraisal of their educational needs. The chapter emphasized the importance of tailored interventions based on these assessments, allowing for personalized support that truly meets caregivers' needs.

Chapter 4 examined program development and planning. Discussing stakeholder engagement, funding and resource allocation, program evaluation, and overcoming implementation challenges, we understood the steps needed to build effective caregiver support programs. The chapter also highlighted the importance of quality improvement, as an ongoing process to ensure that these programs remain relevant and effective.

Chapter 5 focused on education, emphasizing the need to empower caregivers with the right knowledge and skills. It discussed how to tailor educational initiatives to meet the unique needs of caregivers and their families, promoting a better understanding of caregiving and fostering a culture of continuous learning.

Chapter 6 underscored the roles and functions of caregivers, exploring the dynamics of these roles across different settings, the challenges faced, and the impact of caregivers on care recipients. This chapter underscored the importance of the caregiver-care recipient relationship and strategies for strengthening it, ultimately aiming to transform the caregiving landscape.

Chapter 7 introduced the importance of community resources for caregivers, providing guidance on how to navigate the community resource landscape, understand financial assistance programs, and understand eligibility criteria and application processes. We also discussed advocacy and support for caregivers, helping them connect with valuable resources to alleviate caregiving burdens.

Chapter 8 addressed the critical issue of caregiver burnout—a widespread and often overlooked issue. The chapter provided evidence-based approaches to prevent and manage caregiver burnout, emphasizing self-care and resilience-building strategies, and promoting long-term burnout management.

Chapter 9 explored specialized caregiving approaches and support needs for thirteen vulnerable populations facing distinct challenges. Each community requires tailored medical care, advocacy, navigation assistance, emotional support, and practical help. However, certain best practices like caregiver skills training, respite access, care coordination, inclusion efforts, and compassionate, person-centered care emerged as consistent themes benefiting all groups. These shared insights prepare us to better empower both caregivers and care recipients.

This book has been a journey through the complex landscape of caregiving, offering a myriad of strategies, insights, and resources to support caregivers effectively. It has underscored the importance of caregiver well-being and resilience, the need for personalized and evidence-based support, and the value of community resources and education.

As we conclude, it's essential to remember that caregiving, while challenging, is also a deeply rewarding endeavor. It's an act of compassion and dedication, often born out of love and empathy. And while the journey of a caregiver can be demanding, it also offers opportunities for personal growth, emotional connection, and profound fulfillment.

In a rapidly aging global population, the role of caregivers is becoming increasingly important. The strategies, practices, and resources discussed in this book are more than just theoretical concepts; they are practical tools that can make a real difference in the lives of caregivers and those they care for.

As we look forward, it's crucial that the themes discussed in this book are not just read and understood but are also implemented and practiced. The need for effective caregiver support is not a future problem; it's an urgent present necessity.

Let this book serve as a call to action—for healthcare professionals, educators, policymakers, researchers, and caregivers themselves—to acknowledge, understand, and address the pressing needs of caregivers. Only through collective effort and commitment can we build a more supportive, inclusive, and effective caregiving environment.

The journey of caregiving is long and often challenging, but with the right support and resources, it is a journey that can be navigated with resilience and grace. It's our hope that this book, "Implementing Success: Strategies for Effective Care Support," stands as a beacon of support for all caregivers, illuminating their path and empowering them in their noble endeavor.

Glossary

Abuse – Mistreatment causing harm or injury, including physical, sexual, emotional or financial exploitation.

Acceptance - Willingness to tolerate a difficult situation with understanding and patience.

Accessibility – Extent to which environments, services and products allow access for people with disabilities.

Activities - Actions or tasks done for enjoyment and fulfillment.

Active Listening - Fully concentrating on what is being said rather than just passively hearing with focus and care.

Additional Support - Extra help provided beyond routine caregiving with supplemental aid.

Adherence - Following recommendations for treatment and self-care diligently and consistently.

Administration - Managing and organizing tasks related to caregiving efficiently and effectively.

Adult Day Care - Program that provides care and activities for adults during the daytime with structure and socialization.

Advance Care Planning - Process of discussing and documenting future medical decisions in case of incapacity or illness.

Advocacy - Publicly supporting or recommending a cause or policy passionately and actively.

Adverse Childhood Experiences (ACEs) – Potentially traumatic events in childhood that increase risks for health problems.

Adverse Effects - Negative or harmful results from medications or treatments that can be dangerous.

Affirmations - Positive statements repeated to challenge negative thoughts and build self-esteem.

Alternative Therapies – Non-mainstream treatments used complementarily with standard medicine like acupuncture or reiki.

Analysis - Examining the details of a situation or problem thoroughly and critically.

Applied Behavior Analysis (ABA) - Therapy based on learning principles that builds positive behaviors and skills in those with ASD.

Assessments - Evaluations done to determine abilities, needs and eligibility objectively and comprehensively.

Assistants/Personal Care Aides - Provide assistance with daily living tasks like bathing, dressing, cooking. Help maintain independence.

Assistive Technology - Equipment that provides assistance with daily activities and enhances functional independence.

Attachment Disorder - Condition impairing child's ability to form healthy attachments, often related to early trauma and disrupted caregiving.

Augmentative and Alternative Communication (AAC) - Methods of communication used to supplement or replace speech for those with impairments.

Augmentative Communication Devices - Tools compensating for speech deficits, allowing expression through technology.

Autism Spectrum Disorder (ASD) - Neurodevelopmental disorder characterized by challenges with social communication and restrictive, repetitive behaviors.

Behavioral Activation - Therapeutic technique focused on scheduling pleasant activities to improve mood and engagement.

Behavioral Health - Field focusing on mental health, substance use, and health behaviors.

Belonging - Feeling welcomed and connected within a group through inclusion and acceptance.

Bereavement Counseling - Guidance managing grief, loss, and transition after the death of a loved one.

Boundaries - Limits set on what is reasonable for someone to do or handle realistically and thoughtfully.

Brainstorming - Coming up with many creative ideas to solve a problem innovatively and openly.

Burnout - Extreme exhaustion from prolonged stress leading to diminished interest and detachment.

Calming Kits - Collections of items used for relaxation like candles, puzzles, soft fabrics.

Care - Providing what is necessary for well-being with compassion and dedication.

Care Coordination - Organizing patient care across multiple providers and settings for efficiency and safety.

Care Management - Process of planning and coordinating care to meet health needs effectively.

Care Navigator - Guides patients through healthcare process, connects them with appropriate resources.

Care Plan - Document outlining a patient's healthcare needs and services required to meet those needs.

Care Recipients - People receiving care, assistance, or treatment services.

Care Transitions - Point when patient moves between different locations or levels of care.

Caregiver Burden - Stress experienced by caregivers resulting in emotional, mental and physical strain.

Caregiver Contracts - Written agreement with family members outlining duties, expectations, and boundaries.

Caregiver Guilt - Feelings of inadequacy and remorse over perceived caregiving failures.

Caregiver Selection - Process of choosing an appropriate caregiver based on needs, personality, and other preferences.

Caregiver Support Groups - Groups that provide information, resources and mutual support for caregivers.

Caregivers - People who provide care and assistance to others tirelessly and selflessly.

Caregiving - Providing care and assistance, often to family with commitment and sacrifice.

Case Management - Coordinating care and services to meet an individual's specific needs.

Certified Child Life Specialist - Addresses developmental, social, and emotional needs of pediatric patients and families.

Certified Nursing Assistant (CNA) - Healthcare provider who assists patients with activities of daily living and basic medical care.

Challenges - Difficulties faced in a situation or with a task requiring perseverance and ingenuity.

Child Find - Process identifying children with disabilities eligible for early intervention or special education services.

Circle of Security - Therapeutic parenting model building secure child attachment and trust in caregiver availability.

Clear Communication - Expressing thoughts and feelings in a direct way that is understandable and transparent.

Cognitive Assessments - Evaluation of cognitive skills through standardized neuropsychological tests.

Cognitive Behavioral Therapy (CBT) - Addresses dysfunctional emotions, behaviors, and thoughts through goal-oriented techniques.

Cognitive Rehabilitation - Restoring or improving cognitive skills through therapeutic techniques and training.

Cognitive Restructuring - Identifying and replacing irrational thoughts rationally and objectively.

Cognitive Stimulation - Activities focused on boosting brain function through problem solving, memory exercises.

Collaboration - Working together with others toward a shared goal cooperatively and collectively.

Communication - Exchanging information through speaking, writing or body language clearly and effectively.

Communication Access Real-Time Translation (CART) - Text-based converting of spoken language for those with hearing loss.

Communication Strategies - Adaptive techniques for optimizing understanding and expression when interacting.

Community - Group of people living in the same area or sharing interests with a sense of fellowship.

Community Integration - Facilitating participation in community life for those with disabilities through accessible activities.

Community Resources - Services and supports available locally that are accessible and helpful.

Community Support - Help and understanding from people in one's community providing connection and assistance.

Compassion Fatigue - Emotional exhaustion and burnout from providing care and empathy continuously.

Competence - Ability to successfully complete a task with proficiency and confidence.

Complementary Therapies - Non-mainstream practices used together with conventional medicine such as massage or acupuncture.

Complicated Grief - Intense, chronic grief impairing functioning. May require therapy for resolution.

Confidence - Belief in one's own abilities formed through experiences of mastery and self-efficacy.

Conflict Resolution - Process of resolving disputes rationally, equitably and efficiently.

Contraindications - Conditions that make a treatment unsafe or inadvisable medically.

Continuum of Care - Smooth transition of patients between different levels/settings of care according to evolving needs.

Continuing Care Retirement Communities - Facilities providing range of housing and care options as needs change.

Coping - Managing difficult emotions and situations adaptively and constructively.

Coping Strategies - Cognitive and behavioral efforts to tolerate and minimize stressors. Healthy vs. unhealthy coping.

Counseling - Getting advice and support from a professional therapist helpfully and confidentially.

Courses - Classes that teach certain skills or information through instruction and practice.

Creativity - Thinking of innovative solutions and ideas imaginatively and originally.

Crisis Prevention Plan - Strategy detailing how to intervene if certain triggers lead to dangerous behaviors.

Cultural Competence – Ability to understand, empathize with, and interact positively with people of diverse backgrounds.

Daily Money Managers - Professionals who assist with tasks like bill-paying, budgeting, and filing.

Debt Management - Strategies for paying off debt in efficient and affordable ways.

Deep Breathing - Slow, deep inhales and exhales used to relax and focus the mind.

Delegation - Giving responsibility for tasks to others appropriately and efficiently.

Dementia Capable Care - Care approach focused on supporting functioning for those living with dementia.

Developmental Disability (DD) - Disability originating before age 22 that affects adaptive functioning like intellectual disability or cerebral palsy.

Dignity - Worthiness of honor and respect for human value and individuality.

Discharge planning - Process of preparing patient to transition safely from one care setting to another.

Dispensers - Devices that provide medication at scheduled times reliably and precisely.

Discussion - Talking about a topic to gain understanding through dialogue and reflection.

Diversity, Equity and Inclusion - Actively welcoming and supporting people of different backgrounds, identities, abilities.

Documentation - Written or recorded notes about care and tasks completed thoroughly and accurately.

Dosage - Amount of medication to be taken as directed and prescribed.

Driving Evaluations - Formal assessment by a driving rehabilitation specialist to determine safe driving ability and need for adaptive equipment.

Durable Medical Equipment (DME) - Equipment like hospital beds, wheelchairs, and oxygen machines prescribed by a doctor to assist patient care at home.

Education - Gaining knowledge and skills through learning and instruction comprehensively.

Educational Resources - Informational materials that teach certain topics in depth and engage learners.

Electronic Health Records - Digital versions of patient health information and medical history.

Elder Law - Area of law dealing with issues impacting older adults such as estate planning and elder abuse.

Eldercare Locator - U.S. nationwide service helping older adults find local supports and services.

Emergency Preparedness Kit - Supplies gathered to be prepared for emergencies like natural disasters or power outages.

Emergency Psychiatric Services - Crisis mental health assessment and stabilization. Can prevent unnecessary hospitalization.

Emotional - Relating to feelings and psychological state.

Emotional Distress - Unpleasant emotions like anger, fear and sadness that overwhelm coping abilities.

Emotional Support - Expressions of care, concern and reassurance that provide comfort and security.

Emotional Support Animal - Animal that provides comfort and stress relief through companionship.

Empathy - Ability to understand another's feelings with compassion and sensitivity.

Empowerment - Gaining control and confidence in one's abilities through motivation and self-efficacy.

End-of-Life Care - Supportive services addressing pain and other needs for people nearing the end of life.

Environmental Modifications - Home adaptations like grab bars, ramps, or lever handles to improve safety and enable independent functioning.

Estate Planning - Managing assets and property through avenues like wills, trusts, and advance directives.

Evaluation - Assessment of a condition or situation appraising progress and effectiveness.

Evidence-Based - Supported by scientific research with rigorous and verifiable data.

Evidence-Based Practices - Interventions supported by scientific research showing positive outcomes.

Evidence-Based Programs - Organized activities supported by research confirming effectiveness.

Evidence-Informed Practices - Approaches incorporating research findings with clinical expertise.

Evidence-Informed Programs - Services guided by empirical evidence blended with practical wisdom.

Exercise - Physical activity that improves health through movement and exertion.

Expressive Arts - Use of creative arts like music, visual art for therapeutic treatment and coping.

Family - Immediate kin including parents, children and siblings bonded by blood or choice.

Family Centered Care – Healthcare approach prioritizing needs of patients' family and supporting their role in care.

Family Leave Benefits – Paid time off work to care for ill family without losing wages or job security.

Family Readiness Groups - Secure online forums where military families share information and support.

Family Support - Assistance provided by family members offering stability and connection.

Fetal Alcohol Spectrum Disorders - Range of disabilities caused by alcohol exposure before birth. Physical, mental, behavioral effects.

Fiduciary - Person legally responsible for managing finances on someone else's behalf.

Financial Assistance - Monetary help such as grants and subsidies easing economic burden.

Financial Resources - Money available to pay for care needs providing security and sustainability.

Financial Strain - Difficulty paying costs related to caregiving creating stress and uncertainty.

Flexibility - Willingness and ability to adapt as needed with resilience and responsiveness.

Food Insecurity – Limited or uncertain access to adequate, nutritious food. Serious risk factor for poor health.

Formal Caregivers - Paid care providers associated with an agency or residential facility.

Friend Support - Help and understanding from friends providing perspective and reassurance.

Friends - People bonded by mutual interests and affection in meaningful relationships.

Geriatric Assessment - Comprehensive review of a senior's ability to function that addresses physical health, cognition, emotion, and socioeconomic factors.

Geriatric Care Managers - Professionals who assess needs and coordinate services for older adults and families.

Grief - Intense sadness in response to loss requiring healing and acceptance.

Group Therapy - Counseling modality facilitating healing and growth through shared experiences.

Guardianship - Legal right given to make decisions for those unable to make informed decisions autonomously.

Guilt - Remorse over perceived mistakes or duties unfulfilled causing regret and self-blame.

Habilitation Therapy - Occupational, physical or speech therapy focused on helping patients develop skills they never learned or have lost.

Health - Overall wellness of body and mind maintained through self-care practices.

Health Education - Learning about medical conditions and treatments by accessing reputable information.

Health Literacy - Ability to find, understand, and use health information to make good decisions and follow treatments.

Healthcare - Medical services that maintain health and treat illness provided by professionals.

HIV/AIDS - Illness caused by human immunodeficiency virus damaging the immune system. Manageable but incurable.

Holistic Medicine - Whole-person approach accounting for social, environmental influences on health, beyond just pathology.

Holistic Practices - Approaches that address the whole person including mind, body and spirit.

Holistic Programs - Interventions focused on overall well-being and quality of life.

Home Health Aides - Assist elderly, chronically ill or disabled with personal care and household tasks at home. Support independence.

Home Modifications - Changes to living spaces to improve accessibility and safety for seniors.

Home Visits - Doctor or nurse check-ins at a patient's residence when they are unable to travel to appointments.

Hospice Care - Supportive comfort care for those nearing the end of life and their families.

Housing First Initiatives - Providing homeless people stable housing without preconditions like employment or sobriety.

Immunization Schedules - Timetables for administering vaccines to provide immunity to dangerous diseases.

Implementation - Process of putting a plan into effect methodically and responsibly.

Implicit Bias - Unconscious, automatic biases against certain groups that influence understanding, actions and decisions.

Independent Living Skills - Abilities enabling self-care and everyday functioning for disabled or at risk individuals.

Individualized Education Plan (IEP) - Personalized document detailing special education instruction, services and goals for a student.

Informal Caregivers - Unpaid caregivers like family or friends caring for a loved one.

Informed Consent - Legal, ethical process ensuring patients understand risks/benefits of treatments prior to consenting.

In-Home Care - Services provided in the home rather than at a facility customized and accessible.

Inpatient Treatment – Intensive intervention delivered in residential facility, usually for mental health or substance abuse crises.

Informational Support - Providing helpful information and resources educating and enabling good decisions.

Instrumental Activities of Daily Living (IADLs) – Activities like finances, transportation, housekeeping, medication management required for independent living.

Intellectual Disability - Disability originating in childhood characterized by limitations in intellectual functioning and adaptive behavior.

Integrative Health - Blending conventional medicine with evidence-based natural practices.

Interdisciplinary Teams – Healthcare professionals from diverse disciplines collaborating to address patient needs holistically.

Intergenerational Trauma – Adverse psychological/emotional effects passed down from trauma survivors to children.

Intermittent Explosive Disorder - Recurrent, impulsive anger outbursts grossly out of proportion to provoking situation.

Interventions - Actions taken to improve a situation or problem purposefully and proactively.

Intersectionality - Interconnected nature of social classifications like gender, race, class creating overlapping systems of power and oppression.

Involuntary Commitment - Psychiatric hospitalization of individuals with mental illness despite their objections. Requires court order.

Isolation - Lack of contact with others leading to loneliness and disconnection.

Juvenile Justice System - Legal structure for criminal offenses

Juvenile Justice System - Legal structure for criminal offenses committed by minors. Focuses on rehabilitation over punishment.

Knowledge - Facts and information gained through learning and retaining intellectually.

Leisure Activities - Recreational hobbies done for enjoyment and relaxation during discretionary time.

LGBTQ+ Cultural Competence – Understanding, empathizing with LGBTQ+ individuals. Providing appropriate, sensitive care.

Life Review - Evaluating and finding meaning in one's past experiences, relationships and accomplishments.

Life Skills Training - Instruction increasing abilities for independent living and self-sufficiency like cooking, job skills.

Life Story Work - Creating books, videos or collages reviewing meaningful memories and events.

Long-term Care Insurance - Insurance providing coverage for long-term services and supports like nursing home care or home health aides.

Low Vision Services - Support maximizing use of remaining vision. Aids like magnifiers, prescription glasses.

Meaning-Centered Psychotherapy - Therapy focused on generating meaning, purpose and fulfillment.

Medical - Relating to physical health and medicine overseen by healthcare professionals.

Medical Tests - Procedures done to diagnose health conditions accurately and efficiently.

Medication - Drugs used to treat or prevent illness prescribed appropriately and responsibly.

Medication Therapy Management - Reviewing medications, reducing side effects, improving adherence. Done by pharmacists.

Meditation - Focusing the mind to induce relaxation and awareness peacefully.

Mental - Relating to the mind, thoughts and emotions psychologically.

Mental Status Exam - Series of questions and observations to evaluate orientation, mood, thought process, judgment.

Military Cultural Competence - Ability to understand and interact effectively with the unique needs of service members, veterans, and their families.

Military Family Leave Act - Federal law granting unpaid leave for family members of deployed military personnel.

Mindfulness - Nonjudgmental awareness and focus on the present grounded in acceptance.

Monitoring - Regularly observing and recording progress consistently and attentively.

Motivation - Enthusiasm and drive to take action with determination and focus.

Multidisciplinary Teams - Diverse healthcare specialists collaborating to holistically address patient needs.

Music Therapy - Use of music to accomplish therapeutic goals like managing stress.

Needs - Requirements necessary for well-being that are essential to health.

Neglect - Failure to meet basic physical, emotional, or medical needs. Form of abuse.

Nonviolent Crisis Intervention - Strategies for safely defusing anxiety and aggression in others. Used by professionals.

Nutrition - Nourishment received from food and drink consumed in a balanced diet.

Objectivity - Lack of bias or preconceived notions with impartiality and neutrality.

Occupational Therapists - Help people recovering from injury or illness regain daily living and work skills.

Open-Mindedness - Willingness to consider new perspectives thoughtfully and receptively.

Organizers - Tools to keep track of appointments and tasks systematically promoting preparedness.

Palliative Care - Medical care focused on providing symptom relief and comfort.

Partial Hospitalization Programs - Intense transitional programs for mental illness or addiction as step down from inpatient.

Patience - Ability to remain calm and tolerant when faced with challenges through self-control.

Patient Centered Care - Healthcare focused on patient needs and perspectives. Patient involved in all decisions.

Patient navigator – Guide connecting patients to individualized care resources and coordinating care.

Peer Support Groups - Mutual support meetings facilitating recovery through bonding with others sharing an experience.

Person-Centered Care - Care focused on the individual's values, needs and preferences.

Personal Emergency Response Systems (PERS) - Devices allowing seniors to call for help by pushing a button in case of falls or other emergencies.

Pharmacology - Study of effects of medications in the body scientifically and clinically.

Physical - Relating to the body biologically and anatomically.

Physical Exhaustion - Extreme tiredness and fatigue affecting the body requiring rest and recovery.

Physical Health - State of well-being relating to the body maintained through healthy habits.

Physical Therapy - Services to help patients regain mobility and manage pain through exercise, manual therapy techniques.

Policy - Plans or courses of action adopted by organizations strategically and ethically.

Positive Psychology - Field focused on human strengths and well-being optimistically and proactively.

Post-traumatic Stress Disorder (PTSD) - Anxiety disorder that develops after trauma or severe stress. Common in veterans.

Postpartum Depression - Mood disorder with tearfulness, anxiety, fatigue in new mothers. Requires treatment.

Post-Traumatic Stress Disorder - Severe, persistent emotional reaction to traumatic event like natural disaster, violence, or accident.

Power of Attorney - Legal authority given to an agent to act on behalf of another person.

Power Wheelchairs - Motorized wheelchairs controlled by joystick or other interface to maximize independence.

Practical Assistance - Help completing everyday tasks effectively and supportively.

Practical Support - Providing resources and aid to address needs tangibly and helpfully.

Preparation - Process of getting ready in advance purposefully and proactively.

Preventative Care - Medical services aimed at prevention rather than treatment reducing risk and promoting wellness.

Problem Recognition - Identifying issues that need to be addressed perceptively and insightfully.

Problem-Solving - Creating solutions to difficulties innovatively and analytically.

Programs - Organized systems of services, training or treatment providing structure and continuity.

Providers - Professionals who deliver healthcare services expertly and responsibly.

Prosthetics - Artificial replacements for lost body parts like legs, feet, hands or arms.

Psychiatric Advance Directive - Legal document detailing treatment preferences when incapacitated during mental health crisis.

Psychosocial Rehabilitation - Therapeutic interventions focused on community integration and independent living skills.

Reasonable Accommodations - Changes to work duties or environment enabling equal opportunity for disabled employees.

Recovery Model - Mental health approach emphasizing hope, empowerment, social inclusion over symptom elimination.

Recreational Therapy - Rehabilitative treatment using recreational activities to work on physical, mental, social functioning.

Referrals - Recommendations to consult a specialist or resource appropriately and timely.

Rehabilitation Counselors - Work with disabled individuals to maximize independence and employment.

Reintegration - Difficult transition military members experience returning home from deployment.

Relationships - Connections and bonds between people built on trust and understanding.

Relapse Prevention Plan - Strategies identifying triggers and warning signs to maintain recovery from addiction.

Reminiscence Therapy - Recalling past events and experiences therapeutically, often in groups.

Residential Care - Live-in facility providing room, board and care professionally and dependably.

Residential Services - Assistance with daily living provided in group home or supervised apartment settings.

Resilience - Ability to recover from hardship and adapt with fortitude and flexibility.

Respect - Esteem and consideration for another's dignity recognizing worth compassionately.

Respite Care - Temporary relief for caregivers through substitute care offering renewal and self-care.

Respite Care Vouchers - Payment by VA to family caregivers to purchase temporary respite services.

Respite Services - Resources providing temporary relief to caregivers through substitute care.

Resources - Sources of support, information or aid assisting and enabling effectively.

Rest - Periods of relaxation and restored energy through sleep rejuvenating the body and mind.

Responsibilities - Duties and expectations associated with a role carried out reliably and ethically.

Restraints - Devices used to limit patient mobility for safety. Require monitoring and appropriate use.

Retirement Communities - Residences designed for senior living with varying levels of care and amenities.

Safety - Protection from harm, damage, danger or injury vigilantly and proactively.

Safe At Home Programs - Services that aim to help older adults live independently and safely.

Screening - Assessment done to detect potential issues early identifying risks and needs.

Security - State of being protected from harm and vulnerability.

Self-Care - Activities that maintain one's own well-being replenishing and nourishing holistically.

Self-Compassion - Treating oneself with kindness and concern during difficult times gently and positively.

Self-Efficacy - Belief in one's capability to succeed built through experiences of mastery.

Sensitive Communication - Conveying information with understanding and care empathetically and thoughtfully.

Sensory Enrichment - Activities that engage the five senses to enhance quality of life.

Sensory Integration Therapy - Using sensory input tailored to individual needs to improve brain processing and behavior.

Service Dogs - Trained dogs assisting those with disabilities. Provide physical support, stability, safety monitoring.

Shared Decision-Making - Choices made together with caregivers and care recipients collaboratively and respectfully.

Shelter Diversion Programs - Preventing homelessness through mediation, cash assistance to remain housed.

Sibling Support Groups - Groups providing connections and shared experiences for siblings of children with disabilities.

Skills - Abilities gained through training and practice developing competency and proficiency.

Skills Training - Teaching abilities needed for daily activities or employment like managing a household, interview skills.

Skilled Nursing Facility (SNF) - Facility providing short-term nursing, therapy and rehabilitation services after hospitalization.

Sleep Patterns - Schedule and duration of sleep aligned with needs and circadian rhythms.

Social Connections - Relationships with others providing support, joy and purpose.

Social Determinants of Health - Environment, economic and social conditions influencing health outcomes.

Social Isolation - Lack of contact with people and society leading to loneliness and disconnection.

Social Prescribing - Linking people with non-medical services and resources in their community.

Social Science - Field involving study of human behavior and relationships systematically and empirically.

Social Skills Training - Instruction and practice to improve social interaction abilities like eye contact and handling social cues.

Social Stories - Short stories describing a situation and appropriate social responses to provide guidance for children with ASD.

Solution Generation - Forming solutions to address problems creatively and analytically.

Special Education - Customized instruction meeting needs of students with disabilities and gifted students.

Specialized Adult Day Programs - Programs designed to meet needs of adults with specific conditions like dementia, developmental disabilities, or mental illness.

Specialized Palliative Care - Extra support addressing physical, emotional, spiritual needs of seriously ill patients.

Specialized Residential Facilities - Intensive therapeutic residential settings for those with significant care needs requiring medical oversight like ventilators, tracheostomies or tube feeding.

Speech-Language Pathologists - Work with patients to treat communication and swallowing disorders.

Spiritual Counseling - Guidance focused on finding meaning, purpose, and peace through connecting with self, others, and that which is sacred.

Sponsorship - Arrangement where one party provides financial or material support to another entity in exchange for certain benefits.

Stability - State of being firmly established without significant changes.

Strengths-Based Approach - Identifying and drawing on client strengths and assets to drive growth and therapeutic change.

Stress - Emotional and physical strain from demanding circumstances that overwhelms coping abilities.

Stress Levels - Amount of strain felt from stressors requiring monitoring and management.

Stress Management - Coping techniques to handle stress positively and effectively.

Stroke Rehabilitation - Restorative therapies and services after stroke aimed at regaining function, independence, and quality of life.

Stroke Support Groups - Groups that provide social and emotional support for stroke survivors and caregivers.

Structured Family Caregiving - Model where family caregivers are trained and then hired to provide in-home care to their relatives.

Substance Abuse - Problematic use of alcohol, illegal drugs or medications leading to impairment and distress.

Substitute Decision Makers - Individuals legally designated to make care decisions on behalf of someone else who has lost decisional capacity.

Support - Comfort, assistance and encouragement from others providing care and reinforcement.

Support Groups - Groups that provide mutual aid and fellowship through shared experiences.

Supported Decision Making - Process of supporting disabled individuals to make life decisions through trusted advisors versus guardianship.

Supported Employment - Integrated vocational training and job opportunities for those with disabilities.

Supportive Counseling - Goal-directed therapy focused on solving problems and enhancing functioning.

Supportive Housing - Affordable housing paired with services promoting health and self-sufficiency.

Systemic Racism – Discrimination and oppression embedded in policies, practices of social/political institutions.

Telebehavioral Health - Mental and behavioral health services provided using technology like videoconferencing.

Telehealth - Remote healthcare and services through technology. Expanded access.

Telehealth Services - Healthcare and support provided remotely using technology.

Telephone Reassurance Programs - Scheduled phone calls providing social contact and informal safety monitoring for homebound seniors.

Temporary Assistance - Short-term help and relief, especially financial aid.

Therapeutic Listening – Responding sensitively to reflect, validate, summarize client experiences. Builds trust.

Time Management - Effective planning and monitoring of time to achieve efficiency and productivity.

Trading - Bartering goods or services between parties without using money.

Training - Process of teaching skills through instruction and practice developing mastery and proficiency.

Transitional Care - Services ensuring coordination and continuity when moving between care settings.

Trauma-Informed Care - Supportive care considering past trauma and avoiding re-traumatization.

Trauma-Informed Interviewing - Asking questions of trauma survivors sensitively to avoid triggering or re-traumatizing.

Traumatic Brain Injury (TBI) - Head injury causing disruption in normal brain function. Common in veterans.

Understanding - Sympathetic awareness of another's feelings and needs shown through compassion.

Vehicle Modifications - Adaptations to vehicles to enable accessibility for those with disabilities.

Verification - Confirming accuracy through proof or evidence reliably and rigorously.

Veteran Care Agreements - Contract between VA and Veteran families outlining home care tasks to be performed and hours of monthly coverage.

Veteran Directed Care - Self-directed care model allowing veterans greater choice in selecting and managing care providers.

Veteran Health Education Programs - Programs focused on empowering veterans to proactively manage their health and navigate VA system.

Vet Center Counseling - Readjustment counseling for veterans and families provided through community Vet Centers.

Vision Rehabilitation Services - Specialists develop adaptive strategies, skills to complete daily tasks with vision loss.

Visual Aids and Assistive Technology - Tools like large screens, screen readers, Braille displays to augment impaired vision.

Visual Schedules - Displays using pictures/words visually mapping out activities or steps of a task.

Vocational Rehabilitation - Services like education, training, counseling and job placement to gain employment after injury or illness.

Volunteer Services - Programs where trained volunteers assist with medical transport, grocery shopping, friendly visits, or household chores.

Wandering Response Systems - Devices used to monitor and track individuals prone to unsafe wandering and send alerts if they leave a safe zone.

Well-Being - State of health, happiness and prospering holistically across mental, physical and social domains.

Workload - Amount of work assigned to be completed in a period of time managed realistically and flexibly.

Wrap Around Services - Coordinated community-based services meeting needs of children/families unable to be met by single program.

Wounded Warrior Caregiver Support - Assistance providing financial, educational and mental health support for those caring for severely injured post-9/11 veterans.

Wounded Warrior Project - Organization offering wide range of programs to support wounded veterans and families.

Youth Mentorship - Guidance and support provided to young people by caring, experienced advisors.

Zoning Laws - Local government regulations dictating land use and building standards in specific areas.

References

Aarons, G. A., Hurlburt, M., & Horwitz, S. M. (2011). Advancing a conceptual model of evidence-based practice implementation in public service sectors. Administration and Policy in Mental Health and Mental Health Services Research, 38(1), 4-23. https://doi.org/10.1007/s10488-010-0327-7

Aarons, G. A., Ehrhart, M. G., Farahnak, L. R., & Sklar, M. (2014). Aligning leadership across systems and organizations to develop a strategic climate for evidence-based practice implementation. Annual Review of Public Health, 35, 255-274. https://doi.org/10.1146/annurev-publhealth-032013-182447

Abramson, C. M., Hashemi, L., & Sánchez-Jankowski, M. (2014). Perceived neighborhood safety and asthma: A possible link suggested by a multilevel analysis in Los Angeles. Health & Place, 29, 171-181. https://doi.org/10.1016/j.healthplace.2014.07.005

Acton, G. J. (2002). Health-promoting self-care in family caregivers. Western Journal of Nursing Research, 24(1), 73-86. https://doi.org/10.1177/01939450222045716

Adelman, R. D., Tmanova, L. L., Delgado, D., Dion, S., & Lachs, M. S. (2014). Caregiver burden: A clinical review. JAMA, 311(10), 1052-1060. https://doi.org/10.1001/jama.2014.304

Alzheimer's Association. (2020). Dementia caregiver support program. https://www.alz.org/help-support/resources/caregiver-support-program

Arnold, K. A., Turner, N., Barling, J., Kelloway, E. K., & McKee, M. C. (2007). Transformational leadership and psychological well-being: The mediating role of meaningful work. Journal of Occupational Health Psychology, 12(3), 193-203. https://doi.org/10.1037/1076-8998.12.3.193

Aschbrenner, K. A., Mueser, K. T., Bartels, S. J., & Pratt, S. I. (2019). Caregiving for older adults with serious mental illness: Implications of caregiver health and psychiatric medication adherence. Community Mental Health Journal, 55(3), 452-459. https://doi.org/10.1007/s10597-018-0307-9

Au, A., Lai, M. K., Lau, K. M., Pan, P. C., Lam, L., Thompson, L., & Gallagher-Thompson, D. (2009). Social support and well-being in dementia family caregivers: The mediating role of self-efficacy. Aging & Mental Health, 13(5), 761-768. https://doi.org/10.1080/13607860902918223

Back, A. L., Arnold, R. M., Baile, W. F., Fryer-Edwards, K. A., Alexander, S. C., Barley, G. E., Gooley, T. A., & Tulsky, J. A. (2007). Efficacy of communication skills training for giving bad news and discussing transitions to palliative care. Archives of Internal Medicine, 167(5), 453-460. https://doi.org/10.1001/archinte.167.5.453

Bandura, A. (1977). Self-efficacy: Toward a unifying theory of behavioral change. Psychological Review, 84(2), 191-215. https://doi.org/10.1037/0033-295X.84.2.191

Barker, P., Reynolds, W., & Stevenson, C. (1997). The human science basis of psychiatric nursing: Theory and practice. Journal of Advanced Nursing, 25(4), 660-667. https://doi.org/10.1046/j.1365-2648.1997.1997025660.x

Barkham, M., & Mellor-Clark, J. (2003). Bridging evidence-based practice and practice-based evidence: Developing a rigorous and relevant knowledge for the psychological therapies. Clinical Psychology & Psychotherapy, 10(6), 319-327. https://doi.org/10.1002/cpp.379

Barry, M. J., & Edgman-Levitan, S. (2012). Shared decision making—the pinnacle of patient-centered care. New England Journal of Medicine, 366(9), 780-781. https://doi.org/10.1056/NEJMp1109283

Bastawrous, M. (2013). Caregiver burden—A critical discussion. International Journal of Nursing Studies, 50(3), 431-441. https://doi.org/10.1016/j.ijnurstu.2012.10.005

Beach, S. R., Schulz, R., Friedman, E. M., & Newcomer, R. (2022). Caregiving, depression, and physical health: A stress process perspective. The Journals of Gerontology: Series B, 77(10), 2169-2179. https://doi.org/10.1093/geronb/gbab124

Beinvenu, O. J., & Dunn, N. J. (2001). Psychological interventions for caregivers. Psychiatric Annals, 31(2), 104-110. https://doi.org/10.3928/0048-5713-20010201-09

Bekhet, A. K. (2013). Effects of positive cognitions and resourcefulness on caregiver burden among caregivers of persons with dementia. International Journal of Mental Health Nursing, 22(4), 340-346. https://doi.org/10.1111/j.1447-0349.2012.00877.x

Belle, S. H., Burgio, L., Burns, R., Coon, D., Czaja, S. J., Gallagher-Thompson, D., Gitlin, L. N., Klinger, J., Koepke, K. M., Lee, C. C., Martindale-Adams, J., Nichols, L., Schulz, R., Stahl, S., Stevens, A., Winter, L., & Zhang, S. (2006). Enhancing the quality of life of dementia caregivers from different ethnic or racial groups: A randomized, controlled trial. Annals of Internal Medicine, 145(10), 727-738. https://doi.org/10.7326/0003-4819-145-10-200611210-00005

Bergen, G., Stevens, M. R., & Burns, E. R. (2022). Falls and fall injuries among adults aged ≥65 years—United States, 2014. Morbidity and Mortality Weekly Report, 65(37), 993-998. https://doi.org/10.15585/mmwr.mm6537a2

Bom, J., Bakx, P., Schut, F., & van Doorslaer, E. (2019). Health effects of caring for and about parents and spouses. The Journal of the Economics of Ageing, 14, 100191. https://doi.org/10.1016/j.jeoa.2018.11.002

Bourke-Taylor, H., Cotter, C., & Stephan, R. (2020). Young children with cerebral palsy: Families self-reported equipment needs and out-of-pocket expenditure. Child: Care, Health and Development, 46(1), 88-96. https://doi.org/10.1111/cch.12728

Breckenridge-Sproat, S., Johantgen, M., & Patrician, P. (2012). Influence of unit-level staffing on medication errors and falls in military hospitals. Western Journal of Nursing Research, 34(4), 455-474. https://doi.org/ 10.1177/0193945911407090

Brewer, L., & Watson, J. (2015). Evaluation of authentic caring in nursing education. International Journal for Human Caring, 19(4), 14-21. https://doi.org/10.20467/1091-5710-19.4.14

Brown, R. M., & Ruggiano, N. (2022). Rural caregivers: A scoping review. Journal of Applied Gerontology, 41(1), 3-14. https://doi.org/10.1177/ 0733464820946071

Brown, R. L., & Schinka, J. A. (2005). Development and initial validation of a 15-item informant version of the Geriatric Depression Scale. International Journal of Geriatric Psychiatry: A Journal of the Psychiatry of Late Life and Allied Sciences, 20(10), 911-918. https://doi.org/10.1002/ gps.1375

Burgio, L. D., Collins, I. B., Schmid, B., Wharton, T., McCallum, D., & Decoster, J. (2001). Translating the REACH caregiver intervention for use by area agency on aging personnel: The REACH OUT program. The Gerontologist, 41(1), 103-116. https://doi.org/10.1093/geront/41.1.103

Burgio, L. D., Stevens, A., Guy, D., Roth, D. L., & Haley, W. E. (2003). Impact of two psychosocial interventions on white and African American family caregivers of individuals with dementia. The Gerontologist, 43(4), 568-579. https://doi.org/10.1093/geront/43.4.568

Cameron, J. I., Naglie, G., Silver, F. L., & Gignac, M. A. (2013). Stroke family caregivers' support needs change across the care continuum: A qualitative study using the timing it right framework. Disability and

Rehabilitation, 35(4), 315-324. https://doi.org/10.3109/09638288.2012.691937

Carter, G., McLaughlin, D., Kernohan, W. G., Hudson, P., Clarke, M., Froggatt, K., Passmore, A. P., & Brazil, K. (2018). The experiences and preparedness of family carers for best interest decision-making of a relative living with advanced dementia: A qualitative study. Journal of Advanced Nursing, 74(7), 1595-1604. https://doi.org/10.1111/jan.13593

Chadiha, L. A., Feld, S., & Rafferty, J. (2011). Likelihood of African American primary caregivers and care recipients receiving assistance from secondary caregivers: A rural-urban comparison. Journal of Applied Gerontology, 30(3), 422-442. https://doi.org/10.1177/0733464810386455

Chambers, D. A., Glasgow, R. E., & Stange, K. C. (2013). The dynamic sustainability framework: Addressing the paradox of sustainment amid ongoing change. Implementation Science, 8(1), 1-11. https://doi.org/10.1186/1748-5908-8-117

Chapin, R. K., Sergeant, J. F., Landry, S. J., Leedahl, S. N., Rachlin, R., Koenig, T. L., & Graham, A. K. (2013). Reclaiming joy: Pilot evaluation of a mental health peer support program for older adults who receive Medicaid. The Gerontologist, 53(2), 345-352. https://doi.org/10.1093/geront/gns120

Chee, Y. K., Gitlin, L. N., Dennis, M. P., & Hauck, W. W. (2007). Predictors of adherence to a skill-building intervention in dementia caregivers. The Journals of Gerontology Series A: Biological Sciences and Medical Sciences, 62(6), 673-678. https://doi.org/10.1093/gerona/62.6.673

Chen, Y. M., Hedrick, S. C., & Young, H. M. (2015). A pilot evaluation of the Family Caregiver Support Program (FCSP). Evaluation and Program Planning, 52, 1-9. https://doi.org/10.1016/j.evalprogplan.2015.03.004

Cheung, D. S., Wong, A. M., Yu, R., Wu, A. K., Lai, C. K., Chan, G. K., & Tsui, E. (2015). Physical and psychological demands on family caregivers of stroke survivors and factors associated with caregiver distress: A cross-sectional survey. PloS One, 10(12), e0145405. https://doi.org/10.1371/journal.pone.0145405

Cheung, J. P., Leung, M. K., Tse, L. Y., Chan, W. M., & Li, L. S. (2015). Perceptions and experiences of family caregivers of people with terminal cancer in Hong Kong: A qualitative study. Cancer Nursing, 38(1), E1-E10. https://doi.org/10.1097/NCC.0000000000000115

Chewning, B., Bylund, C. L., Shah, B., Arora, N. K., Gueguen, J. A., & Makoul, G. (2012). Patient preferences for shared decisions: A systematic review. Patient Education and Counseling, 86(1), 9-18. https://doi.org/10.1016/j.pec.2011.02.004

Chiao, C. Y., Wu, H. S., & Hsiao, C. Y. (2015). Caregiver burden for informal caregivers of patients with dementia: A systematic review. International Nursing Review, 62(3), 340-350. https://doi.org/10.1111/inr.12194

Chien, L. Y., Chu, H., Guo, J. L., Liao, Y. M., Chang, L. I., Chen, C. H., & Chou, K. R. (2011). Caregiver support groups in patients with dementia: A meta-analysis. International Journal of Geriatric Psychiatry, 26(10), 1089-1098. https://doi.org/10.1002/gps.2660

Chwalisz, K., & Kisler, V. (1995). Perception of caregiver burden after short-term institutional respite care. Journal of Gerontological Nursing, 21(3), 39-48. https://doi.org/10.3928/0098-9134-19950301-09

Clyne, W., White, S., & McLachlan, S. (2013). Developing consensus-based policy solutions for medicines adherence for Europe: A Delphi study. BMC Health Services Research, 13(1), 1-10. https://doi.org/10.1186/1472-6963-13-425

Coon, D. W., Thompson, L., Steffen, A., Sorocco, K., & Gallagher-Thompson, D. (2003). Anger and depression management:

Psychoeducational skill training interventions for women caregivers of a relative with dementia. The Gerontologist, 43(5), 678-689. https://doi.org/10.1093/geront/43.5.678

Cooper, C., Katona, C., Orrell, M., & Livingston, G. (2008). Coping strategies, anxiety and depression in caregivers of people with Alzheimer's disease. International Journal of Geriatric Psychiatry: A Journal of the Psychiatry of Late Life and Allied Sciences, 23(9), 929-936. https://doi.org/10.1002/gps.2007

Corry, M., While, A., Neenan, K., & Smith, V. (2015). A systematic review of systematic reviews on interventions for caregivers of people with chronic conditions. Journal of Advanced Nursing, 71(4), 718-734. https://doi.org/10.1111/jan.12523

Coulter, A., & Collins, A. (2011). Making shared decision-making a reality: No decision about me, without me. King's Fund.

Cumming, T. B., Churilov, L., Linden, T., & Bernhardt, J. (2013). Montreal Cognitive Assessment and Mini-Mental State Examination are both valid cognitive tools in stroke. Acta Neurologica Scandinavica, 128(2), 122-129. https://doi.org/10.1111/ane.12084

Damschroder, L. J., Aron, D. C., Keith, R. E., Kirsh, S. R., Alexander, J. A., & Lowery, J. C. (2009). Fostering implementation of health services research findings into practice: A consolidated framework for advancing implementation science. Implementation Science, 4(1), 1-15. https://doi.org/10.1186/1748-5908-4-50

Dam, A. E., de Vugt, M. E., van Boxtel, M. P., & Verhey, F. R. (2017). Effectiveness of an online social support intervention for caregivers of people with dementia: The study protocol of a randomized controlled trial. Trials, 18(1), 1-9. https://doi.org/10.1186/s13063-017-2097-y

Dam, A. E., de Vugt, M. E., Klinkenberg, I. P., Verhey, F. R., & van Boxtel, M. P. (2016). A systematic review of social support interventions for caregivers of people with dementia: Are they doing what they promise? Maturitas, 85, 117-130. https://doi.org/10.1016/j.maturitas.2015.12.008

Dam, A. E., van Boxtel, M. P., Rozendaal, N., Verhey, F. R., & de Vugt, M. E. (2017). Development and feasibility of Inlife: A pilot study of an online social support intervention for informal caregivers of people with dementia. PloS One, 12(9), e0183386. https://doi.org/10.1371/journal.pone.0183386

Dam, A. E., Boots, L. M., van Boxtel, M. P., Verhey, F. R., & de Vugt, M. E. (2018). A mismatch between supply and demand of social support in dementia care: A qualitative study on the perspectives of spousal caregivers and their social network members. International Psychogeriatrics, 30(6), 881-892. https://doi.org/10.1017/S1041610217002162

Dam, A. E., Vugt, M. E., Klinkenberg, I. P., Verhey, F. R., & Boxtel, M. P. (2016). A systematic review of social support interventions for caregivers of people with dementia: Are they doing what they promise? Maturitas, 85, 117-130. https://doi.org/10.1016/j.maturitas.2015.12.008

Davies, N., Maio, L., Rait, G., & Iliffe, S. (2017). Quality end-of-life care for dementia: What have family carers told us so far? A narrative synthesis. Palliative Medicine, 31(10), 919-930. https://doi.org/10.1177/0269216317690479

Del-Pino-Casado, R., Espinosa-Medina, A., López-Martínez, C., & Orgeta, V. (2019). Sense of competence in dementia care staff (SCIDS) scale: Development, reliability, and validity. International Psychogeriatrics, 31(2), 287-295. https://doi.org/10.1017/S1041610218000799

Department of Veterans Affairs. (2020). Caregiver support program. https://www.caregiver.va.gov

Drake, R. E., Goldman, H. H., Leff, H. S., Lehman, A. F., Dixon, L., Mueser, K. T., & Torrey, W. C. (2001). Implementing evidence-based practices in routine mental health service settings. Psychiatric Services, 52(2), 179-182. https://doi.org/10.1176/appi.ps.52.2.179

Ducharme, F., Lévesque, L., Lachance, L., Kergoat, M. J., Legault, A., Beaudet, L., & Zarit, S. H. (2011). "Learning to become a family caregiver" efficacy of an intervention program for caregivers following diagnosis of dementia in a relative. The Gerontologist, 51(4), 484-494. https://doi.org/10.1093/geront/gnr014

Dunn, N. J., Strain, L. A., Heyman, A., & Fillenbaum, G. G. (2019). A scale to measure activities of daily living in Alzheimer's disease: The PADL-ADL. Journal of Geriatric Psychiatry and Neurology, 2(1), 23-31. https://doi.org/10.1177/089198878900200107

Eifert, E. K., Adams, R., Dudley, W., & Perko, M. (2015). Family caregiver identity: A literature review. American Journal of Health Education, 46(6), 357-367. https://doi.org/10.1080/19325037.2015.1099482

Elliott, A. F., Burgio, L. D., & DeCoster, J. (2010). Enhancing caregiver health: Findings from the resources for enhancing Alzheimer's caregiver health II intervention. Journal of the American Geriatrics Society, 58(1), 30-37. https://doi.org/10.1111/j.1532-5415.2009.02631.x

Elliott, R. A., & Marriott, J. L. (2009). Standardised assessment of patients' capacity to manage medications: A systematic review of published instruments. BMC Geriatrics, 9(1), 1-13. https://doi.org/10.1186/1471-2318-9-27

Elwyn, G., Frosch, D., Thomson, R., Joseph-Williams, N., Lloyd, A., Kinnersley, P., Cording, E., Tomson, D., Dodd, C., Rollnick, S., Edwards, A., & Barry, M. (2012). Shared decision making: A model for clinical practice. Journal of General Internal Medicine, 27(10), 1361-1367. https://doi.org/10.1007/s11606-012-2077-6

Eraut, M. (2000). Non-formal learning and tacit knowledge in professional work. British Journal of Educational Psychology, 70(1), 113-136. https://doi.org/10.1348/000709900158001

Family Caregiver Alliance. (2012). Selected caregiver assessment measures: A resource inventory for practitioners. https://www.caregiver.org/

resource/selected-caregiver-assessment-measures-resource-inventory-practitioners-2012

Family Caregiver Alliance. (2022). Caregiver statistics: Demographics. https://www.caregiver.org/resource/caregiver-statistics-demographics

Farran, C. J., Gilley, D. W., McCann, J. J., Bienias, J. L., Lindeman, D. A., & Evans, D. A. (2007). Efficacy of behavioral interventions for dementia caregivers. Western Journal of Nursing Research, 29(8), 944-960. https://doi.org/10.1177/0193945907303084

Feinberg, L. F. (2022). The dual pressures of family caregiving and employment. Public Policy & Aging Report, 32(1), 33-37. https://doi.org/10.1093/ppar/praa038

Fonareva, I., & Oken, B. S. (2014). Physiological and functional consequences of caregiving for relatives with dementia. International Psychogeriatrics, 26(5), 725-747. https://doi.org/10.1017/S1041610214000039

Gallagher, D., Mhaolain, A. N., Crosby, L., Ryan, D., Lacey, L., Coen, R. F., Walsh, C., Coakley, D., Walsh, J. B., Cunningham, C., & Lawlor, B. A. (2011). Self-efficacy for managing dementia may protect against burden and depression in Alzheimer's caregivers. Aging & Mental Health, 15(6), 663-670. https://doi.org/10.1080/13607863.2011.562179

Gallagher-Thompson, D., & Coon, D. W. (2007). Evidence-based psychological treatments for distress in family caregivers of older adults. Psychology and Aging, 22(1), 37-51. https://doi.org/10.1037/0882-7974.22.1.37

Gallagher-Thompson, D., Lovett, S., Rose, J., McKibbin, C., Coon, D., Futterman, A., & Thompson, L. W. (2000). Impact of psychoeducational interventions on distressed family caregivers. Journal of Clinical Geropsychology, 6(2), 91-110. https://doi.org/10.1023/A:1009560330448

Gallagher-Thompson, D., Solano, N., McGee, J. S., Krisztal, E., Kaye, J., Coon, D. W., & Thompson, L. W. (2003). Coping with caregiving: Reducing stress and improving your quality of life. Stanford University School of Medicine and VA Palo Alto Health Care System.

Gallagher-Thompson, D., Wang, P. C., Liu, W., Cheung, V., Peng, R., China, D., & Thompson, L. W. (2010). Effectiveness of a psychoeducational skill training DVD program to reduce stress in Chinese American dementia caregivers: Results of a preliminary study. Aging & Mental Health, 14(3), 263-273. https://doi.org/10.1080/13607860903420989

Gaugler, J. E., Roth, D. L., Haley, W. E., & Mittelman, M. S. (2008). Can counseling and support reduce burden and depressive symptoms in caregivers of people with Alzheimer's disease during the transition to institutionalization? Results from the New York University caregiver intervention study. Journal of the American Geriatrics Society, 56(3), 421-428. https://doi.org/10.1111/j.1532-5415.2007.01593.x

Gaugler, J. E., Roth, D. L., Haley, W. E., & Mittelman, M. S. (2011). Modeling trajectories and transitions: Results from the New York University caregiver intervention. Nursing Research, 60(3), S28-S37. https://doi.org/10.1097/NNR.0b013e3182126524

Ha, J. F., & Longnecker, N. (2010). Doctor-patient communication: A review. The Ochsner Journal, 10(1), 38–43.

Haley, W. E., Levine, E. G., Brown, S. L., & Bartolucci, A. A. (1987). Stress, appraisal, coping, and social support as predictors of adaptational outcome among dementia caregivers. Psychology and Aging, 2(4), 323–330. https://doi.org/10.1037/0882-7974.2.4.323

Haley, W. E., Roth, D. L., Coleton, M. I., Ford, G. R., West, C. A., Collins, R. P., & Isobe, T. L. (1996). Appraisal, coping, and social support as mediators of well-being in black and white family caregivers of patients with Alzheimer's disease. Journal of Consulting and Clinical Psychology, 64(1), 121–129. https://doi.org/10.1037/0022-006X.64.1.121

Harrison, J. K., Reid, J., Quinn, T. J., & Shenkin, S. D. (2017). Using quality assessment tools to critically appraise ageing research: A guide for clinicians. Age and Ageing, 46(3), 359–365. https://doi.org/10.1093/ageing/afw223

Hartke, R. J., King, R. B., Heinemann, A. W., & Semik, P. (2006). Accidents in older caregivers of persons surviving stroke and their relation to caregiver stress. Rehabilitation Psychology, 51(2), 150–156. https://doi.org/10.1037/0090-5550.51.2.150

Hawranik, P., Strain, L. A., DeForge, R., & Fast, J. (2012). Health of informal caregivers: Effects of gender, employment, and use of home care services. Canadian Journal of Nursing Research Archive, 44(3), 46-72.

Healy, T. C., Peng, C., Haynes, P., McMahon, E., Botler, J., & Gross, L. (2008). The feasibility and effectiveness of translating A Matter of Balance into a volunteer lay leader model. Journal of Applied Gerontology, 27(1), 34–51. https://doi.org/10.1177/0733464807308620

Henriksson, A., & Andershed, B. (2007). A support group programme for relatives during the late palliative phase. International Journal of Palliative Nursing, 13(4), 175–183. https://doi.org/10.12968/ijpn.2007.13.4.23439

Henriksson, A., Carlander, I., & Årestedt, K. (2013). Feelings of rewards among family caregivers during ongoing palliative care. Palliative & Supportive Care, 11(5), 375–381. https://doi.org/10.1017/S1478951512000779

Hiel, L., Beenackers, M. A., Renders, C. M., Robroek, S. J., Burdorf, A., & Croezen, S. (2015). Providing personal informal care to older European adults: Should we care about the caregivers' health? Preventive Medicine, 70, 64-68. https://doi.org/10.1016/j.ypmed.2014.10.028

Hirschman, K. B., Shea, J. A., Xie, S. X., & Karlawish, J. H. (2004). The development of a rapid screen for caregiver burden. Journal of the

American Geriatrics Society, 52(10), 1724–1729. https://doi.org/10.1111/j.1532-5415.2004.52468.x

Hoffmann, T. C., Glasziou, P. P., Boutron, I., Milne, R., Perera, R., Moher, D., Altman, D. G., Barbour, V., Macdonald, H., Johnston, M., Lamb, S. E., Dixon-Woods, M., McCulloch, P., Wyatt, J. C., Chan, A.-W., & Michie, S. (2014). Better reporting of interventions: Template for intervention description and replication (TIDieR) checklist and guide. BMJ (Clinical Research Ed.), 348, g1687. https://doi.org/10.1136/bmj.g1687

Holmes, D., Murray, S. J., Perron, A., & Rail, G. (2006). Deconstructing the evidence-based discourse in health sciences: Truth, power and fascism. International Journal of Evidence-Based Healthcare, 4(3), 180-186. https://doi.org/10.1111/j.1479-6988.2006.00041.x

Hughes, T. F., Chang, C. C. H., Vander Bilt, J., Ganguli, M., & Ganguli, M. (2010). Engagement in reading and hobbies and risk of incident dementia: The MoVIES project. American Journal of Alzheimer's Disease and Other Dementias, 25(5), 432–438. https://doi.org/10.1177/1533317510368399

Institute of Medicine (US) Committee on Quality of Health Care in America. (2001). Crossing the Quality Chasm: A New Health System for the 21st Century. National Academies Press.

Jackson, G. L., Powers, B. J., Chatterjee, R., Bettger, J. P., Kemper, A. R., Hasselblad, V., Dolor, R. J., Irvine, R. J., Heidenfelder, B. L., Kendrick, A. S., Gray, R., & Williams, J. W. (2013). The patient-centered medical home: A systematic review. Annals of Internal Medicine, 158(3), 169–178. https://doi.org/10.7326/0003-4819-158-3-201302050-00579

Jagosh, J., Macaulay, A. C., Pluye, P., Salsberg, J., Bush, P. L., Henderson, J., Sirett, E., Wong, G., Cargo, M., Herbert, C. P., Seifer, S. D., Green, L. W., & Greenhalgh, T. (2012). Uncovering the benefits of participatory research: Implications of a realist review for health research and practice. Milbank Quarterly, 90(2), 311–346. https://doi.org/10.1111/j.1468-0009.2012.00665.x

Janssen, B. M., Van Regenmortel, T., & Abma, T. A. (2011). Identifying sources of strength: Resilience from the perspective of older people receiving long-term community care. European Journal of Ageing, 8(3), 145-156. https://doi.org/10.1007/s10433-011-0190-8

Jensen, M., Agbata, I. N., Canavan, M., & McCarthy, G. (2015). Effectiveness of educational interventions for informal caregivers of individuals with dementia residing in the community: Systematic review and meta-analysis of randomised controlled trials. International Journal of Geriatric Psychiatry, 30(2), 130–143. https://doi.org/10.1002/gps.4208

Joling, K. J., Windle, G., Dröes, R. M., Huisman, M., Hertogh, C. M., & Woods, R. T. (2018). What are the essential features of resilience for informal caregivers of people living with dementia? A Delphi consensus examination. Aging & Mental Health, 22(4), 509-517. https://doi.org/10.1080/13607863.2016.1247431

Joosten, E. A., DeFuentes-Merillas, L., de Weert, G. H., Sensky, T., van der Staak, C. P., & de Jong, C. A. (2008). Systematic review of the effects of shared decision-making on patient satisfaction, treatment adherence and health status. Psychotherapy and Psychosomatics, 77(4), 219–226. https://doi.org/10.1159/000126073

Judge, K. S., Bass, D. M., Snow, A. L., Wilson, N. L., Morgan, R., Looman, W. J., McCarthy, C., & Kunik, M. E. (2011). Partners in Dementia Care: A care coordination intervention for individuals with dementia and their family caregivers. The Gerontologist, 51(2), 261–272. https://doi.org/10.1093/geront/gnq097

Judge, K. S., Yarry, S. J., Looman, W. J., & Bass, D. M. (2013). Improved strain and psychosocial outcomes for caregivers of individuals with dementia: Findings from Project ANSWERS. The Gerontologist, 53(2), 280–292. https://doi.org/10.1093/geront/gns076

Junger, S., Payne, S. A., Brearley, S. G., Ploenes, V., & Radbruch, L. (2017). Consensus building in palliative care: A Europe-wide delphi study on common understandings and conceptual differences. Journal of Pain and

Symptom Management, 53(2), 192–205. https://doi.org/10.1016/j.jpainsymman.2016.09.014

Jutkowitz, E., Brasure, M., Fuchs, E., Shippee, T., Kane, R.A., Fink, H.A., Butler, M., Kane, R.L., McCreedy, E., & Nelson, V.A. (2016). Care-delivery interventions to manage agitation and aggression in dementia nursing home and assisted living residents: A systematic review and meta-analysis. Journal of the American Geriatrics Society, 64(3), 477–488. https://doi.org/10.1111/jgs.13936

Katz, M. G., Kripalani, S., & Weiss, B. D. (2006). Use of pictorial aids in medication instructions: A review of the literature. American Journal of Health-System Pharmacy, 63(23), 2391–2397. https://doi.org/10.2146/ajhp060162

Kent, E. E., Rowland, J. H., Northouse, L., Litzelman, K., Chou, W.-Y. S., Shelburne, N., Timura, C., O'Mara, A., & Huss, K. (2016). Caring for caregivers and patients: Research and clinical priorities for informal cancer caregiving. Cancer, 122(13), 1987–1995. https://doi.org/10.1002/cncr.29939

Kitko, L. A., Hupcey, J. E., Pinto, C., & Palese, A. (2015). Patient and caregiver incongruence in advanced heart failure. Clinical Nursing Research, 24(4), 388–400. https://doi.org/10.1177/1054773814568890

Kumar, S., Nilsen, W. J., Abernethy, A., Atienza, A., Patrick, K., Pavel, M., Riley, W. T., Shar, A., Spring, B., Spruijt-Metz, D., Hedeker, D., Honavar, M., Kravitz, R., Craig Lefebvre, R., Mohr, D. C., Murphy, S. A., Quinn, C., Shusterman, V., & Swendeman, D. (2013). Mobile health technology evaluation: The mHealth evidence workshop. American Journal of Preventive Medicine, 45(2), 228–236. https://doi.org/10.1016/j.amepre.2013.03.017

Kwok, T., Twinn, S., & Yan, E. (2007). The attitudes of Chinese family caregivers of older people with dementia towards life sustaining treatments. Journal of Advanced Nursing, 58(2), 137-145. https://doi.org/10.1111/j.1365-2648.2007.04201.x

Laver, K., Milte, R., Dyer, S., & Crotty, M. (2017). A systematic review and meta-analysis comparing carer focused and dyadic multicomponent interventions for carers of people with dementia. Journal of Aging and Health, 29(8), 1308–1349. https://doi.org/10.1177/0898264316660414

Lee, Y., & Tang, F. (2015). More caregiving, less working: Caregiving roles and gender difference. Journal of Applied Gerontology, 34(4), 465-483. https://doi.org/10.1177/0733464813508649

Lewin, S., Glenton, C., Munthe-Kaas, H., Carlsen, B., Colvin, C. J., Gülmezoglu, M., Noyes, J., Booth, A., Garside, R., & Rashidian, A. (2019). Using qualitative evidence in decision making for health and social interventions: An approach to assess confidence in findings from qualitative evidence syntheses (GRADE-CERQual). PLOS Medicine, 16(10), Article e1002295. https://doi.org/10.1371/journal.pmed.1002295

Llanque, S., Enriquez, M., & Jamison, P. (2016). Concept analysis of health-related quality of life in older adults with Alzheimer's disease. Dementia, 15(4), 704-722. https://doi.org/10.1177/1471301214548521

Lloyd, J., Patterson, T., & Muers, J. (2016). The positive aspects of caregiving in dementia: A critical review of the qualitative literature. Dementia, 15(6), 1534-1561. https://doi.org/10.1177/1471301214564792

Losada, A., Márquez-González, M., Romero-Moreno, R., Mausbach, B. T., López, J., Fernández-Fernández, V., & Nogales-González, C. (2015). Cognitive–behavioral therapy (CBT) versus acceptance and commitment therapy (ACT) for dementia family caregivers with significant depressive symptoms: Results of a randomized clinical trial. Journal of Consulting and Clinical Psychology, 83(4), 760–772. https://doi.org/10.1037/ccp0000028

Lutz, B. J., Young, M. E., Cox, K. J., Martz, C., & Creasy, K. R. (2011). The crisis of stroke: Experiences of patients and their family caregivers. Topics in Stroke Rehabilitation, 18(6), 786–797. https://doi.org/10.1310/tsr1806-786

Lyons, K. S., Zarit, S. H., Sayer, A. G., & Whitlatch, C. J. (2002). Caregiving as a dyadic process: Perspectives from caregiver and receiver. The Journals of Gerontology: Series B, 57(3), P195-P204. https://doi.org/10.1093/geronb/57.3.P195

Mahoney, D. F., Tarlow, B. J., & Jones, R. N. (2003). Effects of an automated telephone support system on caregiver burden and anxiety: Findings from the REACH for TLC intervention study. The Gerontologist, 43(4), 556–567. https://doi.org/10.1093/geront/43.4.556

Malhotra, C., Farooqui, M. A., Kanesvaran, R., Bilger, M., & Finkelstein, E. (2015). Comparison of preferences for end-of-life care among patients with advanced cancer and their caregivers: A discrete choice experiment. Palliative Medicine, 29(9), 842-850. https://doi.org/10.1177/0269216315575681

Martindale-Adams, J., Nichols, L. O., Zuber, J., Burns, R., & Graney, M. J. (2016). Dementia caregivers' use of services for themselves. The Gerontologist, 56(6), 1053-1061. https://doi.org/10.1093/geront/gnv121

McLennon, S. M., Habermann, B., & Rice, M. (2011). Finding meaning as a mediator of burden on the health of caregivers of spouses with dementia. Aging & Mental Health, 15(4), 522-530. https://doi.org/10.1080/13607863.2010.543656

McMillan, S. C., Small, B. J., Weitzner, M., Schonwetter, R., Tittle, M., Moody, L., & Haley, W. E. (2006). Impact of coping skills intervention with family caregivers of hospice patients with

Mittelman, M. S., Roth, D. L., Coon, D. W., & Haley, W. E. (2004). Sustained benefit of supportive intervention for depressive symptoms in caregivers of patients with Alzheimer's disease. American Journal of Psychiatry, 161(5), 850-856. https://doi.org/10.1176/appi.ajp.161.5.850

Mittelman, M. S., Roth, D. L., Clay, O. J., & Haley, W. E. (2007). Preserving health of Alzheimer caregivers: Impact of a spouse caregiver intervention. American Journal of Geriatric Psychiatry, 15(9), 780-789. https://doi.org/10.1097/JGP.0b013e31805d858a

Mittelman, M. S., Haley, W. E., Clay, O. J., & Roth, D. L. (2006). Improving caregiver well-being delays nursing home placement of patients with Alzheimer disease. Neurology, 67(9), 1592-1599. https://doi.org/10.1212/01.wnl.0000242727.81172.91

Montgomery, R. J., Kwak, J., Kosloski, K., & O'Connell Valuch, K. (2011). Effects of the TCARE® protocol for caregivers on care recipient health outcomes and caregiver stress. Journal of Gerontological Nursing, 37(6), 14-22. https://doi.org/10.3928/00989134-20101208-03

Montgomery, R. J., Rowe, J. M., & Kosloski, K. (2007). Family caregiving. In J. A. Blackburn & C. N. Dulmus (Eds.), Handbook of gerontology: Evidence-based approaches to theory, practice, and policy (pp. 426-454). John Wiley & Sons Inc.

Montgomery, R. J., & Kosloski, K. D. (2013). Pathways to a caregiver identity: Transitions related to a relative's cognitive impairment. In R. C. Talley & R. J. V. Montgomery (Eds.), Caregiving across the lifespan: Research, practice, policy (pp. 131-156). Springer Science + Business Media. https://doi.org/10.1007/978-1-4614-4456-2_9

Moran, J. R., & Reaman, J. A. (2002). Critical issues for substance abuse prevention targeting American Indian youth. The Journal of Primary Prevention, 22(3), 201-233. https://doi.org/10.1023/A:1013695201544

Mosquera, I., Vergara, I., Larrañaga, I., Machón, M., del Río, M., & Calderón, C. (2016). Measuring the impact of informal elderly caregiving: A systematic review of tools. Quality of Life Research, 25(5), 1059-1092. https://doi.org/10.1007/s11136-015-1159-4 ↗

Mumford, M. D., Medeiros, K. E., & Partlow, P. J. (2012). Creative thinking: Processes, strategies, and knowledge. The Journal of Creative Behavior, 46(1), 30-47. https://doi.org/10.1002/jocb.003

Musil, C. M., Warner, C. B., Saeid, H., Mutimu, T., LaJoie, A. S., Jeanblanc, A. B., Burant, C. J., & Martindale-Adams, J. (2017). In their own words: Care preferences of older adults with multiple chronic conditions. Geriatric Nursing, 38(2), 118-125. https://doi.org/10.1016/j.gerinurse.2016.08.004

Nichols, L. O., Martindale-Adams, J., Burns, R., Graney, M. J., & Zuber, J. (2011). Translation of a dementia caregiver support program in a health care system—REACH VA. Archives of Internal Medicine, 171(4), 353–359. https://doi.org/10.1001/archinternmed.2010.548 ↗

Nightingale, S., Spiby, H., Sheen, K., & Slade, P. (2018). The impact of emotional intelligence in health care professionals on caring behaviour towards patients in clinical and long-term care settings: Findings from an integrative review. International Journal of Nursing Studies, 80, 106-117. https://doi.org/10.1016/j.ijnurstu.2018.01.006

Northouse, L. L., Katapodi, M. C., Song, L., Zhang, L., & Mood, D. W. (2010). Interventions with family caregivers of cancer patients: Meta-analysis of randomized trials. CA: A Cancer Journal for Clinicians, 60(5), 317-339. https://doi.org/10.3322/caac.20081

Northouse, L., Williams, A. L., Given, B., & McCorkle, R. (2012). Psychosocial care for family caregivers of patients with cancer. Journal of Clinical Oncology, 30(11), 1227-1234. https://doi.org/10.1200/JCO.2011.39.5798

Northouse, L. L., & Northouse, P. G. (2021). Health communication: Strategies for health professionals (4th ed.). Jones & Bartlett Learning.

Nurock, S. A., Wojciechowska, M. H., & Pucko, E. (2015). How to improve communication with palliative care cancer patients at home—A

pilot study of SAGE & THYME©. European Journal of Cancer Care,
24(4), 523-529. https://doi.org/10.1111/ecc.12284

O'Connor, D., Phinney, A., Smith, A., Small, J., Purves, B., Perry, J.,
Drance, E., Donnelly, M., Chaudhury, H., & Beattie, L. (2007).
Personhood in dementia care: Developing a research agenda for
broadening the vision. Dementia, 6(1), 121-142. https://doi.org/10.1177/
1471301207079096

O'Reilly, M., Courtney, M., & Edwards, H. (2007). How is burden
assessed? A review of measures used and discussed in the literature.
International Journal of Geriatric Psychiatry, 22(9), 897-905.
https://doi.org/10.1002/gps.1743

Ory, M. G., Hoffman, R. R., Yee, J. L., Tennstedt, S., & Schulz, R. (1999).
Prevalence and impact of caregiving: A detailed comparison between
dementia and nondementia caregivers. The Gerontologist, 39(2), 177-186.
https://doi.org/10.1093/geront/39.2.177

Ostwald, S. K., Hepburn, K. W., Caron, W., Burns, T., & Mantell, R.
(1999). Reducing caregiver burden: A randomized psychoeducational
intervention for caregivers of persons with dementia. The Gerontologist,
39(3), 299-309. https://doi.org/10.1093/geront/39.3.299

Östlund, U., Wadensten, B., Kristofferzon, M. L., Häggström, E., &
Wengström, Y. (2015). Motivational interviewing: Experiences of primary
care nurses trained in the method. Nurse Education in Practice, 15(2),
111-118. https://doi.org/10.1016/j.nepr.2014.11.005

Oye, C., Sorensen, N. O., & Glasdam, S. (2016). Qualitative research ethics
on the spot: Not only on the desktop. Nursing Ethics, 23(4), 455-464.
https://doi.org/10.1177/0969733014567023

Pagán-Ortiz, M. E., Cortés, D. E., Rudloff, N., Weitzman, P., & Levkoff,
S. (2014). Use of an online community to provide support to caregivers
of people with dementia. Journal of Gerontological Social Work, 57(6-7),
694-709. https://doi.org/10.1080/01634372.2014.901998

Palese, A., Magee, C. A., Caruso, R., Giupponi, A., Agostini, F., Bresadola, V., & Drago, C. (2018). Interventions to maintain mobility and prevent functional decline in older people with cancer: A systematic review. Cancer Nursing, 41(5), E1-E13. https://doi.org/10.1097/NCC.0000000000000534

Papastavrou, E., Kalokerinou, A., Papacostas, S. S., Tsangari, H., & Sourtzi, P. (2007). Caring for a relative with dementia: Family caregiver burden. Journal of Advanced Nursing, 58(5), 446-457. https://doi.org/10.1111/j.1365-2648.2007.04250.x

Park, M., Butcher, H. K., Maas, M. L., & Zanchetta, M. (2004). A thematic analysis of Korean family caregivers' experiences in making the decision to place a family member with dementia in a long-term care facility. Research in Nursing & Health, 27(5), 345-356. https://doi.org/10.1002/nur.20031

Park, S. H. (2015). Caregiver burden and depression among Korean American family caregivers of older adults with dementia: The role of social support. Journal of Evidence-Informed Social Work, 12(4), 384-394. https://doi.org/10.1080/15433714.2014.899173

Parker, D., Mills, S., & Abbey, J. (2008). Effectiveness of interventions that assist caregivers to support people with dementia living in the community: A systematic review. International Journal of Evidence-Based Healthcare, 6(2), 137-172. https://doi.org/10.1111/j.1744-1609.2008.00090.x

Payne, J. L. (2016). The role of inflammation in depression and fatigue. CNS Spectrums, 21(1), 5-8. https://doi.org/10.1017/S1092852916000049

Pearson, A., Field, J., & Jordan, Z. (2007). Evidence-based clinical practice in nursing and health care: Assimilating research, experience and expertise. Blackwell Publishing.

Pearson, A., Wiechula, R., Court, A., & Lockwood, C. (2005). The JBI model of evidence-based healthcare. International Journal of

Evidence-Based Healthcare, 3(8), 207-215. https://doi.org/10.1111/j.1479-6988.2005.00026.x

Perrin, P. B., Morgan, M., Aretouli, E., Burr, J. A., & Arango-Lasprilla, J. C. (2010). The role of culture in caregiver appraisal and coping. In J. C. Arango-Lasprilla & D. L. Perkins (Eds.), Culture and brain injury: Issues in cultural neuropsychology (pp. 319-336). Springer Science + Business Media. https://doi.org/10.1007/978-1-4419-7061-2_16

Peterson, U., Bergström, G., Demerouti, E., Gustavsson, P., Åsberg, M., & Nygren, Å. (2011). Burnout levels and self-rated health prospectively predict future long-term sickness absence: A study among female health professionals. Journal of Occupational and Environmental Medicine, 53(7), 788-793. https://doi.org/10.1097/JOM.0b013e318222b1dc

Phelan, A., McCormack, B., Dewing, J., McCance, T., Slater, P., Wright, J., Brown, D., & Brady, A. M. (2011). Exploring patients' experiences of participating in care delivery and developing a patient-centred, practice-based evidence base: An integrative review. Scandinavian Journal of Caring Sciences, 25(3), 462-472. https://doi.org/10.1111/j.1471-6712.2010.00846.x

Pillemer, K., & Suitor, J. J. (2002). Peer support for Alzheimer's caregivers: Is it enough to make a difference? Research on Aging, 24(2), 171-192. https://doi.org/10.1177/0164027502242001

Pinquart, M., & Sörensen, S. (2003). Differences between caregivers and noncaregivers in psychological health and physical health: A meta-analysis. Psychology and Aging, 18(2), 250-267. https://doi.org/10.1037/0882-7974.18.2.250

Pinquart, M., & Sörensen, S. (2005). Ethnic differences in stressors, resources, and psychological outcomes of family caregiving: A meta-analysis. The Gerontologist, 45(1), 90-106. https://doi.org/10.1093/geront/45.1.90

Pinquart, M., & Sörensen, S. (2006). Gender differences in caregiver stressors, social resources, and health: An updated meta-analysis. The Journals of Gerontology Series B: Psychological Sciences and Social Sciences, 61(1), P33-P45. https://doi.org/10.1093/geronb/61.1.P33

Ploeg, J., Ali, M. U., Markle-Reid, M., Valaitis, R., Bartholomew, A., Fitzpatrick-Lewis, D., McAiney, C., Sherifali, D., & Sohi, G. (2018). Caregiver-focused, web-based interventions: Systematic review. Journal of Medical Internet Research, 20(10), Article e10738. https://doi.org/10.2196/10738

Ploeg, J., Markle-Reid, M., Valaitis, R., McAiney, C., Duggleby, W., Bartholomew, A., Sherifali, D., Hamilton, P., & Gifford, W. (2017). Web-based interventions to improve mental health, general caregiving outcomes, and general health for informal caregivers of adults with chronic conditions living in the community: Rapid evidence review. Journal of Medical Internet Research, 19(7), Article e263. https://doi.org/10.2196/jmir.7564

Ploeg, J., McAiney, C., Duggleby, W., Chambers, T., Lam, A., Valaitis, R., Gifford, W., Markle-Reid, M., Bartholomew, A., Sherifali, D., Hamilton, P., Li, L. C., & Ali, M. U. (2019). A web-based intervention to help caregivers of older adults with dementia and multiple chronic conditions: Qualitative study. JMIR Aging, 2(1), Article e12364. https://doi.org/10.2196/12364

Ploeg, J., Valaitis, R., Duggleby, W., McAiney, C., Fisher, A., Martin-Misener, R., Peacock, S., Donald, F., O'Brien, J., & Williams, A. (2020). A scoping literature review of web-based interventions for older adult caregivers. BMC Geriatrics, 20(1), Article 401. https://doi.org/10.1186/s12877-020-01826-w

Ploeg, J., Valaitis, R., Duggleby, W., McAiney, C., Fisher, A., Martin-Misener, R., Peacock, S., Donald, F., O'Brien, J., & Williams, A. (2020). Web-based interventions for caregivers of older adults with dementia and multiple chronic conditions: Qualitative study. JMIR Aging, 3(1), Article e16820. https://doi.org/10.2196/16820

Port, C. L., Zimmerman, S., Williams, C. S., Dobbs, D., Preisser, J. S., & Williams, S. W. (2005). Families filling the gap: Comparing family involvement for assisted living and nursing home residents with dementia. The Gerontologist, 45(suppl_1), 87-95. https://doi.org/10.1093/geront/45.suppl_1.87

Powell, B. J., Waltz, T. J., Chinman, M. J., Damschroder, L. J., Smith, J. L., Matthieu, M. M., Proctor, E. K., & Kirchner, J. E. (2015). A refined compilation of implementation strategies: Results from the Expert Recommendations for Implementing Change (ERIC) project. Implementation Science, 10(1), Article 21. https://doi.org/10.1186/s13012-015-0209-1

Proctor, E. K., Landsverk, J., Aarons, G., Chambers, D., Glisson, C., & Mittman, B. (2009). Implementation research in mental health services: An emerging science with conceptual, methodological, and training challenges. Administration and Policy in Mental Health and Mental Health Services Research, 36(1), 24-34. https://doi.org/10.1007/s10488-008-0197-4

Proctor, E., Silmere, H., Raghavan, R., Hovmand, P., Aarons, G., Bunger, A., Griffey, R., & Hensley, M. (2011). Outcomes for implementation research: Conceptual distinctions, measurement challenges, and research agenda. Administration and Policy in Mental Health and Mental Health Services Research, 38(2), 65-76. https://doi.org/10.1007/s10488-010-0319-7

Quinn, C., Clare, L., McGuinness, T., & Woods, R. T. (2012). The impact of relationships, motivations, and meanings on dementia caregiving outcomes. International Psychogeriatrics, 24(11), 1816-1826. https://doi.org/10.1017/S1041610212000889

Quinn, C., Clare, L., & Woods, B. (2015). What predicts whether caregivers of people with dementia find meaning in their role?

International Journal of Geriatric Psychiatry, 30(11), 1195-1202. https://doi.org/10.1002/gps.4262

Rainville, C., Skufca, L., & Mehegan, L. (2022). Family caregiving and out-of-pocket costs: 2016-2020. AARP Research. https://doi.org/10.26419/res.00479.001

Ramirez, M., Ford, M. E., Stewart, A. L., & Teresi, J. A. (2005). Measurement issues in health disparities research. Health Services Research, 40(5p2), 1640-1657. https://doi.org/10.1111/j.1475-6773.2005.00450.x

Rapp, T. (2014). Patients' diagnosis decisions in Alzheimer's disease: The influence of family factors. Social Science & Medicine, 118, 9-16. https://doi.org/10.1016/j.socscimed.2014.07.052

Redfoot, D., Feinberg, L., & Houser, A. (2022). Dual eligibles have high levels of need for long-term services and supports: Findings from an analysis of minimum data set assessments. AARP Public Policy Institute. https://www.aarp.org/ppi/info-2022/dual-eligibles-have-high-levels-of-need-for-long-term-services-and-supports.html

Reinhard, S. C., Feinberg, L. F., Choula, R., & Houser, A. (2015). Valuing the invaluable: 2015 update. Insight on the Issues, 104. AARP Public Policy Institute.

Reinhard, S. C., Given, B., Petlick, N. H., & Bemis, A. (2008). Chapter 14: Supporting family caregivers in providing care. In R. G. Hughes (Ed.), Patient safety and quality: An evidence-based handbook for nurses. Agency for Healthcare Research and Quality.

Reinhard, S. C., Levine, C., & Samis, S. (2019). Home alone revisited: Family caregivers providing complex chronic care. AARP Public Policy Institute. https://doi.org/10.26419/ppi.00103.001

Reinhard, S. C., Young, H. M., Levine, C., Kelly, K., Choula, R., & Accius, J. (2020). Home healthcare and caregiver training. Home Healthcare Now, 38(1), 10-19. https://doi.org/10.1097/NHH.0000000000000853

Riffin, C., Van Ness, P. H., Iannone, L., Fried, T., & Wolff, J. L. (2022). Family caregiver burden in the United States: A population-level analysis of secondary stressors. Aging & Mental Health, 26(7), 1347-1356.

Robinson, B. C. (1983). Validation of a Caregiver Strain Index. Journal of Gerontology, 38(3), 344-348.

Roth, D. L., Fredman, L., & Haley, W. E. (2015). Informal caregiving and its impact on health: A reappraisal from population-based studies. The Gerontologist, 55(2), 309-319.

Roth, D. L., Sheehan, O. C., Huang, J., Rhodes, J. D., Judd, S. E., Kilgore, M., ... & Haley, W. E. (2019). Medicare expenditures attributable to dementia: An analysis of the Facing Dementia Survey. Alzheimer's & Dementia, 15(10), 1326-1334.

Rycroft-Malone, J. (2007). Theory and knowledge translation: Setting some coordinates. Nursing Research, 56(4), S78-S85.

Rycroft-Malone, J., Seers, K., Titchen, A., Harvey, G., Kitson, A., & McCormack, B. (2004). What counts as evidence in evidence-based practice?. Journal of Advanced Nursing, 47(1), 81-90.

Sackett, D. L., Rosenberg, W. M., Gray, J. M., Haynes, R. B., & Richardson, W. S. (1996). Evidence based medicine: what it is and what it isn't. BMJ, 312(7023), 71-72.

Samus, Q. M., Black, B. S., Bovenkamp, D., Buckley, M., Callahan, C., Davis, K., ... & Lyketsos, C. G. (2014). Home-and community-based services data elements required for coordinated care of older adults. Aging & Mental Health, 18(2), 171-182.

Samus, Q. M., Johnston, D., Black, B. S., Hess, E., Lyman, C., Vavilikolanu, A., ... & Lyketsos, C. G. (2018). A multidimensional home-based care coordination intervention for elders with memory disorders: The Maximizing Independence at Home (MIND) pilot randomized trial. The American Journal of Geriatric Psychiatry, 26(3), 358-370.

Santos, C. M., Pimenta, C. A., & Nobre, M. R. (2007). The PICO strategy for the research question construction and evidence search. Revista latino-americana de enfermagem, 15(3), 508-511.

Shea, S. E., Goldberg, S., Weatherford, C. G., Aseltine, R. H., Cooper, M. E., Cabral, H. J., & Sansary, J. (2022). Health care worker burnout and patient safety. The Joint Commission Journal on Quality and Patient Safety, 48(7), 420-428.

Sheehan-Smith, L. (2020). Caregiver education needs and preferences for end-of-life care: A systematic review. American Journal of Hospice and Palliative Medicine®, 37(12), 1045-1057.

Sherman, D. W., McSherry, C. B., Parkas, V., Ye, X. Y., Calabrese, M., & Gatto, M. (2013). Recruitment and retention in a longitudinal palliative care study. Applied Nursing Research, 26(3), 167-177.

Sharma, N., Chakrabarti, S., & Grover, S. (2016). Gender differences in caregiving among family-caregivers of people with mental illnesses. World Journal of Psychiatry, 6(1), 7.

Sidani, S., & Braden, C. J. (2011). Design, evaluation, and translation of nursing interventions. John Wiley & Sons.

Siachos, M. P., Vanbakel, A., Foteini, A., Vanbakel, L., & Maria, L. (2018). Burnout syndrome in caregivers of patients with dementia. Archives of Hellenic Medicine, 35(1), 33-41.

Singh, P., Hussain, R., Khan, A., Irwin, L., & Foskey, R. (2014). Dementia care: Intersecting informal family care and formal care systems. Journal of Aging Research, 2014.

Singh, S., Dulku, S., Ramasubbu, B., & Kowal, P. (2022). Prevalence and determinants of loneliness among older adults: Findings from the Study on Global Ageing and Adult Health. Aging & Mental Health, 1-9.

Skufca, L., & Fouts, A. M. (2022). A profile of informal caregivers in rural America. Journal of Family Social Work, 25(2), 124-143.

Smith, J. D., Li, D. H., & Rafferty, M. R. (2020). The implementation research logic model: A method for planning, executing, reporting, and synthesizing implementation projects. Implementation Research and Practice, 1, 2633489520970617.

Smith, M. L., Walker, M. T., Fox, C. H., & Nathaniel, K. C. (2022). Implementation science: Key concepts, frameworks, and approaches. American Journal of Public Health, 112(S1), S28-S35.

Sörensen, S., Duberstein, P., Gill, D., & Pinquart, M. (2006). Dementia care: mental health effects, intervention strategies, and clinical implications. The Lancet Neurology, 5(11), 961-973.

Sörensen, S., & Pinquart, M. (2005). Racial and ethnic differences in the relationship of caregiving stressors, resources, and sociodemographic variables to caregiver depression and perceived physical health. Aging & Mental Health, 9(5), 482-495.

Sörensen, S., Pinquart, M., & Duberstein, P. (2002). How effective are interventions with caregivers? An updated meta-analysis. The Gerontologist, 42(3), 356-372.

Spelten, E. R., Wetsvoort, L. H., van den Beuken, M. H., van Giersbergen, M. Y., de Witte, L. P., & Vernooij-Dassen, M. J. (2020). Palliative care training for informal caregivers of people with dementia: An exploratory review. International Psychogeriatrics, 32(9), 1045-1066.

Srisuphan, W., Moolasarn, S., & Sothornwit, J. (2021). Effectiveness of a mindfulness program on caregiver burden among caregivers of older adults with dementia. Clinical Interventions in Aging, 16, 1305.

Stall, N. M., Kim, S. J., Hardacre, K. A., Shah, P. S., Straus, S. E., Bronskill, S. E., ... & Rochon, P. A. (2019). Association of informal caregiver distress with health outcomes of community-dwelling dementia care recipients: A systematic review. Journal of the American Geriatrics Society, 67(3), 609-617.

Steffen, A. M. (2000). Anger management for dementia caregivers: A preliminary study using video and telephone interventions. Behavior Therapy, 31(2), 281-299.

Stewart, M., Fortin, M., Britt, H. C., Harrison, C. M., & Maddocks, H. L. (2021). Comparisons of multi-morbidity in family practices in Australia and Canada. PloS one, 16(3), e0248091.

Straus, S. E., Tetroe, J. M., & Graham, I. D. (2011). Knowledge translation is the use of knowledge in health care decision making. Journal of Clinical Epidemiology, 64(1), 6-10.

Straus, S. E., Tetroe, J., & Graham, I. (2018). Knowledge translation in health care: moving from evidence to practice. John Wiley & Sons.

Tartaglini, M. F., Safran, D. A., & Phillips, R. S. (2022). Primary care physician home visits prevent healthcare use and improve caregiver quality of life in homebound older adults with dementia. Journal of the American Geriatrics Society, 70(1), 53-60.

Thomas, K. S., Akobundu, U., & Dosa, D. (2016). More than a meal? A randomized control trial comparing the effects of home-delivered meals programs on participants' feelings of loneliness. The Journals of Gerontology: Series B, 73(6), 1049-1058.

Thompson, C. A., Spilsbury, K., Hall, J., Birks, Y., Barnes, C., & Adamson, J. (2007). Systematic review of information and support interventions for caregivers of people with dementia. BMC geriatrics, 7(1), 1-12.

Thornton, M., & Travis, S. S. (2003). Analysis of the reliability of the modified caregiver strain index. The Journals of Gerontology Series B: Psychological Sciences and Social Sciences, 58(2), S127-S132.

Titler, M. G. (2018). Overview of the U.S. Department of Veterans Health Administration quality enhancement research initiative. The Journal of Nursing Administration, 48(10), 481-487.

Tremont, G., Davis, J. D., & Bishop, D. S. (2017). Unique contribution of family functioning in caregivers of patients with mild to moderate dementia. Dementia and geriatric cognitive disorders extra, 4(3), 466-474.

Trukeschitz, B., Schneider, U., Mühlmann, R., & Ponocny, I. (2013). Informal eldercare and work-related strain. Journals of Gerontology Series B: Psychological Sciences and Social Sciences, 68(2), 257-267.

U.S. Department of Veterans Affairs. (2020). Caregiver Support Program. https://www.caregiver.va.gov

Vandepitte, S., Van Den Noortgate, N., Putman, K., Verhaeghe, S., Verdonck, C., & Annemans, L. (2016). Effectiveness of supporting informal caregivers of people with dementia: A systematic review of randomized and non-randomized controlled trials. Journal of Alzheimer's Disease, 52(3), 929-965.

Van Houtven, C. H., Smith, V. A., Stechuchak, K. M., Shepherd-Banigan, M., Hastings, S. N., Maciejewski, M. L., ... & Oddone, E. Z. (2021). Comprehensive support for family caregivers: Impact on veteran health care utilization and costs. Medical Care Research and Review, 78(3), 223-232.

Vázquez, F. L., Torres, Á., Blanco, V., Díaz, O., Otero, P., & Hermida, E. (2014). Comparison of the diagnostic effectiveness of the Mattis Dementia Rating Scale (MDRS) and the Mini-Mental Status Examination (MMSE) for detection of dementia in elderly people. Archives of Gerontology and Geriatrics, 59(2), 302-307.

Vitaliano, P. P., Russo, J., Young, H. M., Teri, L., & Maiuro, R. D. (1991). Predictors of burden in spouse caregivers of individuals with Alzheimer's disease. Psychology and aging, 6(3), 392.

Vitaliano, P. P., Zhang, J., & Scanlan, J. M. (2003). Is caregiving hazardous to one's physical health? A meta-analysis. Psychological bulletin, 129(6), 946.

Wiltsey Stirman, S., Baumann, A. A., & Miller, C. J. (2019). The FRAME: an expanded framework for reporting adaptations and modifications to evidence-based interventions. Implementation Science, 14(1), 1-10.

Wilks, S. E., & Croom, B. (2008). Perceived stress and resilience in Alzheimer's disease caregivers: Testing moderation and mediation models of social support. Aging and Mental Health, 12(3), 357-365.

Williams, A. P., Peckham, A., Kuluski, K., Montgomery, R. J., Morton, F., & Watkins, J. (2021). Reimagining care for older adults: Findings of a citizen panel. Healthcare Quarterly, 24(2), 43-51.

Williams, A. M., Wang, L., & Kitchen, P. (2014). Differential impacts of caregiving across three caregiver groups in Canada: End-of-life care, long-term care and short-term care. Health & Social Care in the Community, 22(2), 187-196.

Wilz, G., Meichsner, F., & Soellner, R. (2019). Are psychotherapeutic effects on family caregivers of people with dementia sustainable? Two-year long-term effects of a telephone-based cognitive behavioral intervention. Aging & Mental Health, 23(4), 474-481.

Wong, C. C. Y., López-Nahas, V., & Molassiotis, A. (2018). Effects of music therapy on anxiety and sleep quality of COPD patients on long-term oxygen therapy: A randomized controlled trial. COPD: Journal of Chronic Obstructive Pulmonary Disease, 15(1), 10-16.

Wong, S. L., Gilmour, H., & Ramage-Morin, P. L. (2016). Alzheimer's disease and other dementias in Canada. Health Reports, 27(5), 11.

Zarit, S. H., Femia, E. E., Kim, K., & Whitlatch, C. J. (2010). The structure of risk factors and outcomes for family caregivers: Implications for assessment and treatment. Aging & Mental Health, 14(2), 220-231.

Zhou, C., Walker, A., & Müller-Riemenschneider, F. (2022). Interventions to improve medication adherence in community-dwelling older adults: a systematic review and meta-analysis. European Journal of Clinical Pharmacology, 78(6), 771-781.

Milton Keynes UK
Ingram Content Group UK Ltd.
UKHW020635110124
435856UK00016B/459